# ERRATA

# DEVELOPMENTS IN PSYCHOANALYSIS

## AT COLUMBIA UNIVERSITY

PROCEEDINGS OF THE 20TH ANNIVERSARY CONFERENCE.
COLUMBIA PSYCHOANALYTIC CLINIC FOR TRAINING & RESEARCH
OCTOBER 1965

edited by

**GEORGE S. GOLDMAN, M.D. & DANIEL SHAPIRO, M.D.**

Page 113    line 16 should read
... She does so by defining quite carefully ...

Page 120    line 16 should read
... obviously manifests later in their meeting ...

Page 123    line 1 should read
In addition to clear message content, ...

Page 154    line 5 should read
... The mother not only fails to define ...

Page 161    Second response of mother should be: 12 (not 15)

Page 302    line 14 should read
the Eskimo has tended to be an amiable,
optimistic and hospitable individual.

Page 317    line 11 should read
maintained by strict observances and taboos.
These observances were in

line 16 should read
correct observance of the details of activities in
these areas. Violation

Page 330    line 33
name transmitted. The subject of depressive
syndromes in Eskimos can

# DEVELOPMENTS IN PSYCHOANALYSIS AT COLUMBIA UNIVERSITY

# DEVELOPMENTS IN PSYCHOANALYSIS
# AT COLUMBIA UNIVERSITY

*Proceedings of the Twentieth Anniversary Conference, Psychoanalytic Clinic for Training and Research, Columbia University, October 30, 1965*

EDITORS

GEORGE S. GOLDMAN, M.D.

DANIEL SHAPIRO, M.D.

19 66

**Hafner Publishing Co.**
**New York      London**

First Edition 1966


Printed and Published by:
    Hafner Publishing Company, Inc.
    31 East 10th Street
    New York, N. Y. 10003



Library of Congress Card Catalogue Number 66-18829

Printed in U.S.A.

# Table of Contents

## IV. APPLIED PSYCHOANALYSIS

## V. SUMMARY

# Contributors

EUGENE B. BRODY, M.D., Professor of Psychiatry and Director, The Psychiatric Institute, University of Maryland.

ARNOLD M. COOPER, M.D., Assistant Clinical Professor of Psychiatry, Columbia University.

B. RUTH EASSER, M.D., Associate Clinical Professor of Psychiatry, Columbia University.

JACK ELINSON, PH.D., Professor of Administrative Medicine, Columbia University.

JOAN FLEMING, M.D., Dean of Education, Chicago Institute for Psychoanalysis.

WILLIAM GOLDFARB, M.D., PH.D., Associate Clinical Professor of Psychiatry, Columbia University; Director, Henry Ittleson Center for Child Research.

GEORGE S. GOLDMAN, M.D., Director, Psychoanalytic Clinic for Training and Research, and Clinical Professor of Psychiatry, Columbia University.

HERBERT HENDIN, M.D., Associate in Psychiatry, Columbia University.

AARON KARUSH, M.D., Clinical Professor of Psychiatry, Columbia University.

PETER H. KNAPP, M.D., Research Professor in Psychiatry, Boston University.

LAWRENCE C. KOLB, M.D., Professor and Chairman, Department of Psychiatry, Columbia University.

STANLEY R. LESSER, M.D., Assistant Clinical Professor of Psychiatry, Columbia University.

DAVID M. LEVY, M.D., Honorary Consultant, Psychoanalytic Clinic for Training and Research, Columbia University; Research Consultant, Henry Ittleson Center for Child Research.

JOSEPH M. LUBART, M.D., Assistant Clinical Professor of Psychiatry, Columbia University.

DONALD I. MEYERS, M.D., Research Psychiatrist, Henry Ittleson Center for Child Research.

LEONARD M. MOSS, M.D., Instructor in Psychiatry, Columbia University.

LIONEL OVESEY, M.D., Clinical Professor of Psychiatry, Columbia University.

EUGENE PUMPIAN-MINDLIN, M.D., Professor of Psychiatry, The University of Oklahoma.

DANIEL SHAPIRO, M.D., Assistant Clinical Professor of Psychiatry, Columbia University.

BLUMA SWERDLOFF, D.S.W., Research Associate in Psychiatry, Columbia University.

JOHN J. WEBER, M.D., Associate Clinical Professor of Psychiatry, Columbia University.

LYMAN C. WYNNE, M.D., PH.D., Chief, Family Studies Section and Adult Psychiatry Branch, National Institute of Mental Health.

# Preface

Within the pages of this book, commemorating the twentieth anniversary of the founding of the Columbia University Psychoanalytic Clinic for Training and Research, are to be found the writings of the second generation of this faculty. They portray a wide diversity of interests, as well as a depth of psychoanalytic penetration attesting to the vigorous growth of this young venture in psychoanalytic education, the initial experiment of its type within a major university medical center.

The steady development of the Clinic over these two decades suggests that doubts and fears of earlier psychoanalysts as to a deleterious influence of formal university structure and medical school setting upon psychoanalysis and its expressions need not necessarily be realized.

It might have been otherwise. The Clinic staff rightly honors those who took such an active role in the early organization and teaching in the newly born university psychoanalytic clinic. Yet the seeds they nurtured were placed in well-tilled and well-fertilised soil. The faculty of the College of Physicians and Surgeons were long since cognizant of psychoanalytic theory and practice. Early in the century, long before the Clinic was born, the first professor of psychiatry, Dr. Frederick Peterson, encouraged his students to study Freud. Dr. Abraham Brill, often spoken of as the father of psychoanalysis in New York City, labored with the neurologists in the old Vanderbilt Clinic, as well as in the halls of the New York State Psychiatric Institute, then located on Ward's Island, and became the respected friend and close associate of the faculties of neurology and psychiatry of the College.

When these institutions moved into the newly built medical center some thirty five years ago, plans to establish a psychoanalytic institute were put forward but could not be realised in those early days in the 1930's. Nevertheless the attention of the medical faculty was attracted to psycho-analytic theory and methods through their application in psychosomatic investigations in the Presbyterian Hospital by Dr. Flanders Dunbar, Dr. George E. Daniels and others. Psychoanalytic concepts were applied to psychiatry at the Psychiatric Institute by Dr. Nolan D. C. Lewis and his associates. Indeed the eventual founding of the Clinic in 1945 within the university medical setting came as a natural evolutionary step. It was not a hurried or impetuous imposition of a strange or unknown entity into the medium of an unprepared medical faculty. Its flowering has taken place amongst a faculty already interested and expectant.

The doubts of the early psychoanalysts as to the wisdom of association with universities, expressed in the opinion that the full-time immersion of the psychoanalyst in his task of data gathering and theory building might be diffused and thereby defeated, may be examined in the light of the two decades of accrued experience in the Columbia milieu. Such doubts, still heard from time to time, sometimes refer to a possible distraction of the psychoanalyst because of pressures on him to collaborate with or assist colleagues in medical or other disciplines through application of psychoanalytic knowledge. He was seen to be deflected thereby from the primary task of collecting the stuff from which psychoanalysis made its beginnings. The experience in the Columbia milieu has proved otherwise. The vast majority of the faculty of the Clinic are occupied and deeply concerned with just those tasks.

Nevertheless, there can be little doubt that the vast resources of the university expressed in the width of interest of its scholars in many disciplines, and its many technical resources have made an impress upon the new faculty of the Psychoanalytic Clinic. As the papers in this volume demonstrate, the psychoanalysts have been influenced by the anthro-pologists, sociologists and psychologists. One finds the beginning of appreciation of the modern computer technology, in an effort to analyze the vast accumulations of data of psychoanalysis which has frustrated the efforts of psychoanalytic advance in the last several decades.

Psychoanalysts, undoubtedly, as with other scientists and humans, will enrich their associational capacities and expand their creativity by closeness with the thinking community—and the modern university offers a wealth of intellectual and technical opportunity beyond that of other institutions.

This testimonial book, then, of the coming of age of the Psychoanalytic Clinic for Training and Research bears good witness to the potential for healthy growth for psychoanalysis within a medical faculty and a university at large.

In closing this preface the sincere appreciation and respect is extended from the faculty of the Department of Psychiatry and from the faculties of other departments in the College who have both benefited from and enjoyed the long and deepening relationship with those so devotedly engaged in the efforts of the Clinic.

Lawrence C. Kolb, M.D.
Professor and Chairman
Department of Psychiatry
College of Physicians & Surgeons
Columbia University

# Introduction

Psychoanalysis has been one of the major tradition-shattering forces of the past seventy-five years. At first it was savagely attacked because it broke with traditional views. In recent decades it has been accused of having developed its own traditions and rigidities. The first university-affiliated psychoanalytic training institute affiliated with the American Psychoanalytic Association was established in 1945, within the Department of Psychiatry of Columbia University. This innovation was a break from the traditional pattern of psychoanalytic education which had been the development of independent psychoanalytic institutes. The creation of the Psychoanalytic Clinic for Training and Research of Columbia University (abbreviated name: Columbia Psychoanalytic Clinic) was a new departure, which brought into psychoanalytic education a number of unconventional features and was accompanied by considerable controversy. Nevertheless, since then four additional university-affiliated institutes have developed within the American Psychoanalytic Association and others are likely. Thus, this pioneering educational venture did open the way for a new kind of training institute.

The twentieth birthday of the Columbia Psychoanalytic Clinic offered an opportunity—a point in time—from which to view its growth and future trends. The growing pains and insecurities of its childhood and adolescence had given way to a confident maturity. It seemed appropriate to mark its *rites de passage* by a suitable celebration which would include a scientific program. A Planning Committee, under the Chairmanship of Dr. Willard M. Gaylin, did an extraordinarily effective and creative job in developing the Twentieth Anniversary Celebration plans. This committee, in addition to the chairman, included Drs. Arnold M. Cooper, George E.

Daniels, George S. Goldman, Herbert Hendin, Aaron Karush, Daniel Shapiro, and Robert Shapiro. The Planning Committee set forth a threefold purpose:

1. to arrange an event that would be noteworthy and memorable for its quality, grace and spirit. The Celebration, which took place at the Waldorf-Astoria Hotel on October 30, 1965, achieved this, particularly the luncheon at which greetings were received from the three former Directors of the Clinic and from others who originally helped to establish the Clinic.

2. to present a scientific program that would represent current work and concepts at the Columbia Psychoanalytic Clinic. This idea was carried still further by the decision that all papers would be presented by staff members who were themselves graduates (or products) of the Clinic. It was hoped that such a program would show the trends in the evolution of the Clinic's theoretical, clinical and research orientations, including the maintenance or change of positions taken in the early history of the Clinic.

3. to invite distinguished members of the national psychoanalytic community to serve as discussants.

The gratitude of the Columbia Psychoanalytic Clinic is extended to the Chairman and members of the Planning Committee for their excellent work; also to Drs. Henriette R. Klein and H. Lee Hall who chaired, respectively, the morning and afternoon sessions of the scientific program. We are indebted to the discussants who came from considerable distances to participate in this conference. We are grateful to Dr. H. Houston Merritt, Dean, College of Physicians & Surgeons, who opened the Celebration by offering the greetings of Columbia University and to Dr. William A. Horwitz, Professor of Clinical Psychiatry, who conveyed the greetings of the Department of Psychiatry. We are particularly grateful to Dr. Lawrence C. Kolb, who has been Chairman of the Department of Psychiatry during the second ten years of the Columbia Psychoanalytic Clinic. Under his encouraging administration the Psychoanalytic Clinic has developed further on the road toward a scientific and psychoanalytic individuality and identity of its own.

We wish to acknowledge the excellent and indispensable assistance rendered by Miss Gail Williams, Administrative Assistant of the Clinic, and by her staff in the planning of the Twentieth Anniversary Celebration and in the preparation of this volume.

Finally, our thanks are extended to those who presented papers on this significant occasion. The scientific program of the Twentieth Anniversary Celebration is herewith offered as a representative cross-section of current work and concepts of the Psychoanalytic Clinic for Training and Research, Columbia University.

George S. Goldman
and
Daniel Shapiro

# Theoretical Considerations

# An Adaptational Approach to Psychic Representation, Perception, and the Psychic Apparatus

*by Aaron Karush, M.D.*

Adaptational theory is an indispensable tool for reconstructing the psychodynamics of morbid behavior. Rado's classic psychodynamic formulation regarding addiction, depression and emergency function,[22,23] Ovesey's lucid studies of paranoid mechanisms and of homosexuality[20,21] and Goldfarb's investigations of the perceptual process in childhood schizophrenia[12] are only a few of the more important clinical applications of the adaptational viewpoint to have been made in recent years.

In trying to clarify the adaptational frame of reference, some of us have published broad critiques of instinctual and energic theories of motivation.[16] Recently I re-emphasized the equivocal position of the concept of the id as part of the psychic apparatus.[18] It must be admitted, however, that adaptational theory in general has not offered convincing alternatives for the classical energic concepts by which psychoanalysts have represented the intensity of mental activity and have tried to account for the selective control over behavior by the forces of motivation. Adaptational theory has so far been no more successful than have other psychoanalytic frames of reference in solving the riddle of choice of neurosis or defining the factors in self-object relationships that lead to arrests or distortions in the development of particular ego functions. Nor, has it dealt satisfactorily with the genetic and psychodynamic origins of the positive *coping* aspects of personality.

In recent years the theoretical emphasis in psychoanalysis has seemed to shift away from the instinctual (id) control of behavior. Major interest has been concentrated more on the super-ego's inhibitive and facilitating functions and on the pathogenic influence that object interaction may exert upon the ego. Much that is being presented today as new had its beginning in the writings of Freud, Ferenczi, Abraham, Reich and others about characterological traits and types. The "new" substructural hypotheses about self and non-self are concerned with questions of "identity" and self-object differentiation which have apparently become the "new frontier" in psychoanalysis. Although seldom acknowledged one of the first clearly defined paths through this new frontier was laid down some twenty years ago by both Rado[22] and Kardiner.[17]

Most recent efforts to deepen our knowledge of ego functions and substructures, especially as they are represented by the concepts of "identity" and "self," have had difficulty in achieving genuine clinical usefulness. To some extent this may be because current analytic theories about the motivational chathexis of self functions are encumbered by such concepts as "neutralization," desexualization" and "de-aggressivization." The result is often an ego theory which is a continuation of the old hypothesis that the vicissitudes of inborn instincts determine the way the ego functions. As we have suggested elsewhere,[16] the truth may well be the opposite—that the structure of the ego decides what happens to the biological drives.

I raise these critical issues now only as a reminder that we need a model of motivational forces which would be consistently adaptational, i.e., derived from the individual's interaction with his environment. To justify itself however the theoretical model would have to account for the variable intensities with which behavior is motivated, for the predisposition to one or another form of psychopathology and for the relationship of motivational forces to the ego's coping devices as distinct from its defensive mechanisms. Even if we cannot complete so large a task, it may be useful to review and redefine certain basic concepts that we now take more or less for granted.

Basic concepts of any science, Freud[4] once wrote, never start out with clear and sharply defined meanings. They remain, of necessity, indefinite until their useful content has been delimited and checked by repeated observations. It is only then that we can correctly formulate these concepts with precision and "progressively modify them so that they become serviceable and consistent over a wide area."[4, p. 117] Psychic representation is one such concept. This paper will discuss the function of psychic representation and its relationship to biological motivational forces of the id on the one hand and to the organ of psychological adaptation, the ego, on the other.

## THE NATURE OF PSYCHIC REPRESENTATION*

In considering the development of the concept of psychic representation in psychoanalysis I shall refer to three broad issues: (1) The relationship of psychic representation to motivating drives and the perceptual function. (2) The relationship of psychic representation to consciousness and unconsciousness. (3) The relationship of psychic representation to energic and structural concepts. Freud first spoke of "representability" in the "Interpretation of Dreams." From the very beginning he delineated two levels of mental representation of inner and external experience, the visual and the verbal. Visual representability referred to thing-representation in pictorial images. Verbal representability depended upon the availability of words which could stand for things and their functions in connection with needs. In each instance representability was based upon the activity of the function of perception. More than twenty years elapsed before Freud presented the id, ego, super-ego model of psychic structure. At that time he assigned the function of perception to the ego; in fact, Freud explicitly stated that the core of the ego was perception. Thus, mental (psychic) representation, visual or verbal, is assumed to arise through the prior activity of the perceptual function and is itself an ego function.

Freud's early definition of the concept of instinct as an internal need did not distinguish between "instinct" and its "psychical representative." ". . . an 'instinct' appears to us as a concept on the frontier between the mental and the somatic, as the psychical representative of the stimuli originating from within the organism and reaching the mind, as a measure of the demand made upon the mind for work in consequence of its connection with the body."[4] Not long afterward,[5,6] Freud began, however, to speak of the instinct as a non-psychical somatic force which could have psychological effects only through its psychical representative. Although the distinction may not seem particularly significant, the latter definition will be the one used in this paper. In Freud's own words: "An instinct can never become an object of consciousness—only the idea that represents the instinct can. Even in the unconscious, however, an instinct cannot be

---

*For the sake of brevity, "psychic representation" will at times be referred to as "P-R" in the text that follows.

represented otherwise than by an idea. If the instinct did not attach itself to an idea or manifest itself as an affective state, we could know nothing about it. When we nevertheless speak of an unconscious instinctual impulse or a repressed instinctual impulse . . . we can only mean an instinctual impulse the ideational representative of which is unconscious."[5, p. 177] Freud seems to treat instinct therefore on two levels. Beginning as a *non-psychical entity*, instinct arises as excitation from somatic sources and is a bio-chemical and physiological process. It undergoes a special transformation, psychic representation, and only then becomes a psychic entity with psychological qualities. As I shall try to show, only those biological processes with unique attributes can engage the psychic apparatus and produce truly psychological effects.

Freud established that an instinct receives its ideational representative only if a sensory experience has left a memory trace. The ideational equivalent of an instinct, its P-R, is derived from the perception of certain features of an impulse or drive. The percept may be formed in visual imagery or in words whose symbolic meaning is learned primarily through the function of hearing. Concerning the difference between excitations which can obtain psychic representation and excitations which cannot, it seems to me that *psychic representation is a potentiality possessed only by those biological processes which depend upon the participation of a perceived object to fulfill the aim of the biological excitation.*

It may be significant that all such processes are intermittently active. They seem to require a period of intervening rest and recuperation which is perceived with pleasure before the drive activity resumes. Psychic representation apparently imposes a delay or slowdown in the stimulus-response pattern and makes possible the selection of effective means of reaching the goal which, temporarily at least, will end the activity of the biological drive. The ego can perhaps be said to inhibit the immediate resumption of drive activity through the perception that rest from that activity is gratifying in itself. The pleasurable recuperation from drive activity frees the ego to pursue other adaptive but non-libidinal aims. By the same token, the biological activities of the heart, kidney, lungs, etc., cannot obtain psychic representation because they do not require the intervention of an external object and cannot excite consummatory behavior that brings the activity to a halt. In a sense that is fortunate since the latter biological functions must remain uninterrupted in order to maintain the very life of the organism.

## PSYCHIC REPRESENTATION AND PERCEPTION

In distinguishing between those somatic excitations that can become psychical from the repetitive excitations which never become psychic processes, we recognize that not all sensation ends in perception and in the formation of mental representatives. Beres[1] has suggested that there is a hierarchy of levels of perceptual experience:

1. A pre-perceptual neuro-physiological level at which are found the sense data of the primary sensory modalities. These are essential to the *reflexive* responses to excitation of nerve endings by temperature, pain, touch, posture, movement and pressure, as well as taste, smell, vision, and hearing.
2. An initial percept formation level which Beres considers to be pre-representational and which involves signals, not mental representations themselves. These percepts are first characterized by gestalts and configurations of space, form and color. At this level they remain dependent upon direct sensory stimulation.
3. An independent mental representation level at which stimuli are organized into concepts of reality. Included in this level are the stimuli which come from the body organs and muscles and contribute to the formation of the concept of self. This is a level of abstraction and conceptualization.

Beres implies first that not all sensation leads to perception and second that the two broad levels of percept formation lead to psychic representations which have different qualities, are subject to different forms of distortion and differ in their ability to reflect reality. His *pre-perceptual level* is based on the activity of the reflex arc in which sensation alerts and releases built-in responses. The *level of so-called pre-representation* includes at least two different mechanisms of perception. One depends upon the conditioned reflex, which occurs also at the first reflexive level. Conditioning leads to percepts made up of imagery that does not reflect an understanding of the connections among events other than in temporal and spatial terms. The second part of this level of perception merges with the first but depends primarily upon the dominance of the visual mode of sensation over the others. Visual images in which objects begin to have spatial, temporal and *functional* relationships to the self make up the percepts of the period of later infancy and early childhood. Furthermore, other forms of sensory experience tend to become integrated around the visual images associated with them. In this way visual mental representations grow in number and develop more and more complex ties to sensations and feelings aroused by the excitation of the other senses. It is hard to imagine a psychic representation of a smell or of a taste or of touch in sighted people except in combination with visual imagery. From these interwoven components of conditioning and vision, we move to the third perceptual level where mental representations are laid down as word presentations or symbols. Rational thought and the conceptualization of true meaning have now become possible. The second level described by Beres is pre-symbolic but is I believe representational nonetheless; the third marks the ability to form concepts and is based on the developmental dominance of the auditory function of the ego over visual perception. Hearing at the first two levels of percept formation has primarily an alerting function which serves the dominant visual apparatus. Its turn to become the dominant form of perception and to decide the nature of psychic representation occurs when language and verbal communication are possible. As for the pre-perceptual level, it alone can be considered to be pre-representational in contrast to the second and third phases of true perception.

In accordance with these conceptions I consider that the perceptual function passes through three successive levels of development. Each level is responsible for psychic representatives with different cathexes or degrees of excitability. The latter are derived from the potential for different degrees of affective arousal which each sensory apparatus possesses. The three perceptual levels consist of the following:

1. *Percepts of sensations* caused by somatic excitation and by external objects by way of contact senses combined with vision.
2. Concrete *percepts of the physical existence, form and functions of objects* and their immediate significance to the subject, e.g., the object as an instrument for the subject's immediate gratification. Vision is dominant but hearing becomes more important.
3. *Abstract percepts or concepts* about objects and their ultimate significance to the subject which now includes recognition of the realistic conditions under which an object will serve as an instrument, as well as recognition of the results of self-gratification for the subject. Hearing is now dominant; symbolic communication has developed.

These distinctions can be observed in some patients. A young woman, a painter with borderline pathology, was able to recognize her preference for direct visual experience rather than for listening to descriptive ideas of others. If she saw something she could accept it. If she thought about it in words and ideas, she remained uncertain about their meaning. The ambiguity of meaning inherent in verbal representations clouded the relationship between the subject and objects and aroused a narcissistic impulse to erase undesirable meanings by wishful magic. Visual imagery is less readily subject to wishful distortion than is the interpretation of what is heard. One can arbitrarily control the meanings given to words that stand for reality, according to one's prior wishes or convictions. To alter visual reality as fully as the above-mentioned patient wished, required an impulse to be blind that would threaten her body image integrity. Auditory reality is alterable at less cost and danger; one can prefer one meaning in words over another without nullifying the ability to hear. External reality can be distorted without threatening body integrity and the self-image. Instead, the altered meaning given to words is ascribed to the object who creates the words (ideas), i.e., projection is a readier defense against the danger of others' thoughts than against direct visual-image representations. Another patient, a man, recalled his intense sensual gratification from touching and caressing his eldest brother's nose and ears when he was a young boy, in clear visual images. His associations during the session moved to his concern with genital weakness and to phantasies about me as a parent. I remarked on his recurrent wish to be close to me and his simultaneous fear of actual contact with me. He became acutely distressed and restless and angrily accused me of considering him "queer." Finally he phantasied that I was really a homosexual trying to seduce him. This defense by projection is a familiar one, but its interest for us lies in the ease with which his auditory perception of what I said could have its meaning twisted and turned into its opposite as compared to his visual memories. The image of himself playing with his brother's face could not have been erased without inducing an intolerable sense of deprivation and isolation. When I put the visual image into words which conveyed meaning in a broader sense, the homsexual implication was clear to him at once. Characteristically, his defense was aimed at my words and at me, their speaker, rather than at the primary sensual gratification he still desired. He could live with minimal conflict with the

visual memory of his infantile erotic play but not with my verbal conceptualization of that vision. The latter was subject to the critical and
punitive activity of his superego. His defense against the resulting shame
and guilt was to project responsibility for homosexual impulses and in
so doing of course to deny the truth of the conceptualization that had
been made of his visual memory. Perhaps because of the superego's
original connection with auditory perception, any verbal conceptualization
of behavior tends to bring its censuring function into play. On the other
hand, psychic representations derived from visual imagery alone, unaccompanied by conceptual representations of the symbolic meaning of an
experience, can be maintained free of the superego's critical scrutiny.
As a result this patient was able to preserve his "right" to infantile sexual
phantasy and behavior without the restraint of the reality principle.

## PSYCHIC REPRESENTATION AND THE ORGANIZATION
## OF THE EGO

Thus far I have discussed P-R as a concept which helps to bridge the
"gap" between soma and psyche. I have suggested that the roots of the
representations of the object world can be traced to successive phases
of percept formation which endow each P-R with its quantum of excitability
(cathexis), its charge of affect. With this conceptualization it is possible
to view the ego as a structure composed of islands of function built up
progressively of direct sensory images, of concrete percepts, and of
concepts, each possessing a different potential for activating behavior.
These islands are discrete ego nuclei with P-R's whose cathexes influence
the intensity and aim of motivational drives toward different goals.

The differences in the structure of the ego nuclei can be understood in
terms of their origins from one or another level of perception. At the
earliest sense-organ level of perception we find ego nuclei that are
comparatively unrelated sense-egos. Thus we can speak hypothetically
of a "tactile ego," a "taste-smell ego," a "kinesthetic ego," a "visual ego,"
an "auditory ego," etc. *Integration* of the ego nuclei begins after psychic
representations are formed, first as sensory images, later as percepts of
objects which have associated functions and purposes of their own. One
might say that integration is expressed in the recognition that various
sensory percepts, by way of their P-R's, signify the physical and psychological dimensions of a particular object or reflect the meaning of a unitary

experience. Depersonalization can be described as a failure to form stable percepts of objects' relationships to the self. A sense of mastery comes with the discovery that our percepts reliably tell us what to anticipate from significant objects and can also help us to organize behavior toward a desired goal. If stable percepts are not formed in this sense, regression to more primitive levels of perception occurs. Regression can stop at the stage where whole objects are perceived as instruments for gratification, or it can proceed along a course of disintegration to the stage dominated by discrete and disconnected sense-egos with a corresponding loss of identity. When an identity crisis occurs, the greater the identity loss that is threatened the more urgent and impulsive will be the actions designed to end the resulting anxiety. The choice of actions may depend on which sense-ego nucleus is dominant in the regression. It is possible to project at least three categories of regressive action according to the prevailing level of perceptual control over the dominant ego nucleus. The following are examples:

1. Tactile-taste-smell dominance leads to oral-intaking behavior and to morbidity such as addictive behavior, anorexia, nervosa, obesity, etc.
2. Visual-kinesthetic dominance leads to acting-out which may appear in the form of primary impulse disorders, as sociopathic behavior or as neurotic acting-out character disorders.
3. Auditory dominance leads to psychoneurotic symptoms or character disorders in which the ability to conceptualize the relation of self to objects is damaged. Superego imbalance or lacunae may also result at the stage of auditory dominance when object relationships have been invaded by anxiety and identifications are weak or conflicted. Regressive admixtures of early sensory ego nuclei complicate the picture.
4. If none of the ego nuclei predominates and all vie for control of perception, the result may be gross psychosis.*

Since ego integration is experienced as a comforting sense of identity, a transient illusion of strength can be fostered at any of the first three regressed levels. The dominant sense-ego can create a pathological solution to the identity-mastery crisis which for the moment at least proves to the person that he *is* whole and has an identity, regressed and infantile as it may really be.

---

*The concept of ego nuclei built about a dominant sensory source of perception is in some respects similar to, but is not identical with, Glover's concept of ego nuclei.[11]

Let us examine more closely how the concept of sense-ego nuclei fits
into the psychic apparatus. The ego's synthetic function brings together
and integrates evolving ego substructures which involve greater percept
complexity as growth proceeds. Each of the substructures is a nucleus
of psychic activity that begins with sense perceptions of both internal and
external stimuli, adds affects and thoughts and culminates in goal-directed
action. The whole complex is bound to a particular motivated aim, that
is to say, the substructure of functions is cathected by psychic energy which
gives the complex its appetitive urgency. The cathexis supplies the aim
(reduction of tension through activity) but not the specific goal which
will end that tension. Cathectic shifts at best account only in part for
developmental changes in the ego. Intra-ego organizations may largely
be based upon the quality of the on-going perceptual process. It is a
quality which reflects the dominant mode of sensation by which the
external world of objects and inner impulses are registered in the ego
as psychic representations. As I have said, each P-R has a different level
of excitability (a different cathected bond of psychic energy) which varies
according to the sense apparatus that has led to the underlying perception.
Tactile, taste and smell sensations end as a rule in P-R's with the highest
cathexis (i.e., affective arousal) and therefore with the lowest threshold
and greatest degree of excitability. Action cannot easily be delayed and
behavior has a reflexive-impulsive quality. Vision permits a longer delay
in response but still invites fairly prompt imitative and responsive actions.
Hearing on the other hand is the one sense excitation that permits a much
less immediate response. The ear not only registers sound signals but is
the main sense organ for concept formation and for learning the words
to create symbolic mental representations. The interval between hearing
something and understanding its meaning is far greater than the time
which elapses from a signal-stimulus to a response when any of the other
senses are excited.

The relationship of P-R to the perceptual function of the ego makes
it easier to define the conditions under which a biological activity can
obtain P-R and can become a psychic entity. I suggested earlier that only
those internal excitations engage the perceptual function and get psychic
representation which depend upon the *intervention of another object for
the fulfillment of the aim of the drive.* Such an object, whether it is external
and separate or is an object that is part of the person himself, is perceived

as an instrument for obtaining the gratification which brings an excitation to an end. Conversely if the activity operates automatically and does not need a facilitating object to fulfill its aim, then no sense-perception is excited which can lead to a P-R; the activity remains somatic and takes on no psychical qualities. In other words, somatic activity without .P-R remains *unmotivated* activity.

The psychic mechanisms that determine the relative precedence which a particular P-R can take over others in integrating behavior are of special interest. There are two aspects of a P-R which can be defined. One comes from the perceptions of the real existence of the external objects needed for the fulfillment of drive aims; the other reflects the perception of the *affective excitations* that are components of the drive itself and are responsible for peremptory expectations of objects. These two aspects fuse with varying proportions of affective arousal in each psychic representation. The nature and intensity of the affective component determine the directions taken by the discharge phenomena which can move toward opposite extremes: to pursue gratification regardless of consequences or to set the object and its requirements above direct satisfaction of instinctual needs. The degree of cathexis by psychic energy parallels the intensity of primary "untamed" affect that exists in association with every motivation.

It seems reasonable to consider that psychic energy, as a polarizing force in the mental apparatus, is simply another dimension of the primary affective arousal that always accompanies sense-perception. When we speak of cathexis we refer to the directing and quantifying aspect of affective excitation that is attached to every psychic representative.

Why one or another P-R triumphs in the competition for psychic energy involves more than inherited genotypes or poorly defined constitutional factors. The answer depends possibly upon which mode of sensory experience was originally responsible for the formation of the psychic representations. Each sensory mode seems to carry with it a greater or lesser potential for affective arousal. For example, excitation of contact receptors of the skin and mucosa readily produces riddance responses to pain as well as incorporative tendencies where pleasure is involved. Affective excitability is the most intense when direct excitation of pain or pleasure is involved. Smell and taste can also stimulate rapid riddance or incorporative responses. Certain kinesthetic sensations such as falling produce instantaneous and massive responses of anxiety at least in the very young. Vision and hearing however extend the shell of the future* far beyond the limits imposed by the other sense receptors. The more the sensory modality is distant from direct contact, the less affective arousal occurs and the less the cathexis of the associated P-R. Pure reason has far less power to activate behavior than does brute emotion. Stated in economic terms rational concepts have a much lower cathexis than do ideas and images which represent concrete sensory experiences. The latter, depending as they do largely on contact, taste, smell and sight, have a powerful affective component that carries with it a *somatic readiness for immediate action*. It is this which supplies the higher cathexis of psychic energy to the associated psychic  representatives and enables them to select and control the ego's motivational interests.

The hypothesis that ego nuclei are built about the psychic representatives created during successive phases of perceptual dominance by the various sense receptors has an obvious resemblance to the classical theory of stages of libidinal development—oral, anal, sadistic, phallic, etc. There is, however, a fundamental difference: perceptual dominance is a bio-adaptive approach to some aspects of ego organization. It does not replace the instinctual hypothesis but rather parallels it. The concept of instincts refers to motivation; the concept of perceptual dominance refers to ego function and structure. Each complements the other but neither is directly derived from the other.

## FURTHER CONSIDERATIONS OF PSYCHIC
## REPRESENTATION AND STRUCTURE

Structural theory has sharpened the distinction between two kinds of unconsciousness, one of which is capable of becoming conscious while the other is not. There is a basic structural significance to the "unconsciousness" of biological activities which can never attain consciousness. These happen also to be the somatic processes which never obtain direct P-R. "Unconsciousness" applied to them has a structural significance, more accurately an infra-psychic structural significance. They do not themselves develop psychical qualities and strictly speaking can produce psychological effects only indirectly if at all. Those biological functions that require the participation of an object (e.g., as in the case of the

*See Rado[23, p. 218-219]

sexual drive), and therefore can excite the sensations which lead to perceptions, develop psychological attributes through their ability to form psychic representations. Only the somatic functions with P-R have psychical qualities—that is to say, have motivational attributes. The distinction between "consciousness" and "unconsciousness" as it pertains to these psychical elements has a descriptive but not a structural significance, unlike the "unconsciousness" of non-psychical processes.

There are people who do get direct sensory reverberations of internal activity that in most of us remains psychically "silent." Even here it is unlikely that the person will perceive that activity as a motivational force. Functions such as respiration, digestion, excretion, etc., form strong associations between resulting physical sensations and intense affects that relate to significant objects. In early life these are objects with whom a symbiotic tie exists. The symbiotic object originally involved himself in the performance of one or more of the subject's automatic body functions. As a result, the P-R's of symbiotic objects serving as instruments through which the subject masters painful tensions seem also to represent the physical functions with which the symbiosis was concerned. That is, a P-R can be *shared* by a body function and an external object. Separation from the object may then for example evoke respiratory dysfunction; a primitive incorporative need for a dangerous object may be expressed as vomiting; rage at a symbiotic object who is frustrating may be represented by a diarrhea. What is particularly interesting in sensitive subjects is that the P-R's of vegetative functions seem to open up a two-way path of psychic activity. Physical sensations can arouse affectively-charged needs for symbiotic objects but the opposite can also occur so that a need for, or a reaction to, an object can be expressed through excitation of vegetative functions. Appetitive behavior requires the intervention of an object. If the object exists in a symbiotic connection to the regressed subject, appetitive impulses tend to arouse broader and more prolonged somatic responses than are ordinarily necessary. The reversibility in the pathway of excitation apparently can occur because the P-R's involved are *shared* by both somatic functions and symbiotic external objects. They become interchangeable as means of discharging the cathexis of psychic energy that is attached to the shared P-R's. Once psychic representation is shared in this way by objects and functions, psychosomatic pathology becomes possible.

The predisposition to form a shared P-R probably depends upon traumatic experiences which occur when a symbiotic object has, for his own needs, injected himself strongly into a biological process that should normally unfold by itself without a mediating object. The danger which a trauma creates is helplessness, loss of somatic control and death. Characteristically, it is pathogenic because it appears during the pre-concept phase of perception when psychic representations are pre-verbal images formed from sensory experiences. It is then that P-R's are still broad and imprecise enough to lend themselves to multi-representation and ambiguity. They can be shared by diverse concrete experiences however unrelated they really are. The P-R's are moreover endowed with especially intense affective components because of the association with *contact* (pre-verbal) sensory experiences. The resulting P-R's are thus intensely cathected and have a low threshold of excitability. A precipitating trauma can excite a psychosomatic attack if it arouses an intense affect, especially of impotent rage, followed by a diffuse sense of helplessness. The level of cathexis is raised of all the P-R's associated with the regressive trend set off by the helplessness. It is then that the two-way channel between a somatic vegetative process and a symbiotic object may be re-opened however long it has been dormant.

## PSYCHIC REPRESENTABILITY AND CONSCIOUSNESS

Freud stated explicitly concerning the transition from unconsciousness to consciousness that, "only something which has once been a conscious perception can become conscious and . . . anything arising from within (apart from feelings) that seeks to become conscious must try to transform itself into external perceptions; this becomes possible by means of memory traces."[7, p. 20] An unconscious psychic event or excitation can reach consciousness only by forming connections with pre-existent images and ideas, or, as Freud himself put it, with the word-presentations which correspond in some manner to the exciting event. In other words, an unconscious entity, whatever it may be, is linked to awareness only through memories existing as visual and verbal images that represent the original experiences. Freud noted that an important exception to this basic rule is that part of the unconscious which comes from internal sensations. Sensations and feelings reflect the activities (aims) of the instincts and according to Freud are experienced only as pleasure or unpleasure.

Unpleasurable feelings seem to impel to some kind of behavioral discharge while feelings of pleasure arouse efforts to hold on to the source of pleasure. Loss of pleasure may also excite discharge-behavior that is designed to recapture the source of pleasure. As sensations, whether pleasant or unpleasant, internal processes can be partly conscious without the intervention of word representation. What does an "unconscious feeling" consist of? The arousal for action of the motor component of an affect is potentially conscious when the subject can identify its behavioral aim and its goal of gratification. If these identifying ideas are not recognizable the affect or feeling may be called "unconscious." It is, to be sure, an inaccurate label since the affective state, unknown as its nature and direction may be, is nevertheless consciously felt as an unpleasant state of arousal and tension.

The structural theory assigned three sets of psychic phenomena to the class of the "unconscious":

1. That which is unconscious because it has been repressed is part of the id.
2. That which is unconscious and produces and maintains repression is part of the ego and the superego.
3. That which is unconscious without ever having undergone regression is the "core of the id."

As Freud put it, the latter is made up of "conative impulses which have never got beyond the id. . . ."

Sets one and two imply that there has been prior excitation of the perceptual function at an earlier phase. Hence, we can assume that the phenomena involved have achieved psychic representation. They are by definition psychical entities capable of motivating behavior or of taking part in motivated behavior. Set number three has always been a source of theoretical confusion. To speak of conative impulses is to speak of appetitive forces which are the instinctual or drive foundations of motivation. When Freud added that these impulses have never gotten beyond the id and must always remain unconscious, he implied that they had no ideational representatives. He left open the puzzling question of how unrepresented strivings can nevertheless set off a *motivational* (as against reflexive or conditioned) sequence of behavior organized and controlled by the ego. It is necessary for the conative core of the id to have at least indirect access to mental representability if it is to become a psychical process and be able to induce motivated behavior. I would go even further and suggest that *unless biological impulses have the capacity for direct or indirect psychic representability and for consciousness they cannot engage the psychic apparatus in motivated activity.* Impulses or urges are subject to indirect representability by way of accompanying affects. It is possible to represent our feelings metaphorically in such expressions as "jumping for joy," "I could cry," "it makes me sick," "I feel like flying," "I could just float along," "I could kick myself," "I could eat you up," etc. These are motor equivalents of affect and suggest that conative impulses obtain psychic representation indirectly when their affective components impinge upon perception through the excitation of motor phenomena. Indirect psychic representation of this kind is easily subject however to accidental associations which may create a distorted reflection of reality.

It is reasonable to conclude that, in general, the less direct the way in which an excitation gets its P-R, the greater the possibility of error in the ego's interpretation of reality and in its selection of appropriate means of attaining gratification. It is no wonder that the conative urges are subject to so much perceptual distortion and lead so commonly to psychoneurotic reactions.

In addition to the instinctual urges which he called the core of the id, Freud assigned ideas and feelings to the id which have been repressed by the ego. These repressed elements are psychic artifacts left behind by the impact of motivating forces upon those ego functions which are active at early phases of development. Both sets of id constituents, the energy of the drives and the repressed ideas and feelings, share the quality of being unconscious but with a basic difference. The primary instinctual energies, the core of the id, according to Freud, can *never* become conscious. The secondary contents of the id created by repression can, on the other hand, become conscious. Freud had stopped thinking of unconsciousness as a structure and regarded it as a common quality possessed by different psychic elements. We are, however, confronted with *two kinds* of unconsciousness: one can change and become conscious, the other cannot. "Unconsciousness" that can change into consciousness is a cornerstone of the psychoanalytic theory of behavior. "Unconsciousness" that can *never* become conscious is another matter. Descriptively, both forms of unconsciousness refer to the same quality. Dynamically the two types of unconsciousness imply very different processes—one has psychical qualities while the other has not.

Processes with "psychical qualities" are those which serve motivation and motivated behavior (as opposed for example to reflexive behavior), whether the ideas that represent these processes are immediately conscious or not. This poses the issue whether the id impulses that Freud considered to be permanently unconscious possess psychical qualities. Stated in another way, I question whether primal energies that are released by biological activity can induce motivated behavior if they can never become conscious. The somatic excitations which develop psychological counterparts do so I believe only under highly specific conditions. Unless these conditions are met the body's activities remain somatic and without psychical qualities.

## PSYCHIC REPRESENTATION AND THE PSYCHICAL PROPERTIES OF THE ID

Freud was aware of the imporance of explaining how instincts obtain psychic representation and how somatic excitation develops psychical qualities. He recognized that psychic representation and the perceptual process are naturally intertwined and suggested that the id, not just the ego, had "its own world of perception." He spoke of the ability of the id to detect "with extraordinary clarity certain changes in its interior, especially oscillations in the tension of its instinctual needs which become conscious as feelings in the pleasure-unpleasure series." He added, "it is, to be sure, hard to say by what means and with the help of what sensory terminal organs these perceptions come about, but it remains certain that self-perception—coenesthetic feelings and feelings of pleasure-unpleasure —governs events in the id with despotic force."[10, p. 199] If the ego alone were given the function of providing representation for somatic excitation then the id would become a lesser organization in the psychic apparatus than was the ego itself. The instinct theory precluded accepting the id as subsidiary to the ego and Freud was compelled to assume a second hypothetical perceptual system.

It is doubtful that the id can create its own ideas and mood representations without involving the ego itself. It will be recalled that Freud himself had said that an instinct, *even in the unconscious,* cannot be represented otherwise than by an idea. This can only mean that unless attached to an idea, or unless perceived as an affective state with ideational associations, we can know nothing of an instinct's existence. It would have no P-R and could have no psychical effect. The "idea" in question is derived primarily from auditory perceptions and to a lesser extent from visual or other sensory experiences, all of which in time become associated with word-presentations. The id as a conceptual entity can be regarded in either of two ways. It can be a non-psychic structure that contains somatically released drive energies while the ego (together with the superego) becomes a broader and more inclusive organization that contains all unconscious ideas; or, we can continue to think of the id as a psychic structure which is the reservoir for the products of repression as well as for the unconscious psychic representatives of the drives. In the latter case the id is subsidiary to the ego which assigns the earliest unconscious (repressed) mental activities to it.

The idea of defining the energies of the somatic drives in their original form as non-psychic functions of the organism is not new. Rapaport[24,25] has noted that while motives, like any other psychological processes, have a neurological and physiological organismic substrate, motives cannot be equated with this substrate. Motives are concepts derived from observation of behavior. If motives are psychological concepts, then so is the concept of instinctual drive providing that we refer to the "psychical representative of the stimuli originating from within the organism and reaching the mind."[4] Rapaport agrees that the concept of instinctual drive is a psychological concept only so long as we mean its "psychical representative." As such it does not conceptualize somatic processes— "neither deficit states, nor homeostatic imbalances, nor hormonal excesses, nor even neural centers of systems—but behaviors." Furthermore, psychological determinism does not require the "assumption of a severance of the mental apparatus from the body but leads to the following two working assumptions: (a) the laws of functioning of the mental apparatus (i.e., the laws of behavioral regulation) can and must be investigated by a study of behavior . . . without reference to molecular, physiological or neural processes; (b) the relationships of the explanatory constructs derived from behavior to somatic processes must be kept vague at least as long as our knowledge of both types of process is meager, lest psychological concepts (or even behavior) be prematurely equated with or tied to specific physiological processes."[24]

Rapaport's careful insistence on psychological concepts for psychological events stands opposed to the strong neurologizing trend of writers like Ostow[19] who has defined the id as "the collection of central nervous system mechanisms concerned with creating, organizing and energizing instinctual needs." He goes on, "in the human . . . the physiological statement of the instinctual need is translated into a psychic statement, a wish. The fundamental element of the psychic representation of instincts is the wish. A wish implies a striving, a tendency, and must be supported by the capacity to mobilize motor acts, an impulse. This impulse to act is spoken of as psychic or instinctual energy or, in the case of the sexual instincts, libido . . . The id therefore creates instinctual needs, translates them into wishes, and provides the capacity to mobilize motor acts." Ostow adds finally, "the id is the central nervous system structure concerned with elaborating instinctual needs, translating them into wishes, providing the wishes with impetus and transferring impetus from wishes which cannot be satisfied to other wishes which can." (In his paper, "Theory of Psychic Energetics," Ostow goes further and speculates that the globus pallidus may be the "source of instinctual energy." The id is located in the basal ganglia.) The speculation is bold and the leap from the neurological and biochemical to the psychological is dangerously seductive. As Rapaport has cautioned such sweeping formulations draw speculative analogies between two very different kinds of data. We would be well advised to respect Freud's own statement[4] that, "The study of the sources of instincts lies outside the scope of psychology . . . An exact knowledge of the sources of instinct is not invariably necessary for purposes of psychological investigation."

## ENERGY, STRUCTURE AND PSYCHIC REPRESENTATION

Keeping in mind the two alternative definitions of the id, the neurological-biochemical vs. the psychological, it is proper to ask how, in the case of the latter, we account for the force and direction of the motivating drives of the id that come to bear on the ego. It is pointless to get involved in a squabble about the biological origins of "psychic energy," or whether psychic energy must obey the laws that hold for energy in general and so forth. Colby[2] had discussed the methodological issues involved in our use of the economic concept of energy in clear and cogent terms. In restating Kubie's position that "a construct of energy must stand for more than some disparate, final quantitative resource in explaining the complex flux of psychic activity," Colby adds that "The chief usefulness of a construct of energy is that it aids us in descriptions of change, of activity, of motion, of acceleration and deceleration of processes of excitement and abeyance." Psychic energy, or as Colby prefers, "cathexis energy," is "a synoptic way of talking about activity and change."

The construct of psychic energy is used in psychoanalysis to account for the following kinds of psychological phenomena:

1. The intensity of aims that temporarily at least seek to end a state of tension by means of specific and repetitive forms of activity.
2. The substitution of one form of activity for another through displacement and fusion.
3. The urgent search for specific objects as tension-relieving end-points of behavior.
4. The replaceability of specific objects by one another, e.g., object vs. self.
5. The relative power of different motivational tension states to take precedence over one another.

Special problems arise when the construct of energy is used to explain the choice of consummatory goals or aims. Freud defined instinct as a quantum of energy that pushed its way toward a particular goal. Many of the modern theories[15] about ego functions continue this assumption that instincts supply their own specific aims. Colby and others[16] have critically discussed the inherent fallacy that instinctual energy can have built into it an aim or an object which alone fulfills the demands of the instinct. Psychic energy in this view has neither aim nor object. Energy activates, it does not direct. Energy can be related to goals only through the psychic representations of sensations excited by needs and of the aims and functions required to carry out the aims, which it activates.

It has become the fashion to postulate four types of instinctual energy, two of which, sexual and aggressive energy, have self-contained aims. The other two, desexualized and deaggressivized energy, have in some unknown way lost their polarizing powers and have become neutral. Their neutrality refers only to their lack of goals since they continue to activate. Colby aptly remarks that all "cathexis" (psychic) energy, by itself, "is simply nondescript." He separates the concept of drive from that of "cathexis energy," which is neutral and goal-less, and proposes that drives be considered structural components of the psychic apparatus which, like the other parts, are activated by cathexis energy. Carried a step further, drives may be defined as functional entities with inborn "meanings" that have psychic representation. This formulation of drive is quite different from that implied in Freud's view of the id as a cauldron of chaotic urges and energy. How the drives get their meaning or purpose remains uncertain (see below), but they possess a somatic source, excite sensations, consist of an aim or activity that strives to re-establish a dynamic equilibrium, and require an object which fulfills the aim and brings the activity to a halt. What distinguishes these attributes of drives from other biological activities is that they are able to obtain psychic representation through arousal of the perceptual apparatus of the ego. There are many biological functions, as I have noted earlier, which are integrated without psychic representation. They operate automatically through strictly humoral and neurological (sub-cortical) regulation. Such activities need no psychic (cortical) intervention to maintain them and cannot be treated as psychic operations of a drive nature. They can engage the psychic apparatus only indirectly through secondary effects upon organic function, effects which may then be perceived and incorporated psychically through mental representation.

To sum up, a drive is the recurrent excitation of a particular form of activity toward the environment. The aim of the drive is that activity which brings the excitation to an end and ushers in a recuperative period of rest. As parts of the psychic apparatus, drives are more than the representations of executive anatomic organ systems. They include the ideational representatives of the activities of relevant somatic structures, of the pain-pleasure aspects of these activities, and of the objects which are associated with arousal and are necessary to end the urge for activity. Among the pain-pleasure attributes of somatic activity are the whole range of pleasure affects, including affection and love, and of pain affects—fear, rage, guilt and grief. Each part of the pain-pleasure complex can become endowed with a symbolic (ideational) representative, with inter-connecting associations to other ideas and with a highly charged anticipation of the future. Genetically, each component is limited in adaptive effectiveness by the maturational level of the perceptual apparatus of the ego through which it first achieved psychic representation.

It may be assumed, if one chooses to use the energic concept, that the P-R's of the drives and their derivatives are invested with psychic energy which defines their relative power to excite activity, but not their purpose.

Energic variations are probably determined by variations in the intensity of excitation coming from somatic sources. But, the psychic (cathexis) energy, or whatever one chooses to call the activating potential of a mental representative, is and remains *neutral* in content. The choice of a goal is the outcome of a specific sequence of processes which begins with perception of the sensory evidence of discomfort or tension and of its location or source, includes the associated memories of similar discomforts and how they previously have been relieved in one's self (or in others), and ends with an emotionally charged anticipation about the future relief of the tension and the achievement of accompanying gratification. It is this set of *affectively* invested ideas and images which seems to release the mental activity and behavior that we call a "drive." If we thus distinguish between the somatic origins of a drive and the psychic entity that is the drive itself, then logically it must be the ego and not the id or its component instinctual elements which selects and organizes the goals of motivated behavior. This distinction corrects a basic weakness in the concept of the id as a structure made up of impelling forces in "a cauldron of seething excitement," but which at the same time is supposedly able to give direction and aim to the activity it excites. It is, I believe (following Colby), more logical to postulate that all energy is neutral, that it impels but does not select behavior. The polarization of functions in one or another direction comes rather from the perceptual meaning of the psychic imagery by which the ego identifies the operating components of a need tension or drive.

The id is therefore no more a source of cathectic psychic energy than is any other part of the psychic apparatus. This holds true especially if the id is defined, as I have done here, as the structure containing the mental representatives of the drives. If the id is "primary," it is so in a temporal rather than a dynamic sense. That is to say, the id is a collection of the *earliest* percepts of internal urges and their activities as well as of the original objects associated with arousal and reduction of need tensions. Such percepts are reflected in the psychic representatives formed of visual images and word presentations with which the ego endowed the sensory and motor experiences of infancy and early childhood. The id therefore begins as a psychic structure made up of prelogical, magical percepts of the narcissistic phase where the self-object world is still partly undifferentiated. Later on there are added the percepts and ideas of later childhood and adulthood in which self and object are more and more differentiated from each other. The latter are derived from more mature egos but for one reason or another have been repressed. In either case, finally, whether we think of the id in the way Freud did in his later years as an infra-psychic structure, or, as I have suggested, as a derivative of the primitive ego, we find ourselves with a truncated id and an expanded ego concept.

The question of the energic dominance of the id over the ego has been studied carefully by Hartmann[13,14] and his collaborators, Kris and Loewenstein.[15] Hartmann[13] noted the existence of "conflict-free avenues of reality-adapted development" in addition to ego-id conflictual factors. Within the "conflict-free ego sphere," he placed such functions as "perception, intention, object comprehension, thinking, language, recall phenomena, productivity, . . . the well-known phases of motor development, grasping, crawling, walking, and . . . the maturation and learning process implicit in all these and many others."[11] In this demarcation of function and development, Hartmann underlined the ego's separate and unique identity as compared to the id. His hypothesis, moreover, not only cast doubt upon the origin of the ego from a pre-existent id, but it questioned the primacy originally attributed by Freud to instinctual energy in shaping the ego's organization. Hartmann tried to resolve the issue by recourse to Freud's suggestion of an undifferentiated ego-id phase out of which both ego and id were distilled. Concerning the directing power of the id's drives after differentiation of the ego and id occurred, Hartmann had this to say however: "We are used to speaking of an oral and anal ego, and so on, and trace specific ego attitudes to specific libidinal characteristics of the correlated phase. This aspect shows the phases of ego development in close connection with the sequences of libidinal phases . . . (however) the ways in which ego attitudes are formed by the characteristics of the libidinal phase are not always clear. I think that in some cases the characteristics both of instinctual tendencies and of the attitudes of the ego may have a common origin in the undifferentiated phase . . . (To) describe ego formation only in terms of its dependence on instinctual development is to give only part of the picture . . . (We) are today very much aware of the fact that cross sections of development cannot be completely described in referring only to libidinal aims—not even if we include the corresponding object relationships in our description . . . *It might well be that even the timing and the individual formation of the typical phases could to some extent be traced to individual variations in ego development . . .*"* In this cautious departure from the classical position, Hartmann says in effect that the ego has the power to determine the intensity and aims by which id forces can express themselves rather than the other way around. If this conception is broadened, the logical hypothesis is that it is perhaps not the drives which develop in successive phases, but rather the ego apparatus whose emergent maturation enables the drives to find a particular form of expression. Changes in behavior hitherto ascribed to the genetic organization of instinctual drives in the id become instead alterations in the ego's capacity for perception, for selection of objects to serve as end-points of needs and for control of the executive apparatus—all under the increasing hegemony of the reality principle of adaptive security.

What role does Hartmann's amended view of the ego-id relationship provide for the id's drive energies? Hartmann postulates that the motor power for the autonomous functions of the ego comes from neutralization of instinctual energy. He has proposed that Freud's hypothesis of desexualized libido be extended to include "deaggressivized aggression" as well. Ego cathexes hence would be derived from neutralized sexual and aggressive energies. According to Hartmann, this neutralization is mediated by the ego and the amount of instinctual energy that can be neutralized is an indication of ego strength. There is a suspicious circularity of reasoning in these hypotheses, but disregarding that, we may ask why not postulate that in the beginning, during the so-called undifferentiated phase, all energy is neutral. Ultimately it would become polarized into libidinal and aggressive activity as the relevant somatic structures become operant, engage the perceptual function of the ego, and gain psychic representation. In this view neither id nor ego "creates" the pool of neutral energy. It is a given, an intrinsic potential of the functional organization of the central nervous system which we call the "mind." The ego promotes psychic representation through the gradual deepening of perception by thought and reason which become a decisive factor in development. The typical phases of libidinal development are really a part of the phases of ego development in which specific somatic structures progressively excite perception by their activity and obtain psychic representatives.

*My italics.

Neutral psychic energy is drawn to these mental images in proportion to the cortical excitation produced by the underlying, infra-psychic, physiological activity and its simultaneous affective arousal. The *quality* of the resultant behavior, libidinal or aggressive, is in part determined by the nature of the psychic representative. The *intensity* of the behavior is determined by the amount of neutral energy cathected by the psychic representatives and their associated ideas. As perceptual thinking is broadened by changes in the appreciation of causality, for example, the earliest psychic representatives are successively replaced—but not obliterated—by new ones. In the ideal sense, maturity signifies the emergence of a balanced perception of self as an object in correct relation to all other perceived objects in the environment. It is not energic cathexis alone—neutralized or polarized—which determines whether an adaptive balance or imbalance takes place but, even more, the accuracy with which perception makes it possible for the ego to select acceptable and attainable aims of motivating drives, aims that include the objects needed to end their activity.

The problem of psychic "energetics" is intimately bound up with the problem of affects and their relationship to the concept of the id. Freud, it will be recalled, prescribed another component of instinct representability, namely, the "quota of affect" which "corresponds to the instinct insofar as the latter has become detached from the id and finds expression . . . in processes which are sensed as affects." Further, "ideas are cathexes—basically of memory traces—whilst affects and emotions correspond to processes of discharge, the final manifestation of which are perceived as feelings."[5] The "ideas" are the psychic representatives of the drives. Affect shows itself on the other hand in motor (secretory, vasomotor, and smooth muscle contractility) discharge which alters the person's own body with reference to the external world. Freud equated the affect component of a drive with its energizing or activating function. Be that as it may, the *specific* feeling tone of an affect cannot be identified with psychic energy or with a particular form of instinctual energy. Feelings have to be linked with the specific ideational content of percepts and their thought associations before they can be differentiated as pleasant or unpleasant in a concrete sense. Without these differentiating ideas, feelings emerge as the general tension states that characterize autonomic excitation. They are without meaning and purpose and are always diffusely unpleasant. These *primary affect components* in the id cannot in fact become *psychic* phenomena until invested by the ego with an identifying ideational label. It is this label which converts subcortical excitation—a purposeless readiness for action—into feelings with recognizable sources, aims, and object-directed activity.

What this amounts to, as I have emphasized earlier, is that every motivating drive is accompanied by affect. Drive, appetitive urgency and affect in its *primary* sense appear to be one and the same. Such a definition accounts for the fact that the drive supplies the conative element, an infra-cortical phenomenon, in an activity complex. It provides the push toward a goal that can end a particular striving for activity. But, drive "energy" or primary affect cannot account for the *specific* organization of psychic processes in the ego by which that striving is consummated.[17] The quota of affect, as Freud noted, generates the motor readiness for activity that ultimately leads to consummation. At the same time, sensory perception marks the beginning of the ego's part in the appetitive activity. It leads in turn to the selective arousal of psychic representations, associations and thoughts which are necessary before a motivated executive action takes place. In the case of the primary biological drive systems, the goals by which consummatory aims can be satisfied are determined by psychic representatives of both the somatic structures involved and the objects that have come to be associated with ending their activity. When the urges come from secondary drive systems supplied by external social directives (e.g., from the superego), the goals are determined by the ideational representatives of the now internalized commands. In the final analysis, the goals of both primary and secondary drives are decided by their psychic representatives. We must distinguish between primary affect states as infra-psychic energizing components of instincts and "tamed" affects with specific feeling tone and psychic representation. Affect and perception (which is the source of the idea labeling the feeling) are the two horses in the team that moves toward consummation of a drive. Primary affective excitation is the somatic source of the hypothetical neutral psychic energy which activates the components of psychic functions.

## SUMMARY

Psychic representation is an essential concept for explaining the transformation of somatic excitations into psychical activity. It is rooted in the successive stages through which the function of perception develops. A biological process can obtain psychic representation, psychical qualities and a motivational significance, if an object is necessary to fulfill the aim of that process.

Perception begins with sensory images that correspond to the sensing apparatus that has been excited by external objects or by the internal affective components of motivational drives. Each set of sensory experiences may be considered to be the core of an ego nucleus. The mature ego represents the fusion of these discrete ego nuclei. The instrument for this ego integration is psychic representation derived from higher perceptual levels where concrete percepts of meaning and broader concepts of object relationship are constructed.

The different cathexes of psychic representatives are conferred upon them by the affective potentials of the various sense-organs, ranging from the most primitive contact receptors to the auditory receptors of verbal symbols. Strong cathexis of psychic representatives (i.e., high level of excitability) is a property of the former, comparatively weak cathexis of the latter. The cathectic properties of each sensory apparatus reflect the capacity for affective arousal to action with which each sensory apparatus is phylogenetically endowed.

Psychic representatives are invested with neutral psychic energy which gives them their relative powers to excite and control mental activity. The goals of such activity are set up by the ego's perceptual function in association with "tamed" affects. Primary affects are without intrinsic ideational representatives and are diffuse excitations which provide the appetitive urgency of the drives. The concept of psychic representation as derived from different phases of perception is useful in making psychosomatic reconstructions.

Psychic representations may be endowed with uniquely intense and mobile cathexes that are derived from the percept level that is dominant during the symbiotic phase of object attachment. The more severe the psychosomatic disorder, the firmer are its genetic roots in the symbiotic phase of development. Symbiosis with its blurred distinction between self and non-self occurs at a time when the dominant sensory percepts are endowed with intense affects. The psychic representatives formed at this time can be shared by internal sensations, especially from the gastrointestinal and urogenital systems, and by symbiotic objects who have intruded themselves into the functions of these systems by interfering with their gratifying activity precisely at a time when they should be operating spontaneously and autonomously.

Finally, the ego gains structural importance at the expense of the id since biological excitations can take on psychical qualities—motivational force—only if they can gain psychic representation. The id becomes a psychic structure containing a residue of the ego's early psychic formations as well as the objects of more recent repressions. As controlling forces over the ego, the motivating drives must share importance with intra-ego perceptual processes. The latter help to determine the adaptive level reached by the ego far more than earlier conceptions allowed. In any case, a broader view of perception and psychic representation relative to their power to shape behavior results in a truncated id and an expanded ego concept.

## References

1. Beres, D. Perception, imagination and reality. *Int. J. Psychoanal.* 41: 327–334, 1960.
2. Colby, K. M. *Energy and Structure in Psychoanalysis.* New York: Ronald Press, 1955.
3. Freud, S. A case of paranoia. *Standard Edition,* Vol. 12. London: The Hogarth Press, 1957.
4. Freud, S. Instincts and their vicissitudes. In *Standard Edition,* Vol. 14. London: The Hogarth Press, 1957.
5. Freud, S. The unconscious. In *Standard Edition,* Vol. 14. London: The Hogarth Press, 1957.
6. Freud, S. Repression. In *Standard Edition,* Vol. 14. London: The Hogarth Press, 1957.
7. Freud, S. The ego and the id. In *Standard Edition,* Vol. 19. London: The Hogarth Press, 1961.
8. Freud, S. Inhibitions, symptoms and anxiety. In *Standard Edition,* Vol. 20. London: The Hogarth Press, 1959.
9. Freud, S. *New Introductory Lectures.* New York: W. W. Norton, 1933.
10. Freud, S. *An Outline of Psychoanalysis.* New York: W. W. Norton, 1933.
11. Glover, E. The concept of dissociation. *Int. J. Psychoanal.* 24: 7–13, 1943.
12. Goldfarb, W. *Childhood Schizophrenia.* Cambridge: Harvard University Press, 1961.
13. Hartmann, H. *Ego Psychology and the Problem of Adaptation.* New York: Int. Univ. Press, 1958.
14. Hartmann, H. The mutual influences in the development of the ego and the id. *The Psychoanalytic Study of the Child,* Vol. 7, New York: Int. Univ. Press, 1950, pp. 9–30.
15. Hartmann, H., Kris, E., and Loewenstein, R. M. Comments on the formation of psychic structure. *The Psychoanalytic Study of the Child,* Vol. 2. New York: Int. Univ. Press, 1946.
16. Kardiner, A., Karush, A., and Ovesey, L. A methodological study of freudian theory, parts 1–4. *J. Nerv. Ment. Dis.* 129: 11–19, 133–143, 207–221, 341–356, 1959.

17. Kardiner, A., and Spiegel, H. *War Stress and Neurotic Illiness*. New York: Paul B. Hoeber, Inc., 1947.
18. Karush, A. The concept of the id. Presented at panel discussion *The Concept of the Id*. Annual Meeting of the American Psychoanalytic Association, Toronto, May, 1962.
19. Ostow, M. The structural model: ego, id and super-ego. *Annals N. Y. Acad. Sci.* 76, part 4, 1959.
20. Ovesey, L. Pseudohomosexuality, the paranoid mechanism, and paranoia. *Psychiatry* 18: 163–173, 1955.
21. Ovesey, L. The homosexual conflict. *Psychiatry* 17: 243–250, 1954.
22. Rado, S. *Lectures on Psychodynamics*. Columbia Psychoanalytic Clinic for Training and Research, New York, 1945.
23. Rado, S. *Psychoanalysis of Behavior*. New York: Grune and Stratton, 1956.
24. Rapaport, D. On the psychoanalytic theory of motivation. *Nebraska Symposium on Motivation*. Lincoln, Nebraska: University of Nebraska Press, 1960.
25. Rapaport, D. *The Structure of Psychoanalytic Theory*. Psychological Issues, Vol. 11, No. 2. New York: Int. Univ. Press, 1960.

# Discussion: An Adaptational Approach to Psychic Representation, Perception, and the Psychic Apparatus  *(Karush)*

*by Eugene Pumpian-Mindlin, M.D.*

Dr. Karush has presented a fascinating exposition of an adaptational theory of perceptual dominance and psychic representation which includes an attempt at a genetic formulation of the role of perception and possible correlations with certain general clinical phenomena.

It is unfortunate that due to the limitations of the program he could only present about one third of his paper—for in the other parts he carries forth the implications of his formulations with regard to current analytic theory, particularly structural theory and the relations and relative roles of ego and id and of the concept of psychic energy. However, the part he has been able to present is self contained—and is exciting in its implications in terms of a rapprochement between classical psychoanalytic theory and adaptational theory.

Moreover it also is of great interest because it seems to me to open up ways for possible experimental or clinical investigative approaches to validate, disprove or modify some of his basic ideas and assumptions. Dr. Karush's emphasis on the role of auditory dominance and the formation of verbal representations in the developmental sequence of psychic representations is of great significance, for it is here that one passes from percept to concept, from thing representation to word representation, from concrete to abstract and by implication from separate ego nuclei to ego synthesis under the influence of concept formation formed by verbal psychic representations. Perhaps herein lies a clue which may be pursued at some other time with regard to the elusive concept of "ego strength" in terms of the ability to synthesize the various sense-ego nuclei and their related differential affective charges into concepts of verbal representations.

One is reminded in this connection of one of the very few diagrams which Freud ever used (in the Ego and the Id),[1] in which he gave a special place to the auditory sphere by having the ego wear the "cap of hearing," although he never elaborated in detail on its crucial role, as is done by Dr. Karush.

However I should like to turn to a question which is rarely touched upon in our discussions—i.e., the question of technique and method—which we all tend to take for granted. Although we refer often to the psychoanalytic method, we rarely stop to think of its limitations as well as its assets. In most other sciences there is an implicit as well as explicit recognition of the limitations of one's technical tools, an acceptance of their specific design and function to meet specific demands. It is peculiar that in psychoanalysis we often hear of the limitations of our theoretical constructs, both with regard to classical theory as well as with regard to its modifications and emendations, but rarely is the question raised as to whether the psychoanalytic method as such is suited to other areas of investigation. Perhaps the very fact that it has been so successful in revealing to us so much of a startling nature has blinded us to the fact that the technical tool and the method itself do have inherent limitations with regard to the nature of the data they can yield to observation. What I should like to examine in the short time allotted to me is the question of the appropriateness of our basic technical instrument—free association —to the investigation of the phenomena which are discussed by Dr. Karush. The analytic observational method consists of certain components: privacy, confidentiality, regularity and longitudinality, which, combined with the technical instrument of free association, serve to reduce the interference of the secondary process in order to expose to observation the manifestations of primary process psychic activity. In other words, logical, rational, structured, ego-oriented, i.e., adaptive, psychic activity interferes with observation of drive-centered psychic processes in the analytic situation. The shift in focus from drive-centered data to the interferences with production of these data represents the shift from an id-oriented psychology to an ego-oriented psychology.

However the focus of the technique of free association is primarily in the direction of the drive derivatives (psychic representations and affects) and only secondarily in the direction of the ego forces which oppose their emergence, as well as the objects of the drives. Moreover the technique of free association appears to favor the emergence of only particular types of data, a point to which I will return shortly. This problem was well summarized by Anna Freud[2] many years ago in the following statement:

> "We are all familiar with the accusation not infrequently made against analysts— that they may have a good knowledge of a patient's unconscious but are bad judges of his ego. There is probably a certain amount of justification in this criticism for the analyst lacks opportunities of observing the patient's whole ego in action."[23-24]

It seems to me then if we are to investigate the areas of perception and psychic representation in relation to adaptation as suggested by Dr. Karush, it may be necessary to re-examine the role and function of our basic technical instrument to see if it is appropriate to elucidate the phenomena which he attempts to delineate. For example, Dr. Karush lays great emphasis on the genetic development of ego nuclei from the predominantly direct contact senses through the visual-kinesthetic modalities to the verbal-auditory, and derives from this a psychopathological nosology in terms of an increasing severity of disturbance as regression occurs from each area.

However our technical instrument is not primarily designed to elicit equally specific material in relation to each of these areas. It appears to be selective in terms of yielding, relatively speaking, more specific information with regard to the genetic aspects of the psychic derivatives of the direct contact senses, somewhat less regarding the visual-kinesthetic and the least specific genetic material in relation to the verbal-auditory (perhaps because the latter encompass the very means of communication for the former and are therefore less observable). If it does succeed in eliciting information regarding these latter areas of function it does so insofar as they interfere with our observation of primary process activity, our principal focus of interest.

Free association as a technique, combined with the psychoanalytic method is an admirable instrument for what it is designed to do—i.e., to investigate motivation (drive, conation), but it is not therefore necessarily equally suited to investigate perception or cognition or interaction with the external world. Under suitable conditions the psychoanalytic method and technique reveals a great deal of systematic material with regard to the orificial relations (i.e., oral, anal, phallic) of an individual to himself and to his fantasies of and feelings about the world. The emphasis on the three areas of transition from the exterior to the interior of the body at the transitions to mucous membranes from the skin is remarkable. It is these areas with their psychological elaborations which we can observe most consistently and with greatest regularity. However observations regarding other areas are much more fragmentary and erratic. For example, we almost never elicit by this method data relating to acquisition of verbal comprehensive or language acquisition so intimately related to verbal psychic representation and concept formation (or even fantasy material regarding these areas.) It seems to me curious that the enormous significance of the symbolic process and of verbalization, which is most distinctly and uniquely characteristic of the human being, seems to be beyond the reach of the psychoanalytic technique and method. With the emphasis on the ability of our method to uncover repressed and unconscious material we seem strangely unaware of this gap in our data-gathering. If one were to counter this by stating that this lies in the so-called "conflict-free" ego sphere and therefore does not come under our scrutiny, one could reply that speech and verbalization do come under conflict and therefore that we should be able to learn more about them— and that relation of verbal psychic representations to concrete thing representations form the crux of the psychological aspects of schizophrenic disorders—and yet we know little of how they come into being and less of how they become distorted and disturbed. From our other areas of psychological knowledge we know that a genetic understanding is not only important but necessary. However in this area we have little or no knowledge. What I am attempting to point out is that perhaps our lack of knowledge is not so much due to lack of theoretical formulations as due to lack of observational data deriving from our technical limitations.

As much as we know about psychosexual developmental stages and the emotional drives and vicissitudes connected therewith, we have amazingly little material regarding the areas which loom large in Dr. Karush's discussion: the role of perceptual dominance, language formation and its relation to word representations and concept formation. As Dr. Karush cogently states: "The concept of instinct refers to motivation; the concept of perceptual dominance refers to ego function and structure. Each complements the other but neither is derived from the other."

Perhaps in order to elucidate further this complementary relationship it may be necessary, as I have attempted to indicate, to critically evaluate the use of our prime technical instrument to see if it is equally suited to elicit the type of observational material necessary to further explore Dr. Karush's provocative ideas. Perhaps we will have to combine our technique and method with other techniques deriving from related scientific fields (e.g., psychology, education, anthropology, etc.) in order to be able to further elucidate the role of perceptual dominance. Such work as that done by Kardiner and others represents the beginnings of such a synthesis and approach.

It appears to me that Dr. Karush presented (and expanded upon in the unread portions of his paper) many areas which may well provide food for thought and stimulus to further investigation and rapprochement with diverse fields.

One is always profoundly influenced by the environment in which one functions. For the past $2\frac{1}{2}$ years I have been working in a setting in which there is a great deal of research activity in the field of psychophysiology— including much work in sleep deprivation, sensory isolation and perceptual isolation. It occurs to me that these investigations, which lead to marked disturbances in perception, might be fruitfully combined with some type of analytic investigation of the subjects in order to investigate further some of the theoretical formulations presented to us by Dr. Karush. Certainly the disintegrative impact of perceptual isolation may possibly cast some light upon the various sense-egos which he postulates. A synthesis of this type of research with analytic investigations of the subjects involved might be most productive and revealing.

May I express my appreciation to Dr. Karush for a significant contribution.

## References

1. Freud, S. The Ego and the Id. *Standard Edition*, Vol. 19, p. 24. London: The Hogarth Press, 1961.
2. Freud, S. The Ego and Mechanisms of Defense. (Second Edition). p. 23–24. London: The Hogarth Press, 1942.

# Clinical Psychoanalytic Studies

# The Phobic Reaction: A Psychodynamic Basis for Classification and Treatment

*by Lionel Ovesey, M.D.*

The phobic reaction can be defined as a defense against neurotic anxiety by avoidance of an imagined danger unconsciously perceived. It is one of the most common defensive maneuvers encountered by the psychiatrist in clinical practice. The mental mechanism of symbolic displacement which terminates in phobic avoidance is always the same, but patients may otherwise differ markedly in developmental history, personality type, and psychodynamic pattern. The purpose of this paper is to provide a simple but operationally useful clinical classification of phobic reactions based on an understanding of these differences. Such an understanding is essential to the therapeutic management of phobic patients because it plays an important role in the choice of psychotherapy as well as in its conduct.

The term "personality" designates the habitual patterns of perception and response used by an individual as he adapts to his environment. There is, of course, no such thing as a pure personality type; there are only mixtures. However, in most people, personality traits are polarized in a predominant direction, and on this basis, personalities lend themselves to classification. Clinically, phobic patients can be grouped under three general headings, in accordance with a personality type and a psychodynamic pattern. Let us consider each of these headings in turn.

## I. THE PHOBIC PERSONALITY AND THE AGORAPHOBIC REACTION

The loose term "phobic patient," as used by most psychiatrists, refers to patients in this category. They comprise the garden variety type of phobic patient, the type most often seen by the practicing psychiatrist.

They seek treatment for an agoraphobic syndrome which consists to a variable degree of fear of being alone, fear of going anywhere alone, fear of traveling, and fear of enclosed spaces, such as elevators, small rooms, subways, and vehicles of all kinds. These patients tend to share a common personality which can be designated the phobic personality. They are immature, passive, easily frightened persons, who are markedly inhibited in both assertion and aggression. They have little confidence in their capacities to meet adult responsibilities, to satisfy their needs, and to insure their survival. In consequence, their predominant mode of psychological adaptation is through magical, infantile dependence upon stronger, authoritative parental figures.

The developmental history of the phobic personality is replete with early failures of mastery over the environment. Multiple childhood phobias, such as fears of being alone, the dark, animals, games, skating, climbing, bicycle-riding, etc. are a frequent finding. Family constellations vary, but they all have one feature in common: they consistently reveal parents, who neglect in various ways to foster the child's attempts to achieve mastery. In many instances, the parents themselves have various phobias and transmit their fearful attitudes to the growing child. Other parents, though not phobic are overprotective and shield the child from hardship, so that he never learns to persevere in the face of adversity. Often, there is a history of negligence, where parents are frequently absent, or, even if present, are distinterested and do not provide the child with support at times of critical failures in mastery. In extreme cases, one finds parents who cripple the child by subjecting his attempts to acquire skills to constant ridicule, derision, and belittlement. Children exposed to such parents perceive their environments as full of unknown terrors. It is small wonder that they fail to become self-sufficient, independent adults.

The phobic personality suffers from multiple phobic anxieties and struggles constantly against multiple phobic responses. He may be afraid to drive, afraid to swim, afraid to fly, and so on. For the most part, the phobias are such that they do not seriously interfere with every day functioning, since the phobic personality either adjusts around them, or, when forced by necessity, makes a special effort and carries out the required action. Phobic responses of this kind are a hangover from the earlier failures to achieve mastery in childhood. They are usually motivated by the unresolved need for dependency, much less often by repressed sexuality. In those instances, however, where an acute agoraphobic reaction breaks out, the onset is characteristically motivated by a forbidden sexual impulse, which then threatens the patient's magical dependence upon his parents. Behind this primary threat to the patient's security lie the fantasied punishments of death and castration.

I have never seen an acute agoraphobic reaction in a phobic personality which was initiated solely by a threat to dependency unrelated to a sexual wish. It would seem, theoretically, that in such a dependent person simply leaving the parental home, for example, and setting up an independent existence, could in itself precipitate an agoraphobic reaction. Clinically, however, in my experience, any step toward independence seems invariably to be unconsciously perceived as a step toward sexual freedom. The patients fears he will lose control over his sexual impulses and, as a result, his parents will withdraw their protection. In effect, then, the anxiety about dependency that sets the acute agoraphobic reaction in motion is derived indirectly from the repressed sexual wish, and not directly from the challenge of independence, per se. This is an important point to keep in mind in the psychotherapy of agoraphobic reactions in patients with phobic personalities. The therapist should not be fooled by an overlay of dependency needs with an apparent absence of the sexual motivation. In all likelihood it is there, no matter how much the patient at first tries to deny it.

I also do not attribute much importance to repressed aggression and fears of retaliation as motivational impulses for agoraphobia in phobic personalities. It seems to me, at most, they play an ancillary role, both in the origin of the phobia and in its perpetuation. This observation is in contrast to my experience with obsessive and paranoid personalities, where repressed aggression as a primary source of agoraphobic reactions is not uncommon. I can only speculate on the reason for this. The phobic personality, as a rule, does not develop very effective patterns of aggression and hence may have little need for defenses against them.

In order to overcome his phobia, the agoraphobe must enter into the phobic situation again and again until he reconditions a new response free from neurotic anxiety. The technical problem that faces the therapist is how best to facilitate this reconditioning process. Here, an understanding of the phobic personality and the limitations it imposes on therapeutic maneuverability is all-important. In any therapy, of course, the patient is helped to achieve his maximum level of self-sufficiency. A few patients with phobic personalities, whose agoraphobic symptoms are minimal, are able to participate successfully in an analytic therapy and eventually become reasonably independent human beings. The great majority, however, irrespective of integrative category—neurotic, borderline, or schizophrenic—are incapable of giving up their dependent adaptation. Their adaptive patterns are fixated on the level of infantile omnipotence and their primary goal in life is to form symbiotic attachments to parental surrogates.

In the conduct of psychotherapy with markedly dependent patients, the therapist must never forget that magical dependency is an adaptive operation. As far as the patient is concerned, it is the only one available to him, however faulty it may be. He is convinced there is no other way to satisfy his needs and to safeguard his security. Once an agoraphobe enters treatment, therefore, he expects the therapist not only to anticipate his infantile need for dependency, but also to defend him from the dangers of the forbidden sexual desires. Such patients seldom, if ever, possess the ego strength to give up their magical dependence. For this reason, they are unable to profit from an orthodox psychoanalytic treatment, where the therapeutic leverage must come from insight and the ultimate therapeutic goal is not merely relief of symptoms, but a reconstructed, self-sufficient personality. Extensive modifications in both methods and goals of treatment must be introduced. Interpretations in dependent patients of this kind do not lead to insights which mobilize adaptive resources, since these resources are not available to begin with. Instead, interpretations serve as a backdrop for the therapist's reassurance that no disaster will occur when the patient experiences sexual impulses. The therapeutic leverage comes from the magical omnipotence with which the patient endows the therapist. This fantasy should not be analyzed away. Rather, the therapist should use it as a protective canopy under which the patient can with a feeling of safety give up his crippling symptoms. In other words, the best one can usually hope for in phobic personalities with an agoraphobic reaction is a symptomatic transference "cure." Periodically, at moments of new stress, reenforcement of the dependent attachment to the omnipotent therapist can often maintain the cure indefinitely. It is very doubtful that the weak egos of these patients can undergo significant analytic reconstruction, no matter how many so-called "parameters" are introduced in treatment.*

Most agoraphobes begin treatment in the same fashion with a recitation of their physical symptoms—the palpitations, the shortness of breath, the faintness, the dizziness, and so on. All they ask is that the therapist relieve them of these handicaps and then they will gladly go into the street. This, of course, is a defensive maneuver in the service of the resistance, and puts the cart before the horse. The first task of the therapist, therefore, is to get across to the patient that the physical symptoms are not organically determined, but are somatic manifestations of anxiety. Furthermore, they will not disappear in advance of going into the street, but only in the course of making the attempt. Next, the therapist must use the patient's free associations and dreams to reconstruct a simplified psychodynamic explanation of the phobic mechanism, how it developed from the past, and how it operates in the present. Such an explanation is a prerequisite to the reconditioning process, which usually cannot be carried out in a sustained way unless the patient at least intellectually grasps the meaning of his phobia. This is no easy task, since agoraphobes as a group do not have a very high order of psychological aptitude and find it difficult to deal with psychological concepts. Nevertheless, with patience and perseverence, given a willing subject, it can in most instances be accomplished within the first several months of therapy. Initially, the explanation is non-specific and deals with the patient's fear that he will be killed should he venture into his phobic area. Later, and only after the patient, himself, has introduced the sexual theme, should the sexual motivation be specifically indicted.

Once the relationship between phobic anxiety, phobic avoidance, the sexual motivation, and fear of death have been established, the patient is ready to recondition a new response. Some patients, of course, unconsciously supported by the magical transference, may already have begun the attempt spontaneously, a few perhaps almost from the very beginning of therapy. These early attempts are usually short-lived, but they should not be discouraged, since every little bit helps. No pressure, however, should be put on the patient until after the psychodynamic reconstruction has been brought into the open. Then the therapist must kindly, but with

---

*See Reference I in Bibliography for an extensive discussion of dependency problems, their psychodynamics, and their therapeutic management.

firmness, take the position that the patient cannot overcome his phobia without facing the phobic situation. Most patients at this point develop considerable resistance and how much pressure can be applied is a matter of clinical judgment. Too much and too fast may push the patient right out of treatment; too little and too slow may lead to endless procrastination.

At the beginning of his re-education, the patient should not be left completely to his own devices, but rather the therapist should set a series of graded tasks for him. In most cases, encouragement and persuasion will suffice to motivate the patient, but at times, when resistance is exceptionally strong, the therapist may have to rely on more forceful methods, such as command or even the threat of termination. The latter is a last ditch device wherein the therapist threatens to throw the patient out unless he does what is required to overcome his fear. On some occasions, as a temporary measure, it may be desirable for the therapist to accompany the patient, or meet him at previously designated places. Sedatives and tranquilizers should be used, particularly for those phobics, where the anxiety is so great it simply cannot be surmounted without pharmacological aid. A few patients do better with a shot of whiskey, rather than with drugs, though often the effect must be purely psychological since it may be achieved almost immediately. I recommend to patients, who are responsive to alcohol, that they carry a miniature bottle of whiskey with them, wherever they go, to be imbibed as necessary.

There are a number of magical devices which arise out of the transference which may be helpful to the patient, especially in moments of sudden anxiety, when he is alone in the phobic situation. These devices symbolically convey the therapist's omnipotence, reassure the patient that he will be safe, and hence allay his panic. For example, I have had patients, who carried bottles of pills with my name on the label in their handbags for years, yet rarely ingested a pill. The sight of the bottle alone usually sufficed to quiet them. Other patients have relied on a good luck charm or a talisman that I had given them as a gift.

A very simple device, yet surprsingly effective with some dependent patients, who are markedly suggestible, is the Certificate of Safe Conduct. I came upon this device quite by accident while explaining the reconditioning process to a woman, who was so phobic she had to be treated at home.* We had reached a point in therapy where with the aid of sedatives and a shot of brandy she could just get outside of her front door, but she absolutely refused to go further. She insisted she would never survive the physical manifestations of her anxiety, but would surely drop dead of heart failure. I reassured her for several months, again and again, but she wouldn't budge. Finally, one day she said sharply, "It's all very well for you to say that nothing will happen to me, but how do I know you are really right?" I retorted, with exasperation, "What do you want me to do? Give you a written guarantee?" To my surprise, instead of getting angry, her face lit up with hope, and she said, with complete seriousness, "Oh, would you?" I felt I had nothing to lose, so I answered, "Bring me a sheet of paper," which she quickly did. On it I wrote the following:

> CERTIFICATE OF SAFE CONDUCT
> I personally guarantee that _____   _____
> can go anywhere she chooses and absolutely no harm
> will befall her.
> Lionel Ovesey, M.D.

She solemnly folded the paper and put it in her purse. The next day, armed with the certificate, she began a sustained attempt to move further and further from her house. (See Case 1.) Since then, I have offered the certificate to other agoraphobic patients. Some laughingly turned it down, and I did not press the matter, but several accepted it, and of those who did, all claimed it helped alleviate their anxiety and bolstered their courage to go on.

In recent years a good deal has been written about so-called "behavior therapy" for phobias, as well as for other neurotic symptoms.[2,3,4] The techniques of this therapy are based on learning theory, ignore the relationship with the therapist, and dispense with insight into the unconscious. Thus, typical of behavior therapy is the treatment of a phobia for blizzards by reciprocal inhibition, the treatment of a homosexual by aversion therapy, and the treatment of an eye tic by negative practice. I have no

---

*This patient provided an especially amusing example of the poor psychological aptitude that characterizes most, though not all phobic personalities. She found it very difficult to comprehend my explanation of reconditioning as the means for overcoming her phobia. To facilitate matters, I told her the story of Pavlov's dog. She listened attentively, but when I finished, she looked very puzzled. "What's the matter?" I asked, "Didn't you understand the story?" "Yes, of course I understood it," she answered, "But I'm not a dog."

personal experience with behavior therapy, as such, and I cannot go along with the wholesale elimination of psychoanalytic concepts, but I do feel there is a place in the more dynamically-oriented psychotherapies for the incorporation of reconditioning devices of all kinds, especially in the treatment of phobic patients.

## CLINICAL EXAMPLES

*Case 1.* A 30-year-old married woman began psychotherapy with me after three unsuccessful attempts at treatment with three different analysts. Her first attempt occurred six years before I saw her when she developed an acute agoraphobic reaction after the birth of her first child and was unable to be left alone. She could leave the apartment in which she lived as long as she was accompanied by someone, and never for distances longer than a few blocks, but she much preferred to stay at home. She entered psychoanalysis five times a week with an analyst across the street and stayed in treatment for two years, but with no improvement. She broke off with him and, thereafter, was too frightened to leave her apartment, even in the company of a companion. She prevailed upon an analyst to treat her at home, but after a year without improvement, during which time she had not left the apartment even once, he gave up. Still another analyst made a similar attempt, again for a year, but with the same unhappy result. The patient did not immediately try again, but now "resigned" herself, quite contentedly, to a completely sheltered life, never budging from the apartment and always in the company of a housekeeper, her husband, her mother, various other relatives, and friends. This went on for two years, when, at the insistence of her husband, she permitted a fourth analyst, myself, to visit her in the apartment.

The patient was raised in a wealthy household. Her father was occupied most of the time with business and she saw little of him. Her mother was an infantile creature, concerned primarily with herself, who delegated the child's care largely to nursemaids. The latter were over-protective and permissive and required nothing of the child, except that she cause them no trouble. The mother did take the time, however, to intimidate the patient sexually. She threatened repeatedly to beat her if she ever caught her masturbating. For many years, well into the patient's adolescence, the mother periodically smelled the patient's hands for tell-tale vaginal odors to ascertain whether she had masturbated or not. Needless to say, the patient, as far as she could remember, never masturbated during her childhood. (She attempted masturbation only once in her life and that was after she was married. This attempt occurred when she became sexually aroused while her husband was away on a business trip. She suffered great anxiety, failed to get an orgasm, and afterwards was consumed with a terrible guilt. Her guilt had been so great that she was unable to reveal this incident to her three previous psychiatrists, and finally confessed it to me during her second year of treatment, even thought the incident had frequently come to her mind and she had consistently denied masturbation upon direct questioning.) She had numerous fears as a child. She was afraid of the dark, afraid to be alone, afraid of social gatherings, afraid to swim, afraid to skate, and so on. She was a pretty girl and popular with boys but was always anxious in their presence. This anxiety markedly increased after the age of 17 when she began to go out on dates. These frequently were accompanied by nausea and vomiting, faintness and dizziness, attacks of diarrhea, palpitations, outbreaks of hives, and violent headaches. Simultaneously, she began to suffer transient fears of the street, the subway, buses and taxis, crowds, and elevators, but she still managed, nevertheless, to maintain some semblance of control over these fears and she continued to engage in the related activities, although she progressively limited the number of boys that she dated. She met her future husband when she was 21, married him in a few months, quickly got pregnant, and by the end of the first year of marriage had her first child by Caesarian section. It was at this point that the acute agoraphobic reaction broke out.

We embarked upon a therapy in which I saw her, sitting face to face, five times a week. She immediately became involved in an explosive erotic transference and after a stormy four months it was possible from her associations and dreams to reconstruct the psychodynamics of her phobia. She was a very immature and dependent young woman, who found her dependency threatened by her sexual impulses. The general anxiety about sexual activity was finally focalized by the birth of her child, which was evidence for the whole world to behold that she had engaged in sexual intercourse. On a deeper unconscious level, she equated her husband with her father and had the Oedipal fantasy that the baby was really her father's. To this fantasy was attached another, that she had killed the mother and taken the father from her. Now it was no longer possible to escape her mother's wrath and she felt not only that her dependency on the mother was threatened, but also that her mother would kill her. She equated being alone or going out alone, first, with taking care of herself, which she felt she could not do, and, second, with being unprotected against the punitive powers of the "bad" mother. Going out, furthermore, represented the original opportunity for sexual adventure. The street, the elevator, and vehicles became places from which she could not escape if she were seen and caught, and since she held her mother to be omnipotent and and all-seeing, she believed detection and punishment to be inevitable. The phobic defense protected her from all of these disasters. She stayed home, never went out, and constantly had someone—symbolically the "good" mother—with her. The good mother not only insured her dependency and protected her against the punishment of the bad mother, but also the good mother by her presence reassured the patient that she, the mother, was still alive and the patient had not killed her after all.

It is most doubtful that the patient had much insight into this psychodynamic formulation, even though its various components were repeatedly documented by her productions throughout the many years she was in treatment with me and were reviewed with her again and again. It seemed to me she eventually grasped that her physical symptoms were manifestations of anxiety, and that the anxiety, in turn, stemmed from an irrational belief that she would die if she ventured anywhere alone. The rest of the scheme I am convinced was beyond her, but it always gave her a great sense of comfort that I, at least, seemed to understand it, and in this way our discussions of psychodynamics were therapeutically useful.

In the fifth month of therapy the patient began her attempts to overcome her phobia. As a first step, escorted by her housekeeper, she took the elevator from her apartment on the fifth floor to the lobby of her building where she was left in the company of a doorman. She practiced leaving her apartment and sitting downstairs for several weeks until she felt comfortable enough to go out of the front door and stand under the canopy. Four months passed and she was unable to go further until the stalemate was broken, as described above, by the issuance of a safe conduct pass. She then practiced walking back and forth in front of the building until she was able to get to the end of the block in either direction. Here, another protracted delay occurred. She could not bring herself either to turn the corner or to cross the street, even in the company of her housekeeper, her husband, or assorted relatives. In order to surmount this obstacle, and each successive new one that might arise, I decided once again to make use of the magical transference and bolster the safe conduct pass, whose effect at this point seemed to be flagging a little, by offering to accompany her in person. I, therefore, suggested that we meet outside and talk while we walked, instead of holding the sessions in her apartment. She was delighted with the suggestion and from then on all of our sessions were held outdoors, except in inclement weather, when we met either in her apartment or, after she learned how to get there, in my office.

The next day, holding my arm, she practiced crossing the street to the other side and then back again, but no further. She also managed to round the corner and take a few steps up the next block. For the next several months our sessions were devoted to lengthening the distance she could cover from her apartment building to my office, which was on the same street, but three long blocks and three intersections away. I always met her in front of her building and then we walked to whatever point she could make comfortably before we turned back. We then repeated the procedure until the session was over. At first, in spite of my reassurances, she had a great fear that I would abandon her or push her further than she felt able to go, but this anxiety was gradually resolved as she learned that I was always guided by her wishes. In between sessions, accompanied by others, she retraced our route and also made short excursions into the side streets. By the end of the first year of treatment, she was able to go with me from her apartment to my office building and up the elevator to my office.

The next step was to teach her to make the trip alone. She would wait on the street in front of her door until I came out of my building and hove into sight. I waved in recognition and waited until she walked toward me. On occasions when she faltered with anxiety and stopped, I went to her. If she were able to continue; we went on; if not, we turned back. In the nineteenth month, I began waiting in my office while she struggled to get there alone, signalling her arrival by ringing the bell downstairs. There was much backing and filling throughout this period. Sometimes she would have an anxiety attack on the way, return to her apartment, and call me by telephone. We would then spend days practicing in the old way, where she could see me, until her courage mounted and, once again, I could wait in the office for her. Eventually she learned to control her anxiety, so that she usually completed the trip and only rarely had to call for help.

In the third year of therapy I began to meet her away from the office at designated places in the neighborhood. In this way, she gradually acquired the confidence to move about freely within a limited area—five to ten blocks in any direction from her house—either alone or in the company of relatives and friends. She has never been able to go outside of this radius, except to the shore for the summer, but life is quite normal inside of her circle, since it is a self-sustaining community in Manhattan, with ever conceivable kind of facility, including several off-Broadway theaters. We had regularly scheduled sessions for six years, but in the fourth year, for financial reasons, I saw her three times a week instead of five, and in the fifth and sixth years, we met only once a week. Ten years have passed since then and she has maintained her gains, although she has not progressed further. She calls me as necessary when problems arise, usually every few months, and we meet for lunch at least twice a year. The therapeutic result is not perfect, but considering where she started, there is little room for complaint.

Case 2. A 24-year-old married woman entered psychotherapy for an agoraphobia of three years duration. She was born and raised in a European country where her parents had been extremely wealthy and traveled extensively. She was usually left at home to be looked after by nurses and other servants. She grew up a markedly timid child with little feeling of inner security and no confidence in her ability to do anything. At the age of 13 she was sent to England to a finishing school. The war came and her parents fled to America. She remained in England. At the end of the war, when she was 19, she left by steamer to join her parents. She was accompanied by a girl friend, who had had several sexual experiences. The patient, however, was a virgin. On board ship, the two girls became friendly with two ship's officers and the girl friend promptly had intercourse with one of them, encouraging the patient to jump into bed with the other. The patient demurred, but not for long, and by the time she landed in America she had lost her virginity several times over. This caused her some anxiety and guilt, but for the most part, on the surface at least, she seemed psychologically none the worse for what had happened. However, she had only been in America a few weeks when a man tried to pick her up on a bus and she reacted with an acute anxiety attack. Thereafter, whenever she got on a bus, she had another attack. She consulted a physician, who misdiagnosed the attacks as asthma and treated them with adrenalin. This, of course, only made them worse, and she solved the problem by avoiding buses. She then met a man with whom she fell in love, had an affair for several months, and subsequently married. She had a number of anxiety attacks during the affair, particularly on her way to clandestine meetings at her lover's apartment, but she was able to surmount them. In contrast, from the day they got married, although she could be alone in the house, she could not go out unless someone accompanied her. She remained in this crippled condition for three years, going from one doctor to another, each of whom treated her medically, until finally she consulted a psychiatrist.

The psychodynamics were typical tor an agoraphobia. She feared death and loss of dependency for her sexual transgressions, first with the officer and then with her husband, both of whom she unconsciously identified with her father. She managed to stave off her phobia fairly well, except for buses, until she got married, but then it was no longer possible to deny that she was sexually active. A dream early in therapy brought out particularly well the threat posed by her sexual behavior.

She and the girl friend, who accompanied her to America, were both young princesses imprisoned by a bad witch in a castle on some cliffs overlooking the sea. The girl friend suggested they escape by diving from a window into the sea and then swimming toward land. The patient was too frightened and didn't want to do it. Her friend insisted and said she would set the example. She dived head first out of the window. The patient watched her make a graceful swan dive and swim to safety. The patient was terrified, but nevertheless, she climbed on the window sill and dove out. However, unlike the friend's, her dive was very awkward and she landed in such a way as to break her neck and drown.

In the dream, she states very clearly that she would like to escape the "bad" mother's restrictions and have sexual relations as does the girl friend, but whereas her friend is independent and can take care of herself, she—the patient—is utterly incapable of self-support, and if she tries to disobey or leave her mother, she shall surely die.

This patient was seen three times a week for three years. She immediately developed an intense dependent transference and after only one week of therapy, without any suggestion from me, she spontaneously walked out of her apartment and went alone to a supermarket down the block. A week later, she was able to take a cab to my office and thereafter came alone without a companion. She continued to improve steadily, though at a slower pace and with occasional retrogressions. Unlike the previous patient, she entered the phobic situation entirely on her own, and I never once went with her. When therapy ended, she was able to move about freely anywhere in the city with a minimum of anxiety—by foot, by car, by subway, and ultimately by bus. Trips beyond the city limits, however, though not impossible, required heroic efforts. For such occasions, she relied on large dosages of sedatives, alcohol, and a safe conduct pass. She has done well in the twelve years since discharge, suffering only infrequently short-lived bouts of phobic anxiety, all of which she has successfully handled.

*Case 3*. A 20-year-old single girl, living at home with two extremely over-protective parents, took a job, her first, as a secretary to a married businessman old enough to be her father. He introduced her to sexual intercourse and they had an affair that lasted for six months. Then, one night, he took her home, parked the car across the street from her house, and informed her the affair was over. Furthermore, she was fired. His wife was becoming suspicious, and although her work was satisfactory—presumably in both respects, vocational and otherwise—he could not afford to take any more chances. She got out of the car and he drove away. As she stepped off the curb to cross the street to go home, she experienced an acute anxiety attack. Thereafter, only when walking, she was phobic about crossing streets and had to have someone with her before she could cross, although she could walk on the street between crossings without any difficulty. She could ride all kinds of transportation, including the subway, go up and down elevators, and stay home alone, but if she got to a corner alone and nobody was in sight, she would have to wait until someone came along and then, without any word to the stranger, she walked at his side until she crossed the street. She gradually extended the phobia to include heights and trips out of town.

In this case, the patient managed to control her anxiety as long as she was in the affair because she felt protected by her lover, symbolically the father. Once he abandoned her, she felt at the mercy of the punitive mother and, therefore, she had an anxiety attack as she crossed the street to enter her house where her mother was waiting. The phobic displacement was to crossing the street, thus permitting her to live with her mother in a state of reasonable comfort.

Currently, the patient is a housewife with two children. She has been in therapy with me on and off ever since I first saw her thirteen years ago. The initial period of therapy lasted two years with some improvement in her over-all adaptation, but with little change in her phobic symptom, which has remained fixed to the present. She can always walk across a street by herself if she wants to, but it requires a force of will that she rarely chooses to exercise. It is much simpler to handle the anxiety by avoidance or by reliance on other people, since the phobia does not seriously limit her movements. She did not drink, drugs were to no avail, and although she was pleased at my offer of a safe conduct pass, she refused it on the grounds it was "magic" and hence could not work. I did cross some streets with her on a few occasions, but that had no effect either. Throughout the years, during crisis in her life such as jobs, marriage, pregnancy, children, etc., she has returned for brief periods of therapy lasting usually from a few weeks to a few months. Sometimes, a single interview has sufficed. The therapeutic technique has been essentially supportive in accordance with the principles for management of the chronically dependent patient.[1]

## II. THE OBSESSIVE PERSONALITY AND PHOBIC EXTENSIONS OF THE OBSESSIVE REACTION

The obsessive personality as a descriptive entity is generally accepted by psychiatrists, irrespective of theoretical persuasion, and does not require elucidation in any detail here. For our purpose, it will suffice merely to list the major obsessive traits: overconscientiousness, a severe conscience, intellectualization, orderliness, emotional control, excessive attention to details, and perfectionism. Symptomatically, pathological obsessive behavior can be subdivided into doubting and brooding, obsessive thinking, and compulsive ritual-making. These, too, like the traits, are well known phenomenologically and need not be described further. There are, however, theoretical differences among psychiatrists about the childhood development of the obsessive personality and the pathological manifestations to which it may give rise.

The developmental origin was first explained by Freud within the framework of the libido theory.[5] Freud had noted a relationship between the so-called "anal character traits" (obstinacy, orderliness, and parsimony) in the adult and harsh anal training in childhood. He ultimately derived these traits from transformations of the sexual instinct and the libido. Thus, the future anal character had an anal fixation and resisted toilet training because of his vested interest in anal erotism. He eventually gave in, but at the cost of repression of the anal libido, which subsequently was transformed into anal character traits by means of reaction-formation, desexualization, and sublimation.

These traits, however, are better understood adaptationally, without resort to the unproved assumptions of the libido theory.[6,7] We need only to introduce a cultural directive—cleanliness—mediated by the parents in the form of toilet training. The traits then clearly emerge as adaptive responses to discipline. The cultural directive comes in conflict with the child's desire to defecate without restriction, whenever and wherever he pleases. In the course of the struggle that ensues, the child shifts his attention from the simple pursuit of unrestricted anal function to the parental demand that he limit his freedom of action. As a result of this shift, anal function, per se, assumes secondary importance, and the power struggle with the parents becomes primary concern of the child. He can respond predominantly with fear, develop a strong conscience, and gradually integrate patterns of cleanliness, orderliness, submissiveness, conscientiousness, reliability, and punctuality, or he can respond predominantly with rage, in which case he will gradually integrate patterns of disorderliness, obstinacy, defiance, parsimony, unreliability, and unpunctuality. Usually, he responds with both emotions, but vacillates between the two. The emotion which gains ascendency determines which group of "character traits" will eventually predominate. Most often fear wins out and hence the obsessive personality is generally defined in terms of the fearbound traits. In some cases, however, the rage-bound traits predominate and lead clinically to an oppositional syndrome.[8]

Once the techniques of coping with authority are laid down, they are no longer limited to anal function, but are automatically applied to other functions as well. In this way, all relations with people are patterned after the original infantile model and are perceived in terms of defiance or compliance, dominance or submission. Adaptationally, therefore, the "anal character traits" described by Freud are merely security devices that operate in accordance with the emergency emotions of fear and rage.

Furthermore, it is important to understand that toilet training is not the only source for the development of obsessive traits. Toilet training is usually the first sustained discipline to which a child is exposed, but obsessive parents hardly confine their demands for conformance to toilet training alone. Rather, they engage the child in struggles for power over disciplinary items in every area of behavior. It is the combined effect of all of these struggles that eventually molds the obsessive personality. There is a kind of social heredity that operates in this child–parent interaction. Given an obsessive parent, particularly a mother, who, without wavering, demands that her standards be met, a child doesn't have much of a chance. Under such circumstances, she will mold him in her image, and he will emerge from childhood with the obsessive chain unbroken.

Every aspect of obsessive behavior can be traced to the original struggles for power in childhood. The rage experienced by the child is unconsciously misinterpreted as murderous violence and carries in its wake the threat of equally violent retaliation. The child in reality is weaker than his parents and he comes to believe that retaliation in kind is inevitable. Rage, of course, integrates aggressive thought and action. The concept of violence, however, is not limited only to aggression, but becomes symbolically extended to include any transgressive impulse. Thus, any act that is forbidden by the parents, or any thought of such an act, is equated with murder of the parents and evokes a fear of retaliation. The symbolic extension of aggression can even go a step further and eventually encompass most forms of self-assertion. The nuclear conflict, therefore, in obsessive behavior is the control of rage and its symbolic derivatives.

The motivational basis of obsessive symptoms becomes clear in this context. The three subdivisions of pathological obsessive behavior listed before—obsessive doubting and brooding, obsessive thoughts, and obsessive ritual-making—all reflect the same ambivalent conflict, a vacillation between the polarities of rage and fear. The obsessive patient, like Hamlet, is unable to decide whether to do or not to do. Should he be defiant, unleash his rage, and commit a transgressive act, or should he give in to guilty fear, hold the rage in check, and so ward off punishment? In the end, he settles for safety, and his symptom is inevitably designed to inhibit the rage, thus protecting him from retaliation for his prohibited desires.

The primary defense of the obsessive personality is, of course, an obsessive reaction. Frequently, however, the obsessive symptoms do not suffice to control the anxiety and are secondarily reenforced by phobic avoidance. These are the cases I classify as obsessive personalities with a phobic extension of the obsessive reaction. The phobic manifestations in such patients, in contrast to the agoraphobic syndrome of the phobic personality, can rarely be treated directly with any measure of success. They are too intimately a part of the obsessive reaction and will usually go away only as the obsessive symptoms, themselves, are resolved.

Unhappily, psychotherapy of the obsessive reaction is notoriously difficult and successful resolution is not easily attained. An agoraphobe can respond to suggestion and control his anxiety long enough to take effective action. Not so, the obsessive. It is useless to suggest he cease his obsessive thinking or put an end to an obsessive ritual. Magical attempts of this kind, even in the framework of a well-established dependent transference, simply do not work with obsessive patients. What seems to be required is an integrative change, best achieved, in my experience, by an analytic therapy; that is, one which provides the patient with insight into his unconscious motivations. Here, the underlying integration of the obsessive reaction is crucial. Psychoanalysis, or some modification of it, such as so-called psychoanalytically-oriented psychotherapy, are most feasible where the integration is neurotic; they have little, if any, application to obsessive reactions in boderline cases or in the frankly psychotic. For that matter, obsessive symptoms in the latter instances are usually so rigidly fixed that they don't seem very responsive to any of the established forms of psychotherapy. Their severity ebbs and flows, but within a framework of chronicity, and when there is temporary improvement, it is difficult to demonstrate that psychotherapy had much to do with it. Tranquilizers may be helpful, but they, too, are limited in their usefulness. The fact is, psychiatry has yet to devise adequate tools for helping these patients. Perhaps the newer and experimental forms of therapy, such as the behavior therapy[2,3,4] previously mentioned, or milieu therapy[9] with hospitalized patients will be more successful. Or perhaps new drugs will provide the ultimate answer.

## CLINICAL EXAMPLES

*Case 4.* A 26-year-old married man was referred for psychotherapy by an internist because of a chronic diarrhea which did not respond to medical care. The patient displayed all the characteristic traits of an obsessive personality, acquired through a prolonged struggle with an overprotective, markedly obsessive mother. In the initial interview, he revealed that his symptoms began after he experienced intercourse for the first time at the age of 21. A few days later he began to suffer severe griping and urgency, but with only a mild diarrhea. At the time, he did not draw any connection between the symptoms and his sexual adventure. The symptoms gradually died down within the week, but in the ensuing years he had many intermittent attacks of a similar nature, each following sexual episodes with different women. He became obsessively preoccupied with the fear that he would soil himself in public because he would not be able to get to a toilet in time. As a result, he began to plan all his daily activities around proximity to a toilet. Wherever he went, either for social or business purposes, he always had to know in advance where a toilet was located to which he could have ready access in the event of an emergency. In this way, by phobically avoiding those places where toilets were not available, he managed to move about and keep himself reasonably free from anxiety. He continued his sexual adventures and in due course, at 24, got married. After two years of marriage, his symptoms took a sudden turn for the worse. He began to complain of chronic, unremittent diarrhea, not severe, to be sure, but enough to increase greatly his obsessive concern with bowel function and with toilets. Simultaneously, there was a sharp rise in his phobic anxiety. It was at this point that he consulted his internist.

This patient underwent psychoanalysis, four times a week, for four years. At first, he could not account to the therapist for the exacerbation of his symptoms. As it turned out, the relapse coincided with an increasing desire for extra-marital intercourse. He had become involved with a young woman in his office, who had not yet acceded to his overtures, but from his account of their relationship, she was on the verge. It turned out he was right, for it was not many weeks before she invited him to her apartment. He went, but with trepidation, and as she was serving him a drink, he suddenly experienced such a terrible urgency to move his bowels that he broke out in a cold sweat. He was too embarrassed to ask if he could use her toilet. Instead, he pleaded illness and departed in haste. He jumped into his car and managed to maintain control until he reached the rest room of a gas station, where he had an explosive bowel movement.

For the next several days he was anxious, depressed, and stayed very close to toilets, even though his diarrhea had returned to its pre-explosive state of mild chronicity. He offered no explanation to the therapist, but during this period he was very penitent. He felt very guilty about his extramarital excursion and expressed the self-punitive opinion that what happened damn well served him right. He then had a series of dreams that revealed the underlying dynamics of his conflict. These dreams brought to light childhood fantasies of illicit sexual activity with both his mother and sister for which he feared castration from his father. It soon became clear that his concern with bowel function was a displacement of these repressed infantile fantasies via the equation, sex = feces. His fear of soiling himself in public was really a fear that he would lose control of himself and do something sexual, that is, symbolically, something "dirty." This construction explained why the symptom had broken out coincidentally with his first sexual experience and why it had become so intensified during his unsuccessful attempt at an extramarital relationship.

This patient is a good example of a neurotically integrated, obsessive personality where the obsessive pathology is accessible to analytic psychotherapy. He achieved a good therapeutic result. The many unconscious ramifications of his conflict were uncovered and analyzed in depth. By the time treatment ended, he was symptom-free, except for very infrequent minor exacerbations from which he quickly recovered. These gains have been maintained for more than ten years.

Case 5. A 27-year-old married woman with one child entered treatment for an obsessive fear of becoming "dirty." She compulsively scrubbed her entire body for many hours a day in order to wash off the "dirt" and phobically avoided anything and anyone that she considered "dirty." Her mother was an unpleasant woman, obsessive, domineering, controlling, and overprotective, utterly lacking in warmth and affection. She was distrustful of people, very argumentative, and got along poorly with others. The father was ten years older than the mother. He was somewhat more loving, but very weak, and it was the mother who ran the household. The patient was an only child. The labor was difficult and in its course the mother suffered a dislocated hip. The infirmity became chronic, necessitated several operations throughout the years, and caused her a lot of pain. The mother held the patient responsible for her disability and never let her forget it.

The patient was a feeding problem and was spoon fed by the mother until she was 12. She demanded such treatment or refused to eat and the mother complied. Toilet training was said to have been severe and completed by the age of 1. The mother was fanatical about cleanliness and neatness. The patient was made to feel that if she soiled anything or got dirty herself, it would give the mother additional work and aggravate her bad hip; in other words, dirt would hurt her mother. The patient was so imbued with this concern that even as a small child she always cautioned visitors to the house not to bring in any dirt. The mother was hypercritical of her in every respect and demanded rigid conformance to perfectionist standards of behavior. She also taught the patient not to trust people and the patient grew up without any close friends. Instead, she was attached to her mother in an almost symbiotic way: "Mother was my only and closest friend. We were one." The mother had to leave home several times in order to have surgery on her hip. Each time the patient felt abandoned, rejected, and angry.

The mother was very prudish and sexually inhibited. She boasted virtuously about being sexually "cold" and spoke with contempt about the father for being sexually "hot." The patient was at first curious about sex, but the mother condemned her questions as "dirty" and refused to answer them. When the patient entered menarche at 11, the mother told her this was punishment for her sexual curiosity. She did explain intercourse a year or so later, but put it in such terms that the patient felt it was "too dirty." Throughout adolescence, the patient had sexual fantasies about her father or about men who looked like him. One day, when she was 15, her father brought home a book on sex which she read. She became sexually aroused, masturbated for the first time, and achieved an orgasm. Later, she felt her room was dirty and began compulsively to clean it, as well as all the other rooms in the house. Thereafter, the same thing occurred each time she masturbated, especially on Sundays when her parents were away and she was alone in the house. She would masturbate and clean. She became increasingly guilty and finally confessed the masturbation to her mother, who reprimanded her strongly and warned her she would go crazy if she did not stop. The patient promised she would never masturbate again and, as a matter of fact, she didn't. At 18, she began to go out with boys. She necked with them, but permitted no petting, although several tried. She now began to feel subways were "dirty" and was unable to sit on the seats. At 23, she married a man very much like her father, non-assertive, passive, and ten years her senior. She felt no sexual desire, but could have intercourse mechanically, without orgasm. The obsessive symptoms began to increase at this time. She had a son three years later and after his birth the symptoms became so severe they began to incapacitate her. All public transportation became "dirty." People became "dirty." The house became "dirty." She phobically avoided all such contacts and spent most of her time scrubbing herself. As a result, she was unable to take care of the house or the child, and her husband brought her to the psychiatrist.

The psychodynamics in this case are typical for the obsessive reaction. The mother, herself, was very obsessive and the power struggle between herself and the patient was intense. The patient ultimately gave in, repressed her anger, and became submissive. Simultaneously, she collected her reward. She became excessively dependent on the mother, who, in turn, fostered the dependency by spoon-feeding, overprotectiveness, and instilling distrust of others. The repressed hostility toward the mother produced guilt with a feeling of responsibility for the mother's injured hip. The patient learned early that "dirt" would hurt the mother, and, therefore, she began obsessively to carry out the mother's demands. Later, she learned that sex, too, was dirty, not only in its own right, but for its forbidden Oedipal meaning. Thus, as she grew older, sex particularly meant hurting the mother and losing her support. For these reasons, the patient's symptoms were intensified by masturbation, became worse with necking on dates, increased further in severity with intercourse after marriage, and became full-blown after the birth of her child. Each of these events was a sexual milestone. The last two, especially, were public announcements of sexual activity and heightened her anxiety markedly. In the end, by obsessively scrubbing herself, she demonstrated to an imaginary mother that she was a good, clean, obedient girl, who meant no harm and deserved to be protected. For secondary defenses, she instituted phobic avoidance, not only of dirt, itself, but also of its many and varied symbolic representations.

This patient is a good example of an obsessive personality where the underlying integration is probably psychotic and not readily accessible either to psychotherapy or to any other kind of psychiatric treatment. Her clinical course over the past 10 years has been all too characteristic of many patients with obsessive pathology of such severity. She was in psychotherapy with the first psychiatrist twice a week for a year and a half. She improved a little, at least enough, she thought, to leave treatment and try again on her own. She almost immediately relapsed and her condition became as bad as ever. She re-entered treatment, but with another psychiatrist. This time she remained for three years, had some ups and downs, but was never significantly free from symptoms. Dissatisfied, she transferred to a third psychiatrist, who hospitalized her for one year. Again, there was minor improvement, but as soon as she got home, it was the same old story. A fourth psychiatrist put her in still another hospital, again for a year, but with no better results. She has had every conceivable type of tranquilizer, as well as electric shock, but nothing has been to any avail. At the present writing, she is again scrubbing at home while negotiating to re-enter psychotherapy with the second psychiatrist, who, understandably enough, is reluctant to accept her back.

## III. THE PARANOID PERSONALITY AND PHOBIC EXTENSIONS OF THE PARANOID REACTION

The paranoid personality is characterized by the following traits: intense ambitious strivings, excessive concern with self-esteem, status, and prestige; exquisite sensitivity to slights, real or imagined, in interpersonal relations;

marked self-referential tendencies expressed by suspiciousness, distrustfulness, and seclusiveness; use of projection as the predominant mechanism of defense. Developmentally, these traits result from exposure during childhood to a persistent climate of intimidation, not infrequently violent, in a family setting that is severely authoritarian, harsh, and cruel. At least one parent, often both, at times abetted by siblings, are hostile and controlling persons, who reject the child and through abuse, accusation, disparagement, and humiliation produce fear of attack, feelings of inadequacy, and a conviction of unlovability. The child learns to perceive his environment as dangerous and grows up with this perception intact. Thus, the paranoid personality is ever alert to the same damage from others that he suffered from his family.

The mechanism of projection can be used as a defense against any repressed impulse,[10] and the projection can, in turn, be secondarily defended by phobic avoidance. Clinically, however, phobic extensions of the paranoid reaction occur most often where the central conflict, as in the obsessive reaction, is with the control of rage. The paranoid child would like to strike back at his parents and siblings, but the power arrayed against him inevitably is too great. He ends up with the same inhibition of assertion and aggression that ultimately cripples the obsessive child, and for the same reason: hostile action is unconsciously equated with murderous violence and must be restrained to avoid certain retaliation. The two personalities differ, of course, in the primary defense used to contain the rage. The obsessive relies on obsessive thinking and ritual-making, whereas the paranoid resorts to projection.

Psychoanalytic therapy is usually the therapy of choice in phobic extensions of the paranoid reaction. In some cases, the phobic extension will respond to suggestion in the course of a predominantly supportive therapy, and the patient can be reconditioned by using the techniques described for phobic personalities with the agoraphobic reaction. Most often, however, the phobic extension in paranoid patients can no more be treated directly than in obsessive patients. In both, the primary reaction must be resolved first, before the patient can deal with the phobic problem. Fortunately, paranoid personalities are more accessible to an insight therapy than obsessive personalities, and although treatment is fraught with difficulties, there is a much greater chance of success. This is particularly true where the underlying integration is neurotic, less true, but still feasible, where it is borderline. Psychotic paranoid reactions, on the other hand, are very resistant to psychotherapy of any kind.

## CASE EXAMPLES

*Case 6.* A 35-year-old engineer of Jewish extraction, married and the father of three children, entered treatment because of the following symptoms: chronic anxiety with acute anxiety states, multiple phobias, hypochondriasis, and a peptic ulcer. The presenting illness developed gradually from a clearly defined traumatic situation that occurred twelve years ago when the patient was 23. At that time, he was overseas as a lieutenant in the Army, doing well, and on good terms with everyone. Then a new outfit joined his, bringing with it a six-feet-two Gentile captain, who hated Jews and drank heavily. One day, while drunk, and not knowing that the patient was Jewish, he delivered an anti-Semitic tirade to a group of officers gathered in the patient's tent. The patient was furious and prepared to "beat the hell out of the Captain." He baited the Captain into a fight, and when the Captain finally accepted the challenge, the patient suddenly felt paralyzed and couldn't move. He collapsed on his bed shaking with fear. The news of his cowardice quickly spread throughout the camp. He was subjected to constant derision by his bunkmates and he became the butt of frequent anti-Semitic remarks. For two months he was in a state of severe anxiety. He became increasingly sensitive to the anti-Semitism and gradually developed a phobic fear of drunks and "loudmouths." He also began to avoid crowds. At the end of two months the Gentile captain was separated from the group and the patient's symptoms greatly subsided.

The War ended and he was discharged from the Army. This brought a recurrence of acute anxiety attacks. He had liked the uniform despite all the trouble he associated with it. He felt it had afforded anonymity, prestige, and security. Civilian life threw him on his own resources and confronted him with the need for independent assertion. Nevertheless, he got a good job, fell in love and married, and quickly had three children. He worked very hard and received several promotions until he became a key executive in his firm. The bigger his vocational success, the more anxious he became. He fell into a depression and found himself wishing that he were ill. Finally, one morning, at the age of 34, while driving through a long tunnel on the way to work, he suddenly experienced an acute panic. He turned around, went home and got into bed, where he stayed for twenty-four hours. The next day he attempted to go to work again, but now he was phobic about the tunnel. Within two weeks the phobia spread from the tunnel to cars, bridges, trains, and all forms of transportation, until the patient was almost completely confined to his home. He saw a psychiatrist for a short period and got his phobic symptoms sufficiently under control so that at least he could go back to work, but he still had recurrent episodes of acute anxiety. Gradually, the phobias again became worse and at the same time he began to suffer from a mild general hypochondriasis. He had several hysterical "heart attacks" and then developed a bleeding peptic ulcer. His internist then prevailed upon him to return to a psychiatrist.

The developmental history throws considerable light on this patient's illness. His father was a hard-driving, ambitious, very successful head of a corporation who demanded absolute obedience from the family. The patient was terrified of him and considered him "the stranger and the enemy" in the house. The mother was an affectionate, but markedly fear-ridden woman, who was overprotective with the patient and inflicted her fears of physical exertion, injury, and disease upon him. There was one sibling, an older brother, who was defiant and willful, in contrast to the patient, who was docile and compliant. The brother, like the father, was always highly successful in whatever he undertook. As a child, the patient was both enuretic and asthmatic until the age of 9. He was fearful of sports, bodily contact, and physical harm. In school he always worked hard enough to be moderately successful, but if he began to approach leadership, he immediately slacked off. He had a repetitive nightmare throughout childhood which symbolized his weakness in the struggle with his father. He dreamt that someone was holding him by the scrotum and squeezing his testicles. He tried desperately to get away, but he never made it, and hence inevitably awoke in terror.

The combination of a strong, sometimes violent, terrifying father and an overprotective, anxious mother resulted in a submissive, fearful child. Assertion, very early, was equated with the capacity for violence. In fact, as a child, the patient recalled that he envied juvenile delinquents. The pattern for the future neurosis was thus laid down in the key formula: self-assertion = violent aggression → violent retaliation. In spite of his inhibitions, the patient aspired to at least match, if not surpass, his father and his brother, but he always made sure he stopped just short of success. The episode in the Army with the drunken captain represented an end point in which the patient attempted dramatically to solve his problem by facing the violence head on. Unfortunately, he collapsed with fear and succeeded only in proving his own inadequacy. The subsequent symbolic representations of this initial episode—the drunk, the anti-Semite, the loudmouth, the crowds—all confronted him with the threat of violent retaliation for his hostile impulses. The primary defense, therefore, was a paranoid reaction, secondarily reenforced by the phobic extensions. Later, the responsibilities of civilian life forced him to be assertive and to compete vocationally with other men.

The now fixed equation between assertion and violence generated greater and greater anxiety until finally, near the peak of vocational success, the phobic symptoms set in and he had a rationale to stay home. Here again, the primary defense was a paranoid reaction, the fear of violent retaliation for his success. The initial phobic extension was a hidden one, a "success phobia," or an unconscious fear of vocational success.[11] The success phobia was further symbolically extended and became manifest as an agoraphobic syndrome. These, alone, did not suffice to contain his paranoid fears, but he had to resort in addition to hypochondriasis and ultimately to physical illness. It should be noted that the repressed motivation for the agoraphobia in this patient, a paranoid personality, was assertion misconstrued as aggression, and not a sexual impulse which, as cited before, is responsible for agoraphobic reactions in phobic personalities.

This patient was treated psychoanalytically three times a week for two and one-half years. His phobic anxiety and the related phobias diminished sufficiently in two months so that he was able to return to work. He continued steadily to improve and by the end of two years of treatment he was relatively symptom-free. He worked with top efficiency on his job and experienced only infrequently outbursts of phobic anxiety, which he easily controlled. He was observed for six more months, maintained his improvement, and treatment, therefore, was terminated.

Case 7. A 38-year-old man, the son of a college professor, entered the same field as his father, and eventually, himself, became a professor, but in a larger university, where his status was much higher than his father had ever been able to achieve. His appointment was the culmination of a life-long ambition to surpass his father, an egocentric tyrant, who treated his wife and children with complete disdain. However, instead of being elated, as he had expected, he shortly fell into a depression, and as the time approached for his first lecture, his anxiety mounted. He managed to get to his classes, and forced himself to lecture, but by the end of the day he was in a panic. He continued to teach for almost a month, each day a repetition of the first, when finally he became so phobic about the classroom that he gave up altogether. He was offered treatment in the University facilities, but since the school was located in a small "college" town, he feared his illness would become public knowledge, and, therefore, he turned the offer down. Instead, he took a leave of absence until the next semester, three months distant, and came to New York, where he stayed with relatives and entered psychotherapy three times a week.

It was not difficult to demonstrate from his associations and dreams that he was suffering from a typical "success phobia." He could not tolerate surpassing his father, because he unconsciously equated such an achievement with patricide. Thus, instead of sustaining his victory, he succumbed to his sense of guilt and the fear of retaliation, which led to his eventual collapse in a self-imposed defeat. At the end of three months of therapy, armed with "insight" into the psycho-dynamics of his conflict, he returned to his job, seemingly improved—and promptly fell apart on the first day of class. It was as though he had never even heard of a psychiatrist, let alone seen one. This time, his condition deteriorated even more rapidly than the first time, and by the end of the week he was finished. He retired to his home, afraid to venture out, and remained ensconsed there for several weeks. Instead of abating, his anxiety only increased until in the end he went into an acute schizophrenic paranoid-hallucinatory episode for which he had to be hospitalized. He was taken away in a panic, screaming that he was being chased by men, who wished to assault him homosexually and to kill him.

## SUMMARY

The phobic reaction is a universal mechanism of defense, but patients who resort to it differ markedly in personality type, developmental history, and psychodynamic pattern. In accordance with these differences, phobic patients can be classified as follows:

I. The Phobic Personality and the Agoraphobic Reaction.
II. The Obsessive Personality and Phobic Extensions of the Obsessive Reaction.
III. The Paranoid Personality and Phobic Extensions of the Paranoid Reaction.

The differential features between the three categories are demonstrated in Table 1.

Any patient with a phobic reaction must, of necessity, fit into the classification. Phobic patients, whose predominant personality type falls outside of these headings, or whose personality type is mixed, nevertheless have in component form personality traits and psychodynamic patterning in common with one or the other of the three listed categories. For example, the agoraphobic reaction of a hysterical personality would be classified under the first heading (the phobic personality) as a hysterical personality with a phobic component and an agoraphobic reaction; the phobically extended obsessive ritual of a passive-aggressive personality would be classified under the second heading (the obsessive personality) as a passive-aggressive personality with an obsessive component and a phobic extension of the obsessive reaction; the success phobia of an obsessive personality would be classified under the third heading (the paranoid personality) as an obsessive personality with a paranoid component and a phobic extension of the paranoid reaction. The point is, it is impossible to have an agoraphobic reaction without a phobic component in the personality, or a phobic extension of an obsessive reaction without an obsessive component, or a phobic extension of a paranoid reaction without a paranoid component. Thus, once the therapist determines the primary defense, the classification of the phobic reaction under the proper personality heading follows as a matter of course.

The clear comprehension of psychodynamics is essential to the conduct of dynamic psychotherapy. The classification of phobic reactions proposed in this paper facilitates psychodynamic reconstruction and, therefore, can be clinically useful in the psychotherapeutic management of phobic patients.

TABLE 1

| PERSONALITY TYPE | DEVELOPMENTAL HISTORY | CENTRAL CONFLICT | PRIMARY DEFENSE | SECONDARY DEFENSE | EFFECTIVE PSYCHOTHERAPY |
|---|---|---|---|---|---|
| PHOBIC | Lack of parental support for acquisition of skills | Control of sexual impulse | Agoraphobic reaction: phobic avoidance | — | Usually supportive therapy |
| OBSESSIVE | Power struggle with obsessive parents about conformance to parental standards | Control of aggressive impulse | Obsessive reaction: obsessive thoughts and rituals | Phobic avoidance: phobic extension of obsessive reaction | Usually insight therapy |
| PARANOID | Intimidation, often violent, by abusive and authoritative parents | Control of aggressive impulse | Paranoid reaction: projection | Phobic avoidance: phobic extension of paranoid reaction | 1. Usually insight therapy 2. Occasionally supportive therapy |

## Bibliography

1. Karush, A., and Ovesey, L.: Unconscious Mechanisms of Magical Repair, *Archives of General Psychiatry*, 5: 55–69, 1961.
2. Costello, C. G.: Essentials of Behavior Therapy, *Canadian Psychiatric Association Journal*, 8: 162–166, 1963.
3. Eysenck, H. J. (Ed.): *Behavior Therapy and the Neuroses*, New York, Pergamon Press, 1963.
4. Wolpe, J.: *Psychotherapy by Reciprocal Inhibition*, Standford University Press, 1958.
5. Freud, S.: Character and Anal Erotism. In *The Standard Edition of the Complete Psychological Works of Sigmund Freud*, London, Hogarth Press, Vol. 9, pp. 167–175, 1959.
6. Kardiner, A., Karush, A., and Ovesey, L.: A Methodological Study of Freudian Theory: The Libido Theory, *Journal of Nervous and Mental Disease*, 129: 133–143, 1959.
7. Rado, S.: Obsessive Behavior, in *American Handbook of Psychiatry* (Ed. Arieti, S.), New York, Basic Books, pp. 324–344, 1959.
8. Levy, D.: Development and Psychodynamic Aspects of Oppositional Behavior. In *Changing Concepts of Psychoanalytic Medicine* (Eds. Rado, S. and Daniels, G.), New York, Grune and Stratton, pp. 114–134, 1956.
9. Mesnikoff, A. Therapeutic Milieu for the Seriously Disturbed. In *International Psychiatric Clinics*, Boston, Little, Brown & Co., Vol. 1, No. 4, pp. 891–910, Oct. 1964.
10. Ovesey, L.: Pseudohomosexuality, the Paranoid Mechanism, and Paranoia: An Adaptational Revision of a Classical Freudian Theory, *Psychiatry*, 18: 163–173, 1955.
11. Ovesey, L.: Fear of Vocational Success, *Archives of General Psychiatry*, 7: 82–92, 1962.

# Transference Resistance in Hysterical Character Neurosis— Technical Considerations

*by B. Ruth Easser, M.D. and Stanley R. Lesser, M.D.*

Hysteria was considered for many years the diagnostic entity most amenable to the psychoanalytic method. In the more recent past, clinical experience has questioned this postulate. Therapeutic failures have led to a reassessment of the prognosis;[7] a questioning of the original dynamic and developmental etiology of the disorder;[8] also to the promulgation of modified therapeutic techniques and therapeutic emphasis.[12] Thus Knapp, et al.,[7] suggest that prognostic evaluation is extremely capricious. Marmor[8] places the primary conflict in the oral rather than the oedipal phase of development. Winter[12] advises that technically the analysis should be based upon the oral relationships with the mother and the triangular relationships of the oedipal conflict be de-emphasized, i.e. the father left out.

We believe that there are two prime reasons why the clinical analytic method has, in many instances, failed to effect a resolution of the underlying conflicts which produce both hysterical character traits and hysterical symptomatology. The first is diagnostic misevaluation, lack of differentiation of the hysteric from other groups displaying similar overt traits and symptoms. We have attempted in a previous paper "Hysterical Character: A Re-Evaluation"[2] to discriminate the hysterical character neurosis from other diagnostic categories which we have lumped together under the rubric "Hysteroid." Two, even when a correct diagnosis has been established, we feel that inadequate attention has been given to the ego attitudes and relational modes of the hysteric personality. These attitudes and modes, if unattended, preclude the development of a transference neurosis which would enable the resolution of the underlying conflicts. The question of the nature of the transference in the hysteric is, we believe, a key issue. The zest with which the hysteric approaches the therapeutic task and so readily seems to absorb insights frequently obscures a relationship in which the patient has indeed been an onlooker observing and reacting to the analyst at work rather than working through his own problems. There may be some change in the behavior but the basic inhibitions, the quality of object relations and the emotional way of life remain unmodified.

Wilhelm Reich[9] stressed that character traits, "character armor," must first be analyzed since he visualized that its function was to defend the patient against the stimuli of the outer world and against repressed inner impulses. Nevertheless, he followed Freud's original dictum in stating "apprehensiveness and coquetry defend against genital sexuality and that one should interpret more or less directly the genital sexual nature of the defense . . . the fact that this sexual behavior also expresses other, secondary strivings, such as primitive narcissism, or the wish to dominate or to make an impression is not important in this context." We would agree with Reich as to the core sexual problem. We also agree with the need to loosen the "character armor" before the patient can allow himself to enter a therapeutic alliance. We would most emphatically disagree that the so-called "secondary strivings are not important to this context." Rather we feel, that the analysis of these "secondary strivings" e.g., "the need to impress" are resistances which, if not resolved, will color, impede and frustrate the entire course of the analysis.

Edward Glover,[6] in his concept of "transference resistance," describes an aspect of transference in which childhood reactivity bedevils the analyst as infantile memories are approached, particularly those about the oedipal situation and leads to stagnation or exacerbation of the symptoms. He regards this transference resistance as a regressive phenomenon concomitant with the development of a transference neurosis. This would imply that these character resistances are necessarily secondary to the formation of a transference neurosis. Our observations lead us to emphasize that the character resistances confronting the analyst are an integral part of the life style of the hysterical patient both before he encounters the analyst as well as immediately present in the opening phases of the analysis. In this, our concept would be much closer to the concept of resistances to the transference. In other words, we suggest that the therapeutic behavior in analysis is usually a mere repetition of the patient's behavior in numerous contemporary and past interpersonal transactions rather than the manifestations of a transference neurosis.

In this paper we wish to highlight certain common ego maneuvers and ego attitudes that are utilized in resistance to the transference and must be differentiated from transference phenomena:

1. The ease of emotional lability;
2. The maintenance of the child self-image;
3. The derivatives of the unconscious construction of a fantasied role;
4. The ability to evoke a response in the analyst that establishes and maintains the gratifications from the secondary gains.

The hysterical character depicts what may be characterized as "the emotional way of life." The understanding of the emotional way, in analysis, is a prime requisite for successful treatment. Manifest emotionality or, more properly, emotional reactivity is the outward manifestation of the self as an involved emotional participant. Obversely, the interreactivity with the object (in this case the analyst) seems to the patient essential for his immediate security, the perpetuation of the character mode and the defensive guarding against specific unconscious conflicts. The latter concept of emotionality as a defense is similar to Valenstein's[11] proposal of the term "affectualization" as a defense mechanism. ". . . affect, and its intensification and excessiveness, with unconscious use or exploitation for defensive purposes to avoid the cognitive appreciation of emotionally charged issues and the rational recognition of explanatory connections, i.e. affectualization." The ubiquitous proneness to this behavior in every relational and adaptational aspect provides a most effective character armor. Dreams, associations, symbolizations, infantile memories, transference reactivity, current events are all pervaded. Interpretations presented without a constant alertness to this proclivity will only become new grist for this already well-established emotional mill. Since affect-laden ideation is in most instances a principal road to effective interpretation, it is easy for the analyst to view these highly emotional associations as meaningful. However, the hysteric has the tendency to relish the emotive role of a dreamer, free associater, a creator of symbols or an abreactor, or counterwise: a resister, antagonist, provocateur, or for that matter, any role that seems necessary or appealing. The analysis may seem to be going well or badly but in fact is not going at all.

The hysteric views (consciously and unconsciously in varying degrees) this emotionality as a jewel to be exhibited, fondled and cherished. Any attempt to move beyond it or to remove it is viewed as an attack and is defended against with the total personality, i.e., with a new surge of affectivity. The tenacity with which this character trait is guarded is not surprising when one considers its multi-determination and the multiple psychic functions served. Analogously to a neurotic symptom it provides a source of pleasure (even when seemingly painful), a source of pride (even when consciously disparaged and deplored), and a preservation of the self-image as an affectively involved being, which becomes a useful commodity in evoking the interest and involvement of others (even when viewed by others as an irritant). Most importantly, for analytic consideration, it provides a secondary defensive barrier against the experience of the more painful and feared core affects; the illumination of unresolved infantile conflicts and the true awareness of their role in present and past relationships. Siegman[10] in his paper "Emotionality—A Hysterical Character Defense" both emphasizes the defensive use of the histrionic emotionality and also suggest a developmental line through which the hysteric may avoid responsibility for his dyscontrol and the internal pangs of conscience:

> "Patients are sometimes surprised to find that not everyone experiences similar emotions and that the particular stimulus does not really warrant all the emotionality. At the same time, the patient may be able to distinguish these 'hysterical' emotions from other affects and may also become aware of a certain attractiveness and pleasure in the experiencing of these feelings. . . . the hysterical affectivity is utilized by the ego as a fixed mode of adjustment to the demands of the superego, id, and reality. Hysterical emotionality is a dramatic and exhibitionistic demonstration to the superego that the ego is 'well-behaved,' 'proper,' and experiences the correct emotions, in order to avoid the displeasure of guilt or loss of love. Similar demonstrations are offered to superego surrogates, parents, the public, or fate. . . . The hysterical defense seems to be directed toward, and to have its genesis in, the oedipal period. Hysterical behavior is strongly reminiscent of the child's dramatic and exhibitionistic efforts to win the parent's love and approval and avoid rejection and punishment by showing the expected behavior and emotions after having done something 'bad.' "

A reciprocal relationship exists between the emotional lability and the defensive uses of a child self-image. "If I am a child how could I indulge in adult sexual activity, and moreover, if I find myself there I cannot know what I do; how to do it; why I do it; or to be responsible for my actions." The emotionality lends a childish cast to the patient and the patient utilizes this childish self-image in several interlocking defensive maneuvers. Many of these defensive maneuvers are utilized to sustain inhibitions and to avoid the acceptance of adult responsibilities. An emotional storm ensues whenever there is an internal impulse toward or an external demand for the adult role, e.g., a housewife panics because after preparing for a dinner party, she forgot to light the oven; a young man flies into a rage at his girl friend while she is engaged in a provocative strip because he suddenly recalled that she had been critical of the restaurant he had chosen for dinner. The childish emotionality and juvenile coquetry provokes others into an adoptive role. The hysteric then renews his pride by seeing himself as more sensitive, more empathic, more responsive than the parentified object. Rather than hide the anticipated non-fulfillment of duties the hysteric dramatizes and exhibits his incompetence. The emotional dyscontrol itself is proferred to himself and to the external world as a "logical" rationalization for his inability to engage in unemotional thinking and behavior and hence he is incapable of adult tasks or role fulfillment. Furthermore, a role reversal takes place in which the hysteric induces others to seemingly force him into an area of his own desire, e.g., the competitive or genital-sexual.

The patient is at once using his emotional lability to deny that he sees or knows what lies in these inhibited adult areas; that he himself has desires to enter these areas; that he is capable even if he did wish to break through these inhibitions; that the emotionality itself gives him substitutive satisfaction and even pride. Furthermore, he is able to induce parental attitudes in those with whom he is close. These parental responses are first converted by the patient into demands for maturity, responsibility and adult action. At this point he attacks the surrogate parent for making unrealistic and unattainable demands. The analytic situation presents a tailor-made forum for a repetition of these dynamics. Unless the analyst can go behind these resistances he runs the danger of falling into the Scylla of being viewed as an indulgent parent or the Charybdis of being viewed as a taskmaster in his activity should he agree or confirm what the patient has already underlined as his "irresponsibility."

The key to the solution of this resistance lies in the understanding of the specific utilization of these ego maneuvers by the hysteric. Repression and inhibition are the core defenses. These cannot be attacked frontally without arousing the aforementioned secondary defensive cycle. The externalized defensive cycle depends upon the use of the mechanisms of denial, projection, and reversal of roles. Insight into the use of these projections and distortions in his current life experience, both within and without the analytic situation, is the first order of business.

A school teacher raged at her principal for demanding that she correct her chronic lateness. She rationalized her lateness as a life-long characteristic. Why couldn't she be accepted as she was and secondly why should this be demanded of her when it was well known that she was a superior teacher.

On further exploration clarification ensued. She had provoked her principal to phone and awaken her each morning.

Interpretation and formulation allowed the patient to accept her own role in inducing the principal to replicate the childhood situation and to shift the responsibility for promptness from herself to the principal. In treatment the external situation is presented as a defense and a confirmation of her own incompetence. She is still a child, accepted as a child and thus incapable of assuming responsibility for her own behavior, desires or feelings. It is at this point that a challenge to this self-image is possible and often mandatory. This working through process is repeated in various behavioral areas each time a seeming demand for more mature functioning is perceived. A gradual recognition of the defensive use of the infantile self-image becomes possible, which in turn, increases awareness of greater competence and permits confrontation of the areas of inhibition.

Exaggerations, psuedo-ignorance and perceptual distortion are well-known attributes in the hysterical presentation. This presentation, while often at first appearing ubiquitous and randomized soon, when closely observed is the manifest form of underlying fantasies. These fantasies when grouped, epitomize a preconscious and/or unconscious role in which the patient has cloaked himself. These roles, which determine many aspects of the distorted ego function are centered around such images as that of "the prince," "the femme fatale," "the hero," "the martyr." Dramatizations and distortions protect the patient from reality confrontation, conscious awareness which might expose his role playing and limit the ease with which he turns the world to his psychic purpose. His illusions determine many attitudes (often unconscious) that are derivatives of this central role. In turn, as with the child self-image, they compensate for and protect against insight into the primary conflicts and inhibitions.

A young matron emphasized her personal dedication to humanitarian and philanthropic causes. She entered an analytic session distraught and grieved at having encountered what she described as a wretched, deprived group of people marching up the street before the analyst's building. She was particularly moved by her "empathy" for these people who were being superciliously watched in this wealthy neighborhood.

When this unhappy scene was further explored there unfolded a description of a group of festive marchers on their way to the annual political picnic. Upon seeking the motivation for such obvious distortion, it became apparent that this patient had retained the fantasy that she herself was of true aristocratic character and feeling, relegating the analyst and his co-tenants to the category of upstarts. She could afford to practice *lese majeste*. Interpretation led to the production of new material, the essence of which was that this lady had been pursuing a covert mode of life through purchases indicative of high aesthetic taste, such as elegant furnishings and gourmet foods in accord with her fantasied, aristocratic, high-born self-image and in marked contrast to the sympathetic, suffering worker of humanitarian endeavors. Furthermore, it shed new light on her sexual refusal of her "peasant" husband. By presenting to the world and particularly to her husband, confusion, incompetency, inability to keep house, to maintain household budget, she successfully diverted her husband and others from any knowledge of this secret, highly invested and carefully maintained, aristocratic self-image. Better to be an exasperating little girl than to be challenged and perhaps ridiculed for these strivings.

As long as such a fantasy remains unrevealed and unexplored, interpretations actually fortify the fantasy and maintain the analyst as inferior and impotent. Exploration of behavioral and perceptive modes and confrontations of distortions and non-perceptions are a *sine qua non* in enabling the therapist and the patient to ferret out and expose underlying attitudes and their correlated fantasies. These fantasies and attitudes are invested with guilt and shame in contrast to the child self-image which is often quite ego syntonic. They are moreover, heavily narcissistically invested for they are derivatives and residual bastions of strong excitatory infantile experiences. They are a mode through which the oedipal situation is perpetuated and unresolved. If these character attitudes are not worked through, they permit parallel attitudes to prevail in the "transference" which effectively blocks the analysis. Furthermore, these character attitudes often carry within themselves exaggerated and labile emotionality. Once these fantasies are confronted, one begins to observe rages, sorrows, injured feelings etc. which become more meaningful to the patient and to the therapist.

As these fantasies are derivatives of childhood experiences and conflicts they serve as a bridge to forgotten and distorted childhood memories. The aristocratic fantasies of the aforementioned young matron led to a recall of a formerly repressed memory of her father fostering and cultivating this aristocratic pose through his own elegance and the stimulation of this elegance in her. This allowed for the undoing of a tenaciously held image of her father as unfeeling, uncouth, and obstructing her femininity. In turn, this revived a flood of bodily excitations emanating from the recollections of her relationship with her father.

One must anticipate that at each point of exposition, the analyst is confronted by a new round of hyper-emotionality, hyperincompetence and irresponsibility and, not infrequently, symptom formation. This display is usually accompanied by the oral demands expected of an angry child, a whining child, a suffering child and a frightened child.

Of course, transference behavior by the patient finds a potential echo in the countertransference attitudes of the analyst. There is no patient like the hysteric to prove Franz Alexander's[1] dictum, "Since the phenomenon of countertransference has been recognized, we know that a completely objective attitude of the analyst exists only in theory no matter how painstakingly he may try to live up to this requirement." The evocation of emotionality in others is, as has been mentioned above, prime psychic stock and trade of the hysteric. The analyst finds his day enlivened by this patient's hour. He is courted and flattered. He is made a cherished spectator to an ever unfolding psychic drama. He is invited to become a principal player within the drama, the key to its resolution. Almost no analyst is beyond these temptations. Secondly, the analyst's expectations of his curative powers are mobilized by the apparent simplicity of the defenses, the clarity of the meaning of the behavior, the lucidity of the symbols, the openness of the underlying conflict and the obviousness of the sources of gratification, both conscious and unconscious. Furthermore this therapeutic zeal is abetted by the inference of suggestibility as the patient reiterates the ease with which he is supposedly influenced and led by others.

Even as the analytic drama is being enacted one notes that large and significant areas are avoided, cloaked in vagaries and/or presented but never pursued. A mother may not be mentioned; sexual behavior cannot be discerned. One patient would not use the word "woman," always substituting lady or girl. Amnestic material is presented with large sectors forgotten. Situations both past and present are given preliminary exposition but their resolution remains buried. The dreams have similar vagueness, incompleteness and lack of resolution. It is in attempting to probe the clearly distorted, displaced and repressed that the true intransigence of the defensive structure becomes apparent. It is at these points of resistant roadblocks that the analyst may find himself prone to, or in fact, replicating the emotional attitudes of the parents or later parental surrogates, in fact responding as would the patient's friends, mate, employer or relatives. He may protect his patient from shame and anguish; he may exhort; he may reassure; he may threaten. In each he is conspiring in the maintenance of the patient's neurotic defense.

This by-play, i.e., the actualization within the transference, is in fact a repetition of the secondary gains which have enabled the patient to maintain his conflicts and inhibitions. Whenever the manifest content of the dreams contain the same elements of seductiveness and flattery it is strongly indicative of an intact defensive structure. The secondary gains achieved by the hysterical character neurotic are almost exactly analogous to the classical description by Freud of the secondary gains achieved through a conversion symptom.[3-5] However little attention has been paid to the analyst's indulgence in his own secondary gain as enhancing and endangering the resolution of the neurosis. In fact, the major mechanism through which the hysteric achieves his secondary gain is the evocation in others of emotional interest, responsiveness and pleasure. The analyst's emotional response reassures the patient that he is, as he was in childhood, continuously cherished without the necessity of intrusive physical sexuality nor of the harsh reality that might shake those illusions and fantasies that have been substituted for genital sexuality. If this undesirable transference situation should eventuate, the patient has a repetitive experience rather than a corrective emotional experience; he sustains those inhibitions and repressions that allow him the relational experiences which have been his stock and trade from childhood until his entrance into analysis, and permit him a continued self-imposed blindness to the motivations underlying his behavior.

Although this paper is primarily devoted to the mechanisms of the secondary gains, facades and hyperbolized emotional reactivity of the hysteric, nevertheless, to avoid a therapeutic and theoretic skew, it is essential to stress the psychic pain endured by these patients and to touch upon some of its sources. The therapeutic danger of accepting secondary gain as primary gain is matched by the danger that the therapist's disillusionment and frustration may lead him to ignore and deny the quality of his patient's pain. Hysterics hyperbolize their responses to external events. This externalization defends against the arousal of anxiety-laden body sensuality. This body sensuality is of course much more closely related to inner impulses. These inner impulses are unconsciously assumed to be perenially in danger of arousal and once aroused are feared to be uncontrollable and overwhelming. These diffuse and specific somatic excitements and pleasures are poorly discriminated from sexual impulses and the sexual arousal of the body. These interconnections are not surprising when one considers the developmental pathogenesis of this disorder. Repression and displacement occurred in childhood in response to the genital sensations that were evoked in relation to parental figures. Pleasure derived from the genitals and other parts of the body hazily discriminated during childhood have, for the hysteric's ego, remained but little further discriminated. Two sources of sensuality have remained less repressed and inhibited: (1) The evoking in others of sensuality and even more its concomitant emotionality. The patient's sensation then is limited mainly to the reflexion of this arousal in others;[13] (2) The expression of emotionality dissociated from sensuality is permitted and is, in fact, hypertrophied.

Certain milestones mark the penetration of the emotional character facade of the hysteric. It is at these points that a therapeutic alliance and a working transference are established. One sign of the development is the dampening and deepening of the florid emotionality. The emotions are more enduring and tend to be focused on the analyst and a few close affective objects. The patient's assumption of responsibility for his own emotionality lends greater self-consciousness to his behavior and emotional display. Guilty apprehensiveness begins to become manifest through the increased concern and feared anticipation of retaliation and threatened withdrawal by the therapist. As the patient becomes more conscious of the relation between his own emotionality and the response of others his emotionality becomes more tentative and better controlled. This increased consciousness of the significance of his role leads to increased self-awareness and awareness of bodily feelings and sensations. Transient conversion symptoms and psycho-physiological responses often occur. (e.g., urinary frequency).

Bodily feelings, beginning genital sensations instigate body exploration and arouse masturbatory temptations. The gratification of these impulses within a strong affective tie arouses the original fears and guilts. These tend to manifest themselves in feelings of loneliness and the expectation of withdrawal by the analyst. One patient rather succinctly stated ''orgasm is my graduation and I am not ready to be graduated.'' This separation anxiety with its depressive hue, marks the onset of the second stage in the analysis of the hysteric. Paradoxically, in the face of mounting guilt and anxiety, there is a growing sense of pride and gratification. This pride and gratification is the resultant of decreasing inhibitory barriers both internal and external. These positive affects permit further analytic work and increases the scope of interests, accomplishments and pleasures both within and outside of the analysis.

## CONCLUSION

Particulate ego reactivity and ego maneuvers characterize the defensive organization of the hysterical character neurosis. These same characteristics serve as a resistance to the development of an effective analytic transference. This defensive purpose is often difficult to discern and if discerned, to modify. The hysteric's use of emotionality as a defense often results in important secondary gain for the patient. This secondary gain is the evocation in others of affective counterreactivity. As in all interpersonally useful secondary gains it is difficult in itself for the patient to forswear in the expectation of lessened future suffering.

In the hysteric a special analytic difficulty in this regard is operant. The analyst himself is potentially susceptible to this form of stimulus and evocation of emotional response. It is this very mutuality of gratification that tends to permit the acceptance of quasi-transference in the same way that the defensive emotionality is misread as basic emotional response. Furthermore, the quasi-transference does not permit the analysis of the defensive use of the self presented as a child, rather, it reinforces and sustains it. As long as the child role is indulged, interpretations are rendered impotent and neither the underlying fantasied role, nor its attitudinal derivatives can be explicated. The authors deem it necessary for this fantasy complex to be brought into conscious awareness before the infantile memories and emotional experiences long since repressed can be recovered. Once this phase of the analytic task has been accomplished, a transference neurosis evolves and the second phase of the analytic process can proceed.

## References

1.  Alexander, F. *The Scope of Psychoanalysis*. New York: Basic Books, 1961, p. 264.
2.  Easser, B. R., and Lesser, S. R. Hysterical personality: a re-evaluation. *Psychoanal. Quart.* 34: 390–405, 1965.
3.  Freud, S. A case of hysteria. *Standard Edition*, Vol. 7. London: The Hogarth Press, 1953.
4.  Freud, S. *A General Introduction to Psychoanalysis*. Lecture 24. New York: Liveright Publishing Corp., 1935.
5.  Freud, S. Inhibitions, symptoms and anxiety. *Standard Edition*, Vol. 20. London: The Hogarth Press, 1959.
6.  Glover, E. *The Technique of Psychoanalysis*. New York: Int. Univ. Press, 1958, p. 68.
7.  Knapp, P., Levin, S., McCarter, R., et al. Suitability for psychoanalysis: a review of one hundred supervised analytic cases. *Psychoanal. Quart.* 24: 459–77, 1960.
8.  Marmor, J. Orality in the hysterical personality. *J. Amer. Psychoanal. Assoc.* 1: 656–71, 1954.
9.  Reich, W. *Character Analysis*. New York: Orgone Institute Press, 1949, pp. 189–192.
10. Siegman, A. Emotionality—a hysterical character defense. *Psychoanal. Quart.* 23: 339–54, 1954.
11. Valenstein, A. The psycho-analytic situation. *Int. J. of Psychoanal.* 43: 315–324, 1962.
12. Winter, H. Pre-oedipal factors in the genesis of hysterical character neurosis. *Int. J. of Psychoanal.* 45: 338–42, 1964.
13. Wisdom, J. A methodological approach to the problem of hysteria. *Int. J. Psychoanal.* 42: 224–37, 1961.

# Discussion: The Phobic Reaction (Ovesey); Resistance to Transference in Hysterical Character Neurosis (Easser and Lesser)

by Joan Fleming, M.D.

Dr. Klein, Dr. Goldman, and members of the Columbia Psychoanalytic Clinic for Training and Research—my congratulations on this anniversary of your beginning and my best wishes for a continued development extending far into the future.

Today the papers we have just heard and those to follow are celebrating the scientific work which has been going on at Columbia these past twenty years. Offered as a record of productivity, these papers serve also as a bench-mark for the journey Columbia has made—a bench-mark which measures progress and which serves as a point of take-off for the next period of advance.

When I read the two papers you have just heard, I was puzzled as to how to discuss them both in a meaningful way. I found myself comparing them in response to two questions: 1) What is the function of a scientific paper; and 2) how can it be useful?

Obviously, the function of a scientific paper is to communicate to a large audience the thinking of the author and the evidence on which that thinking is based. Time does not permit me to explore my responses to this first question any further, since they would lead us into the realm of scientific philosophy, the large subject of scientific creativity and the motivations and values of individual scientists.

My responses to the second question seemed more practical and more pertinent to the task today. The papers are similar in many respects. Each

81

deals with a particular psychiatric syndrome. Each is concerned with differential diagnosis and with special aspects of treatment technique. Yet they differ in the kind of information they offer and even more significantly in the way they communicate that information.

It seems to me that to be useful, a scientific paper aims first to provide information which may take the form of opinions on a controversial topic, or attempt to clarify and reformulate established concepts; or it may present new data which illuminate areas not yet perceived and which eventuate in modifications of existing theory. Second, a scientific paper aims to stimulate questions—questions about unsolved problems, new angles of approach, new methods of investigation—questions which stimulated the author to study a problem and questions which the author's report raise in the mind of the reader. Often this thought provoking aim of a scientific paper gives it more value than the author's answers. A third way in which a scientific paper can be useful is to demonstrate the relationship between the author's message and other contributions on the same subject. For example, terms should be clearly defined with reference to established meanings so that new meaning can be easily differentiated. The originality of a new formulation needs to be highlighted by underlining what aspects of the old formulation have been modified or why they have been excluded.

With this simple and compressed framework for ordering my responses, I come to the papers we have just listened to.

Dr. Ovesey's paper on the Phobic Patient describes a familiar syndrome. He attempts to contribute to our understanding of the phobic reaction by clarifying the diagnostic problem. In other words, he asks the question, do all phobic reactions have the same dynamics, economics, and genetics, the same ego structure and adaptive function? Unfortunately, the paper which we heard is only one segment of his thinking on this question of differential diagnosis. Having had the opportunity to read the entire argument, I regret that he did not concentrate on the diagnostic problem but permitted the equally stimulating question of treatment technique to become the main part of his presentation here. He lets us look at four cases which he treated with a special technique. This is a fascinating account of his experience with agoraphobes, but I feel quite inadequate to evaluate the usefulness of his recommended procedures. "Reconditioning" and various magical devices accomplished relief of symptoms, but statements about their effectiveness were not accompanied by a satisfactory attempt to explain why they were successful. For me it was not enough to speak of magical dependence on the therapist's omnipotence or to call it "transference cure." These terms by themselves do not help the reader to follow Dr. Ovesey's conceptual thinking. They did, however, emphasize the fact that the symbiotic tie between child and external object, so appropriate at very early levels of development, can be re-established in bizarrely distorted form in adult life; and, that we know very little about the disintegration of the intra-psychic structure which permits this regression. These challenging questions lead us into the theory of transference and require a deeper explanation of the function of the object in the integration of adult ego structure and in the reconstruction of mature ego structure in therapy. I hope that Dr. Ovesey's pessimism implied in his statement that his therapy resulted in "only a transference cure" will not prevent his attempt to penetrate further into this unilluminated area.

The second paper by Dr. Barbara Easser and Dr. Stanley Lesser gives us valuable information not simply in the description of the phenomena of hysterical reactions, but more especially in the picture of the authors' thinking as they formulated a problem and proceeded to try to solve it. Their method of approach follows a model for the use of psychoanalytic data in clinical investigation. Starting from clinical observations which raise questions not answered by established theory, they proceeded to hypothetical answers which can be checked by further clinical observations confirming or modifying what is already known.

The basic question which the authors asked themselves is stated clearly—why has psychoanalysis failed so often with hysterics when according to early theory, this symptom complex was thought to be the neurosis par excellence for treatment by analysis? They too focus on a problem of diagnosis, an attempt to explain a particular form of resistance to the efforts of psychoanalytic technique. The behavior which stimulated their curiosity is clearly delineated as a pleasurizing of the analytic relationship in such a way that analytic work itself serves as a resistance to the analytic goal. The "tendency to relish the emotive role" inhibits the operation of the observing function of the ego and the patient "does nothing but experience" discharge of tension over two pathways, simultaneously experiencing the forbidden wish and the defense against it—the discharge of tension and the punishment for the pleasure involved. They describe how both pleasure and punishment are tension-laden; how the ego moves in relation to the id and the superego forces simultaneously, thus keeping a balance that blocks analytic progress. Analytic investigation brought out that this problem constituted a repetition of a childhood solution to a conflict at the oedipal level of development. The childhood solution, with or without admixture of pregenital patterns, had been continued into adulthood as a perpetual acting-out of oedipal success permitted by an ego-superego maneuver which condoned childish emotionality and the personal myth of being a child, not an adult.

The authors make many interesting points which the time allotted for discussion does not permit me to go into. The most interesting bear on the theory of transference. They raise the question of how to diagnose the dynamics of various transference phenomena. They try to differentiate the intrapsychic balance of forces in a defense transference from the balance in a transference neurosis. They ask what is the difference between an ego that can tolerate an analyzable transference neurosis and one that cannot; what is the structure of an ego that adapts by a continual repetition of a childhood fantasy, attempting to make it come true in many relationships at different ages; what role does regression play in these maneuvers; and what type and degree of regression is observed?

In the cases described, resistance is offered by a transferred fantasy in which the patient is play acting without knowing that it is make-believe. Transforming a dream into a myth and dramatizing it is a form of resistance different from reproducing an actual childhood experience. The amount of energy used by the hysteric in denying reality and the wide area of perceptual experience which the denial mechanism covers increase the effectiveness of this resistance against the usual regressive transference neurosis. Here we see very clearly the way in which this childhood solution is a repetition from childhood and how this repetition is a defense against the disillusionment with infantile omnipotence which reality thrusts upon the child. The authors outline the technical dilemma of the analyst when faced with the transferred attempt to "parentify" him. One is reminded of Nunberg's article on Transference and Reality published in 1951. In these cases, as in Dr. Ovesey's Phobic reactions, there is regression in the reality testing function of the ego. But in the hysteric, the conflict seems to be with reality whereas in the agoraphobe the conflict is more instinctual and anxiety producing. The hysteric compromises for make-believe infantile gratification, settles for this and so avoids the painful struggle with reality. The agoraphobe runs away and regresses temporarily to a level of relationship where the tension of the conflict can be avoided.

The way in which the hysteric's repetition of his childhood fantasy serves 1) as a resistance to a therapeutic alliance, 2) a stimulus for countertransference in the analyst, and 3) a protection of infantile narcissism is beautifully elaborated in this paper. The authors speak of this state of affairs as a quasi-transference. This statement surprised me and brings us to a crucial difference of opinion. According to the dictionary "quasi" means "seeming" or "as if," giving a connotation of falseness. I see the phenomena they describe as a pretending but not as only seeming-to-be-transference. In my opinion these phenomena are of the essence of transference. The problem is created by the difference in what the analyst is aware of compared to what the patient is aware of. For the analyst, the patient behaves "as-if," but the patient has no sense of his behavior being a fiction until this denial in fantasy is confronted by analytic interpretation. Until then the patient transfers—reproduces—the defensive fantasy and the oedipal situation recreated in the analytic relationship remains "perpetuated and unresolved." An interesting question left unanswered should be asked. In these patients, was the oedipal conflict ever solved on a more mature level? Or, has the hysteric described in this paper remained at an oedipal level continuing to act out defensively one component present in every oedipal conflict, the fantasy of being an oedipal success. This fantasy of being successful is usually covered secondarily by various kinds of distortions and by the fantasy of being unfairly rejected.

The authors touch on the aggressive component of the triangular oedipal conflict when they mention the storms stirred up if the defensive self-image of being just a child is disturbed. It seems to me two aspects of the aggressive component deserve more attention than the authors were able to give them in this presentation. The influence of the defensive regression stemming from homosexual rivalry certainly has its own set of fantasies and undoubtedly reinforces the fixation on the self-image described here. The component of the oedipal conflict which struggles with the rage at the heterosexual parent for not going along with the fantasy of oedipal success needs to be better integrated into the total picture. The authors' contribution, however, is their sharp focus on the secondary defenses which present the most intense resistance and reinforce the more primary repression and inhibition. They have elaborated on the problem of diagnosis, interpretation, and working through this transference resistance which achieved defensive gratification behind the denial of competition as an adult.

I believe they are to be congratulated on the clarity of their exposition of this difficult resistance and on calling attention to the subtle ways in which the character defenses of the hysteric and the narcissistic counter-reactions of the analyst tend to support each other in perpetuating this particular solution to the oedipal conflict. To return to their original question about the value of psychoanalytic treatment for hysteria, I would like to stress the opinion that difficult as this resistance may be, psycho-analysis provides the only situation in which this pleasurized defense against the childhood narcissistic injury by disillusionment can be penetrated and the infantile conflict be re-worked and resolved.

# Research

# The Verbal Encounter Between the Schizophrenic Child and His Mother*

*by William Goldfarb, M.D., Ph.D., David M. Levy, M.D., and Donald I. Meyers, M.D.*

In the present report we shall consider a strategy which we have employed in observing schizophrenic children and their mothers in a verbal encounter. The earlier portion of our report states why we wish to study the schizophrenic child in social interaction and, more particularly, in verbal interaction with his mother. To assist us in the enterprise of establishing a connection between the deficits of the schizophrenic child and the verbal behavior of his mother, we shall formulate a set of presumptions regarding dyadic communications generally and the mother-child verbal engagement more particularly. We shall discuss the schizophrenic child's central adaptive impairment and the characteristic deficits which we presume are accessible to communication influence. Then we shall summarize some environmental failures which we have noted clinically and which we may assume have influenced the developmental aberrations of the children. These presumptive failures are defined in communication terms so that they may offer us leads for the analysis of the verbal responses of the mothers in the experiment. The latter portion of our report implements our general discussion by presenting a specific technique for eliciting, recording and analyzing conversation between child and mother. Errors in communication of mothers of schizophrenic children are illustrated. Finally, one important parameter, namely the clarity of the mother's verbal behavior, is statistically compared to other measures

*Childhood Schizophrenia Project of the Henry Ittleson Center for Child Research under support of the Ittleson Family Foundation and NIMH Grant No. MH 05753-04.

89

of the family in order to cast light on our theory of etiology in childhood schizophrenia.

## OBJECTIVES IN INTERACTIONAL INVESTIGATIONS
## OF CHILDHOOD SCHIZOPHRENIA:
## VERBAL BEHAVIOR OF MOTHER AND CHILD

The analysis of communication between schizophrenic child and his mother is one study in a program of investigation which has reflected a broad interest in all the relational experiences of schizophrenic children. In our experience, the schizophrenic child has emerged as human, understandable and individual only when observed in life process. Merely tagging a child "schizophrenic" is a non-descriptive as calling him "normal." We needed to see him in active engagement with his human and non-human environment; and his responses became meaningful when we interpreted them as adaptive accommodations to the pressures and challenges of his surrounding environment. We presumed that systematic observation of the schizophrenic child as he is engaged with important persons in his life will cast light on the development of those traits of behavior which are characteristic for each child under scrutiny. The general objective of our investigation has thus been to delineate the part played by socialization in influencing the development of these very deviant children; and to do so by a direct view of their particular interaction with their mothers at the very moment of mutual impingement. The current investigation has focused on the mothers of the schizophrenic children because of their important social influence on the children. Since mothers exercise their influence very largely through communication, the specific objective of this experiment has been to evaluate its effect on their children.

It seemed that the profit to us in studying the direct interactional impact of any mother and child on each other at the point of encounter and in terms of the interactional episode itself could not be duplicated by other methods which did not rely on direct observations. Psychoanalytic therapy of the mother of the schizophrenic child has explained the unconscious motivational sources of her observable behavior with the child and has been an essential basis for therapeutic efforts to alter this behavior. However, in our experience, individual psychoanalytic investigation of the family members has not provided all the interactional data pertaining to mother and child which we have been seeking. The chief value for us of psychoanalytic exploration of the family members has been the clarification of the unconscious roots of the relational responses. The details of overt interaction and communication could not be predicted, so that their social and communicative behavior needed to be studied directly. Beyond this, the schizophrenic children we have studied have manifested their characteristic modes of response from the earliest days of life; and in common with all children, in the crucial early months and years, these children lack the cognitive capacity to react to the complexities of adult behavior. Rather, the children responded to what was ostensive in the interaction itself. In addition, what was of most pertinence to the child in the relational transaction could be articulated best in the very terms of the act itself. As an illustration, we have observed in the history of one schizophrenic child that his mother responded to his hypersensitivity to all stimuli by withdrawing totally from him. He was kept in his crib all alone except for necessary physical care. It is our presumption that the environmental failure was experienced by him as an infant in simple terms of isolation from stimulation and human contact whatever the cause, explainable in terms referable to his mother's development, her own history of affective deprivation, her schizotypal personality, her unconscious narcissism, and her paralyzing ambivalence about her maternal role. What was most pertinent in this schizophrenic child's early months was that he was not held, fondled, talked to, played with, offered the usual experiences involving maternal care, including predictable gratifications and relief from physical discomfort—all these being factors which can be made known by direct observation of mother-child observations.

It also seemed reasonable to assume that the verbal messages directed toward any child, whether schizophrenic or normal, by the most important provider of early sustenance and stimulation, the mother, directly affected the child's self-regulative and adaptive behavior. In the case of the schizophrenic child, this assumption suggested the further possibility that the mother's communications to her child would have an immediate bearing on his major adaptive impairments. It is this link between the mother's verbal behavior and the schizophrenic child's deviant manifestations that has interested us.

What bearing might such a communication study have on an understanding of the etiology of childhood schizophrenia? Therapeutic study of schizophrenic children throughout a 24-hour day has confirmed the fluctuant character of the symptoms and characteristics of schizophrenic children. It seems reasonable, therefore, that in a measure, at least, the manifestations of childhood schizophrenia are situationally determined; and they are inseparably linked to time, space and social context. Not unlike normal children, the schizophrenic child reacts sensitively to his immediate environment. The schizophrenic child's symptoms reflect his adaptive adjustments to the influences and demands of his social environment. In turn, his responses provoke reactions in his environment and thereby influence his outer situation. The study of the schizophrenic child in interactions with other persons, such as his mother, must of necessity reflect the impact of the child on the adult as much as the impact of the adult on the child.[6] In our study of interaction, we do not propose to pinpoint a single and ultimate cause of childhood schizophrenia. Rather, we attempt to bring into sharp relief relational processes which adversely affect the adjustment of the schizophrenic child. Since we are assaying social interaction as expressed in communication, we can say more specifically that we are attempting to discover those errors in communication between the schizophrenic child and his mother which are potentially disabling to him. In other words, we are striving to delineate in a highly individualized fashion for each child the dynamic relationship between the communication failures on the part of the mother, to which the given schizophrenic child is repeatedly exposed, and his characteristic adaptive impairments.

## A THEORY OF COMMUNICATION WITH
## IMPLICATIONS FOR CHILDHOOD SCHIZOPHRENIA

In order to refer our more general theoretic propositions regarding the mutual impact of mother and schizophrenic child to the communication episode, a simple definition of communication will be offered and a number of attributes of communication will first be explored. These attributes are implicit in every communicative interchange but for purposes of our study, need to be explored and made explicit.

By definition, the process by which the mother and child influence each other is termed communication. In this process, an intimate relationship between mother and child is established; and intellectual and emotional meanings are exchanged through a common set of symbols, variously designated as words, gestures, signs, cues and, more globally, as speech and language. Language—verbal as well as non-verbal, and emotional as well as intellectual—is composed of highly specific, detailed and ritualized conventions.

The child learns these conventions. Each person is born with the anatomic structures and the capacity for language; but language itself is learned. Although there is no reason for doubting the evolutionary selection of individuals with the physical structures and functional capacities for language attainment, the somatic structures involved in communication are not themselves primary speech structures. We mean by this, for example, that the lungs are primarily for breathing and the mouth for eating. The individual must obviously learn to use for purposes of communication structures which mainly serve non-communicative functions.

For the learned cues to be useful in social interchange, the communicants need to agree on the meanings to be assigned to the symbols and gestures. In each culture, a different set of communication signals are agreed upon. To insure that the participants in any communication accept the same cues for comparable meanings, supplemental efforts and devices ("clarity aids") are an essential part of the communication. (These will be specified in our discussion of the analysis of clarity.)

Finally, the child learns his language from the adults or those more mature individuals who already possess the complex, highly differentiated language forms the child must learn as a basis for socialization. Left without instructions, the child cannot arrive at the full and precise repertoire of incoming and outgoing signals required of him. He needs to have suitable models available so that he may imitate other persons with more acceptable or mature verbal skills. We are aware, too, that ordinarily the child is actively encouraged and supported in his learning of speech. He is emotionally prepared to speak and also goes through a number of essential preparatory phases before learning more mature verbal skills. We mention this inasmuch as errors in socialization during the infant period of preparation for language may explain later aberrations in communication.

The dyadic communication in which any child may participate implies that the child has agreed to talk. It is an expression of his wish to communicate. As stated above, it indicates he has attained the mutually agreed upon signals for communication of meaning, that is, the normal, expected speech skills. It further indicates he has had an environment which has presented him with suitable speech models to emulate and which has responded to his communication efforts in a manner which reinforces interest and capacity in communication.

It is significant, therefore, that schizophrenic children are deficient in speech skills[5,13] and, as a group, are less motivated to engage with others through verbal interaction. Some special features which are characteristic of schizophrenic children also influence their failures in the development of communication skills. These special features of the children reflect especially their aberrant patterns of over-all adaptive response. An awareness of these qualities is important to us because any inclusive analysis of the communicative interactions of schizophrenic children with their mothers would have to recognize that in their communication responses these children present unusual tasks to their mothers. The mother has to contend constantly with the extraordinary difficulty she experiences in engaging with the schizophrenic child, in initiating and maintaining a continuous chain of conversation with her child, in understanding his meanings and in conveying meanings to him. It is also important to recognize that the responses of the adult may either weaken or strengthen the child's characteristic modes of interactive adaptation.

One adverse effect of the schizophrenic child's adaptive responses which influence his communication behavior may be a resistance to human engagement. The "bridging" defects may be represented by a disinterest in sounds, in regard to both listening and vocalizing. Sometimes there is a very specific disinterest in the human voice. Just as crucial a response may be the visual avoidance of the human face or person.

In examing the perceptual behavior of schizophrenic children, however, we have been particularly impressed with their deficient use of their own vocalizations to monitor their speech production in a finely discriminated fashion.[5,12] Similarly they are inattentive to the vocal and gestural responses of other individuals who might communicate with them and influence their speech.[4]

Such deficiency in the use of acoustic and visual information to monitor speech production reflects an over-all aberration of ego. However, even when we have reversed the schizophrenic child's avoidance of the visual and the auditory, we find that he often suffers from a primary incapacity to perceive or to organize patterned form from elemental acoustic and visual stimuli.[5] This perceptual impairment in itself is a hindrance to communication development.

We have also stressed that the schizophrenic child's deficiencies in self-awareness (identity) are a hindrance to his attainment of communication skill.[8] The learning of communication signals for emotional or private discriminations requires a consciousness of differentiated inner states. The child who has not achieved a finally discriminated awareness of his private experiences will be unable to learn the verbal and gestural cues which our culture has designated to specify such inner states. This is particularly true of affective reactions. Schizophrenic children are often unaware of sharply etched states of emotion and sentiment such as anger, joy, love and fear; and they do not, therefore, have a basis for learning the appropriate word cues for these feelings.

The following two examples from our case records illustrate the point that a vocabulary deficiency in words for feelings may both reflect and actually affect awareness of feeling:

(1) Ben did not know the meaning of the word "hunger"! He would eat and never know when he was satiated. In discussion with his therapist he revealed that the only way he knew that he had had enough and was not "hungry" was to touch his stomach. His psychiatrist inquired about this. "Don't you know inside of yourself when you have had enough?" Ben replied in the negative, stating that he always had to feel and to see the full stomach before he was sure he wanted no more food.

(2) For about six weeks after admission to the Center, Moses was in a state of marked confusion and anxiety. The dominating factor seemed to be that of disorientation. One day his physician found him smiling and she said, "You're smiling." He responded to this with apprehension. He said, "Isn't it all right?" His psychiatrist replied, "Yes, it's fine. You must be happy." He responded, "Is that why you smile? What do you mean smile? What do you mean happy?" His physician replied, "Look, I'm smiling because I like to be with you." The child still looked worried. His physician said, "Let's look in the mirror together." As the physician continued to smile, the child finally began to look more like the physician and became somewhat more relaxed. It was necessary to do this repeatedly in therapy until the child finally learned the implications and communicative value of a smile. There was every evidence that he gradually learned to relate the signal of a smile to the experience of warmth in his relationship with his physician.

Apart from the likelihood that deficits in the schizophrenic child's ego as a whole retard his communication skill, recent evidence has confirmed that the average mother of a schizophrenic child is also deficient in speech.[15] She, therefore, presents her schizophrenic child with a poor speech model to emulate. In addition, because she communicates meaning and affect less competently than the average mother of a normal child, we may presume that she is also a poor teacher of acceptable speech patterns.

## MOTHER'S OBJECTIVES IN COMMUNICATION AND THE SCHIZOPHRENIC CHILD'S CENTRAL ADAPTIVE IMPAIRMENTS

Up to now we have referred to certain fundamental generalizations regarding communication and its attainment. We have also discussed factors influencing the poor speech of schizophrenic children. We should now like to propose also that in every communicative transaction between any mother and her child, the mother is profoundly impelled by a number of objectives, directed particularly toward affecting her child's behavior and all determined by her role as mother. Intuitively she responds continuously to her child's behavior in accord with her maternal objectives; and she alters her child's responses by an amazing array of supportive, reinforcing, punishing or simply passive techniques. In this regard, the mother must react to constantly shifting interactions by appropriate choices of responses. We may first ask, therefore, what do mothers do in the course of their "natural" interactions with their children. Here we refer to the usual, hence expected interactions. How do her responses to the child influence his learning and development? These are enormously involved questions and we have selected for discussion only those maternal objectives which will assist us in the analysis of communication of schizophrenic children and their mothers.

In brief, we are postulating that in her many varieties of interaction with her child, every mother, to a degree, performs tasks whose effects include (1) the enhancement and support of the child's relational and affectional responses and, (2) the enhancement of the child's feelings of familiarity and predictability in a fluid and changing world.

The mother encourages her child's attachment to her because it increases his security. On the other hand, she also has to assist him to separate himself from her. If she overstresses attachment she increases his potentiality for separation anxiety and reduces his resourcefulness and independence. On the other hand, overstress of separateness and distance and the avoidance of attachment leads to emotional privation. Quantitative variations in these experiences may be noted.

The mother thus educates her child in the awareness of affectional feelings and in the communication of such feelings. In addition, while encouraging his response of tenderness, she assists him also to cope with separations from her. She does so by anticipating and helping the child to grasp temporal limits of separations, by building trust in her inevitable return and, generally, by encouraging the attainment of a mental representation of a mother who is permanent and continuous even when she is physically out of view.

Related to training in warm human relationship is the enhancement of the child's feelings of familiarity in a more general sense. This requires the mother's anticipation of her child's surprise at unfamiliar events and her ability to dissipate his puzzlement arising from incomplete construction of reality, deficient schematization and feelings of incompleteness. We assume that the mother's vigilance in anticipating surprise assists her in accustoming the child to unfamiliarity. This anticipation enables her to control the dosages of strangeness with which the child can learn to cope. We believe this to be an elemental task of the mother which constantly orders her response to her child from the earliest months. The mother spends an enormous proportion of her time with the child explaining to the child and giving novel experiences a meaning which the child can grasp, accept and relate to previously achieved understandings. The mother will have had many examples of her child's response of surprise beginning very early in the child's life. (Such surprise and related fear has been noted as early as the third month of life.) Of course, in many different cultures, one observes early play of covering and uncovering the face with verbalizations such as "Here I am." This game may represent a useful device for training the child for strangeness.

The mother's intuitive behavior for diminishing the distress of surprise and strangeness is stimulated by the child's expressions of puzzlement, fear or protest in an obvious context of unfamiliarity. The mother's inclination to anticipate and to respond sensitively to the child's reaction to strangeness is an aspect of general adult responsiveness to a child's state of helplessness. However, mothers have a uniquely profound commitment to their children and an intense investment in supporting the children's testing of reality and adaptive efforts for the purpose of achieving understanding and familiarity in changing situations. We would further speculate that the strong motivation of mothers to counteract their children's keen distress resulting from strangeness aids in diminishing the dependency and thereby the fears of separation from the mother's physical person.

These general tasks, which the mother assumes in every interaction with her child may now be expressed in terms specifically pertinent for the communicative interaction. In communication, as in any kind of interaction, she takes steps to support the child's developing attachments and to educate and stimulate his adaptive functions in order to improve his ordering of reality and diminish the anxieties that are a consequence of confusion and strangeness. Among the adaptive functions which the child is stimulated to attain, of course, is his own capacity to communicate. We shall proceed to discuss each of these maternal tasks in communication with the child in more detail.

We presume that in every communicative encounter the mother ideally attempts to enhance, deepen and maintain the relationship between herself and her child. In the face of the enlarging physical distance between herself and her growing child, she attempts to bridge the gap between herself and her growing child. This "bridging" function is performed by stimulating and sustaining the child's interest in and attention to her. She maintains the contact by use of visual and acoustic cues, although other cues, such as touch, are also present.

Of importance in the maternal maintenance of affectional response are the comprehensive steps she takes to diminish the child's prototypic fear, that is, the primary anxiety of separation. The mother encourages an attitude of trust that she will return after each separation; and she supports the child's internalized representation of her permanence even when she is absent from view. She thereby assists the child to tolerate physical separateness. It has seemed to us that this experience between mother and child in which the child learns to accept the physical separateness and, even more, the absence of the mother is an important part of the education of the child to anticipate the continuity of all familiar objects and places absent from immediate view and to develop a temporal concept of past, present and future. It is also a factor in supporting the child's consciousness of every act as a unit characterized by the rhythmicity of a beginning, middle and end.

In the mother's communicative efforts to stimulate and educate the child's ego functions she encourages some of his responses and thereby enlarges and maintains important ego functions. She diminishes other responses, including those which result in errors, deficiencies and aberrations from the acceptable. There is a constant, vigilant investment in enhancing functional growth by pertinent response to the child's behavior. Among the supporting responses of the mother, as observed in her communications, are an enormous variety of behaviors including praising, permitting, contacting, guiding, directing, expressing affection, assisting, offering to cooperate, playing with the child, explaining and teaching. Among her restraining communications are disapproving, criticizing, interfering, refusing to cooperate, removing herself and breaking contact, setting bounds or restraining the child.

Among the important adaptive functions which the mother enlarges via communication is communication itself. By voice and gesture, the mother encourages an interest in acoustic and visual experiences and in a reciprocal interchange of cues. In addition to stimulating the initial engagement by language, the mother encourages the continuation of the communicative encounter. She teaches the child the acceptable cues in a precise fashion. Most importantly, she effects an implicit agreement to communicate in which both participants agree to a symbolic interchange. They agree to strive to understand each other so that they may each be able to communicate, (1) "I want you and me to understand the signals we each transmit," or (2) "I want to understand what you understand," or (3) "What you understand in my signals is what I understand."

In the light of our theoretic analysis of the mother's goals in her verbal engagements with her child, it is important to stress that the schizophrenic child is deficient in exactly those functions which, we maintain, the mother would be most anxious to stimulate and strengthen. These functional deficiencies among schizophrenic children include a serious lack in the elements of relational and affectional response and a dramatic impairment in capacity to observe order, continuity and predictability in reality. They are less able to love reciprocally than normal children and they are more confused about reality.

These characteristic deficiencies of schizophrenic children are presumably influenced by the processes of mother–child interaction. But how important are they and to what extent do they reflect the core or primary adaptive impairments of schizophrenic children? The answer to this question would be useful for analysis of verbal encounter between these children and their mothers. Therefore, we have asked ourselves: What, in our view, are the primary adaptive disturbances common to all childhood schizophrenics? What factors contribute to these impairments? In answer to these questions, we shall turn to some conceptual speculations regarding childhood schizophrenia that have guided the Ittleson Center investigations of childhood schizophrenia. These speculations, rooted in clinical and experimental observation, have encouraged our interest in communication. They have, in addition, suggested a set of propositions applicable to the analysis of communication.

We are first proposing that the central impairment common to all childhood schizophrenics is a pervasive defect in all levels of self-regulation.[5] This global defect is represented in aberrations in virtually all adaptive and purposeful functions including human attachment, communication, perception, abstraction and motility. The deficiencies in purposeful functions account for all the commonly accepted criteria for the diagnosis of childhood schizophrenia, including disorders in human relationships, disturbed identity, failure in perception and conceptualization, communication incapacity, abnormal motility, unusual preoccupations, and not infrequently gross intellectual retardation. More precisely, the schizophrenic child fails to organize his sensory input into patterned forms, to categorize and generalize the information, and to manipulate the environment effectively through psychomotor response. Related to these failures, the schizophrenic child is seriously disabled in his body control and coordination, in his postural balance and in discrimination of body cues. His failure to achieve a unified and confident awareness of his body hinders the development of a well differentiated self, clearly distinguished from non-self.[8] This, in turn, seems to be a factor in the schizophrenic child's limitations in differentiating important from unimportant persons.

The key functional impairments, that is those which are common to all schizophrenic children, are abnormalities in receptor response, self awareness, and communication. Their relative avoidance of the distance receptors, vision and hearing, adversely affects the adequacy of their orientative efforts. Their defects in self-awareness reflect their overwhelming weakness in categorizing and schematizing the data of inner and outer experience. Their communication deficiencies adversely affect their human relationships as well as cognitive potentialities; so that they are socially isolated and slow to learn.

A major outcome of all these ego impairments is a state of pronounced puzzlement. The children repeatedly manifest the overt attitude of bewilderment when unable to organize orderly relationships in what they experience. Always, however, they strive to draw pattern and familiarity from their experiences. It is also striking that their desire to extract pattern and familiarity is, in a sense, as strong as their incapacities in making sense of reality.

Puzzlement in the schizophrenic child embodies the inner experience of cognitive unfamiliarity, a primary and non-conflictual emotional response of intense anxiety to unfamiliarity accompanied by a persistent drive to attain familiarity and understanding. His continuous sense of strangeness diminishes the schizophrenic child's capacity to cope with the novel and unfamiliar. It also reduces the gratifying feelings of complacency which are the natural accompaniments of familiarity. In previous reports we have suggested that the characteristic anxiety and defenses of the psychotic child against anxiety are secondary to his fluid, disordered organization of reality.[5,9,14]

In looking for the cause of childhood schizophrenia, therefore, we are actually seeking explanations for a diminished repertoire of adaptive and purposeful functions which the child requires to orient himself to reality and to give it meaningful form. We include among these adaptive responses in which the schizophrenic child is deficient those internal discriminations which are the constituents of self-awareness, that consciousness which accompanies each person's purposeful actions. We also include among his deficits in self-directive response his failures in affectional response, human relationships and communication.

How can the existence of all these functional impairments and the disordered construction of reality they entail be explained? It is clear that such functional deficits can be primary manifestations of intrinsic incapacity. For example, poor speech and communication may reflect cerebral dysfunction and related errors in perception and execution of the spoken word. On the other hand, deviancy or deficit may reflect extrinsic or environmental error. For example, poor speech and communication may reflect the absence of a good speech model[15] or a poor learning environment in which suitable reinforcers are absent; so that the child does not progress through the various stages of communication attainment. Unless facilitated by a responsive environment, the child may lose his interest in and attention to sound making, babbling, sound imitating, and the whole complex emotional preparation for speech. Also, as we have previously stated, the more complete explanation of the ultimate ego manifestation in the schizophrenic child lies in the way that intrinsic and extrinsic factors interweave in their effects.[6]

## FAMILY FAILURES AND DERIVATIVE PROPOSITIONS RELATIVE TO THE MOTHERS' COMMUNICATION

We have thus suggested more generally that the preferable explanation of each of the self-regulative deficiencies of schizophrenic children is one which accepts a multiplicity of contributing factors, including those which refer to deviations in the child himself and those which refer to his social environment. This conceptual scheme has received support from investigations of the families of the children and of their neurological status.[2,3,5,7,25] Subclusters of brain damaged and of non-brain damaged children have been noted, which differ in behavioral competence and family adequacy. However, it has also been our theoretic conviction, supported by experimental and therapeutic data, that the impairments in self-awareness and in self-direction of schizophrenic children are not static. They shift considerably in response to changes in the inner states and the external milieu of the children; so that ego deficits which determine the diagnosis of childhood schizophrenia are strongly affected by interactions between the child and his family. In short, each symptom is a final outcome of a series of relational episodes involving in sequence the child's unique impact on each of the family members, their response to the child and finally the child's own adjustment to the conduct of his family in the light of his own survival requirements and capacities. In considering the influence of families, and even more specifically, of mothers in the aberrant development of adaptive functions of schizophrenic children, what hunches are provided by clinical and therapeutic experience with the children and their families?

For purposes of corrective reversal of the deviant expressions of schizophrenic children, we have always investigated whether the family environment has failed to meet the child's special requirements for growth. This approach has encouraged us to examine the interaction between the child and his surroundings and to appraise the child's capacities and inclinations, his impact on others, and the responses he provokes in others. We have sought particularly to determine what in the environmental response has diminished the child's orienting behavior, his perception of reality, his mental organization of reality, and his ability to manipulate reality to meet his needs.

In assaying the family and mother–child interactions clinically, we have first reached a decision regarding the child's intrinsic capacities. We have thus distinguished children who give evidence of cerebral dysfunction from those who do not give such evidence. Certainly the child who is lethargic, inattentive, and unresponsive on the basis of physical factors has an effect on his mother's behavior and is different from that of the baby who is energetic, attentive and responsive. It is also clear that the behavior of a placid baby leads to responses in his environment, which are quite different from those provoked by a tremulous, hyperactive baby. Following this subdivision of the children by neurological assay, we have sought to distinguish two general categories of failure in family response; that is, failures of omission and failures of commission. Responses and discriminations by the child can obviously be facilitated or diminished by a variety of positive environmental responses, either rewarding or punishing; and they can also be affected by a quantitative absence of environmental response. We shall offer some illustrations below.

In considering the schizophrenic child who in our judgment is physiologically and neurologically intact, we have been impressed by evidence that the environment has indeed often failed to provide essential parental response to the child. Examples of such environmental failure are particularly represented in families characterized by a paralysis of parental function which we have termed "parental perplexity."[11,21] "Perplexity" refers to the following set of parental responses to the child's behavior; extreme passivity; an absence of clear, assertive, constant parental presence; lack of spontaneity; marked uncertainty; absence of empathy with the child so that awareness of the child's needs are not perceived; bewilderment and inactivity in the face of unacceptable or bizarre behavior and dramatic lack of control of the children. An example of "perplexed" parental response, which we have already reported,[21] is that of the mother of a schizophrenic girl who reported the following incident involving the girl and a younger brother:

> "She plays with his sex organs and then she shows him her genitals. Then she plays with his sex organs and he plays with hers and they laugh like it is low, not nice. I just cry that it should be over, but I don't say 'Don't do it.'" Am I acting the right way?"

The most strikingly outlandish symptoms of this schizophrenic child was an extreme lack of normal sexual control. The mother's disciplinary passivity was obviously an important factor in the child's uncontrolled sexual expression. The mother did not teach her child control of impulse— an essential aspect of ego. This inference is supported by the fact that the child learned to control her sexual behavior by active encouragement.

The family environment may be an active agent in confusing the child's efforts to order reality in meaningful fashion. Again we quote an incident that we have already reported.[10]

> At a family meal, the father of one of our schizophrenic children pointed to milk and, with serious expression, demanded "Pass me the ketchup." His son looked bewildered and said that his father was pointing to milk. The father mocked anger, insisted he was pointing at ketchup, instructed his son not to argue, and again demanded the ketchup. His son passed the bottle but was speechless, uncomprehending and confused.

We may also infer family failure when the family has been unable to cope with special demands of children who have primary incapacities. This is commonly seen in families of children in whom cerebral dysfunction accounts for intrinsic incapacities in functions essential to a child as he attempts to organize meaningful relationships in reality. The deviancies of the child which reflect the brain damage lead to consequences in the family environment. These environmental responses in turn foster the development of those special characteristics which cause the child to be included in the over-all population of children designated as schizophrenic. Clear examples of this interactive process are to be seen among children who manifest sensory hypersensitivity as a result of altered cerebral function. Hypersensitive children represent a special kind of challenge to their parents who often may respond to the child's hypersensitivity in such a way that the child is encouraged to evade perceptual engagement.

Confusion in the child may result from parental overstimulation, or understimulation, or active distortion of the stimulation. An interesting example of cruel hyperstimulation[10] has been reported.

Ben, a seven-year-old schizophrenic boy, was being given a birth-day party by his parents. Although his father knew of Ben's hyper-sensitivity to sudden noises, Ben's father purchased noisemakers. These were gunpowder toys which made a very loud gunshot sound when a string was pulled. Ben's father encouraged his son to be the first to pull the string of the noisemaker. His father thought it would be fun to begin with Ben, since Ben was so easily startled. When Ben pulled the string, there was a loud explosion and the toy disinte-grated. Ben screamed with fright, attacked his father and then plunged a fork repeatedly into the birthday cake. In subsequent discussion with Ben's psychiatrist, the father showed a complete lack of empathy for his son's fear, and, instead, he focused on the struc-tural aspects of noisemaker construction.

In summary, we have postulated that the families of schizophrenic children, whether the children are neurologically normal or not, frequently show gross deviances in response to the children's behavior such that the children are not guided to develop very basic adaptive capacities and to construct reality effectively. The massive gaps of psychotic children in those functions which are required to order reality distinguish them from neurotic children. Among the latter group of children, intrapsychic conflict, rather than perceptual and orientative failure, is the central problem for the child; and we infer that these neurotic children will ordinarily have been adequately provided with nurturant experiences which support the development of those capacities which constitute the normal ego. The psychotic child lacks elementary resources for orientation and adaptation which the neurotic possesses. We have proposed that the neurotic child, with more ego, is occupied with conflict; whereas the psychotic child is occupied with pre-conflictual failures in ego and the adaptive responses to his serious ego defects. This is of significance in our present study since we are led to propose that the study of the behavior of the child's family with the disordered child is most directly illuminating in the case of psychosis. In other words, it is presumed that failure by the parents to provide responses which assist the children to construct reality and which induce ego growth is a primary cause in psychosis—more so than in neurosis where we presume that the family failure encourages intrapsychic conflict in the child.

It will also be noted that we have stressed the central symptomatic significance of childhood confusion in childhood schizophrenia. Confusion is a common enough experience of all childhood. Overcoming the child's confusion is an important aspect of normal rearing, and occupies the mother in a very high proportion of her verbal responses to the child. The mother supports and augments the growth of those adaptive functions and inner discriminations which are essential to the child as he tries to order reality and to give it form, permanence and predictability. In the event such schematization of reality is not achieved, the child is constantly propelled into a state of anxiety. We may reasonably ask what occurs in the event the parent does not rescue the child from the distress of his own bewilderment and does not reassure him? We may presume, of course, that the anxiety will persist. In our clinical experience, the anxiety even burgeons and may frequently reach a state of catastrophic panic. Beyond this, however, the adult loses his attractiveness to the child as an agent who will relieve the child's anxiety and gratify him. The child withdraws; and then the adult has to meet a new challenge since he is no longer acceptable to the child as a source of approval and direction in the development of the child.

Examples of confusing family behavior follow. We refer first to Mary, who has never attained a sure and certain sense of body integrity, and to the behavior of her family which—we may presume—influenced her body concepts.

At various times Mary has verbalized anticipation of body disintegration. ("Will my hands fall off?") She has also talked of loss of body contents, of body incompleteness and castration. Her very uncertain body self has been linked to fears which, on occasion, have reached panic proportions. In an investigation of her family's conduct during her early childhood, we uncovered a remarkable history of parental response which repetitively increased Mary's body confusion and body anxiety. "We were both afraid to touch her. We thought she would break. Both of us got up in the night and one gave her the bottle and one held the baby. I put a handkerchief in his hand to hold the baby's head because I was afraid that if he would touch her with his bare hand her head would dilapidate (sic)."

Quite remarkably, the first minute of communicative interaction between Mary and her mother in our experiment illustrates her mother's failure to overcome Mary's disordered and fragmented body concepts as well

as Mary's deviant means for communicating affectional need. The brief
segment* of verbal interaction between Mary and her mother follows:

Mary:      "Finger." As she smiles and motions to her finger.
Mother:    "What's that?" As she looks at the child's finger.
Mary:      "Finger." As she smiles broadly.
Mother:    "What is it?"
Mary:      "I love finger." As she smiles.
Mother:    No verbal response. Mother adjusts Mary's sweater.

In contrast to this mother's failures in conteracting confusion, the corrective alleviation of the same child's confusion and consequent anxiety
about her body by active communicative intervention of an Ittleson Center
worker is illustrated in the following anecdote:

On passing the doorway of the school toilet, a staff member
heard Mary groaning painfully. When asked, Mary informed him
that she had struck her arm against the sink. At the sight of the slight
red bruise mark Mary went into a panic. "I'll die" she cried repeatedly. "I'm going to bleed to death; my arm will fall off!" Her agita-
tion increased with each prediction of dying. Examination of Mary's
arm did not show any break in the skin. The staff member assured her
that her fears were baseless but Mary would not be consoled. All else
failing, the adult proceeded to examine Mary's arm with a serious
medical attitude. He examined her fingers carefully; bent her elbow
several times and finally informed Mary that he was *sure* he could
make it better in a few minutes. He told Mary to watch the red mark
get lighter when he patted her arm. Mary watched eagerly, the tears
subsided a bit although she continued to ask if she would die or bleed
to death. He informed Mary authoritatively that there was absolutely
no possibility of dying from the bruise. As proof of this he showed her
that the redness was already disappearing. Mary looked hesitantly
and then expressed dismayed surprise that the redness was really
gone. A moment later she complained disappointedly that it still hurt.
"In that case" the staff member commented, "there's still one more
thing I have to do." Then ceremoniously he proceeded to put cold
water on the injured area. Patting the arm dry, he commented, "Now
it's definitely all better; doesn't that feel better now?" Mary looked
tenderly at her arm and then up at him and said "Yes," and walked
quietly back to her classroom.

Another anecdote illustrates how the failure to dispel a child's confusion
by clear explanation hinders his construction of reality and disturbs his

*See Example 3 on pages 140–143.

emotional complacency and relationships. This is one of many similar episodes we have been able to observe.

During a visit home, John decided to play one of his records. He noticed that one side had a big scratch on it. He showed the record to his mother and asked who had scratched his record. His mother insisted no one had touched the record, though it was evident she was lying. John insisted logically that the scratch could not have occurred unless someone had handled the record and scratched it. His mother persisted in saying "It just happened." John could not understand and became agitated. Then his sister said that John himself had scratched the record; but John could not grasp how this could have happened. He became more and more bewildered, asked repetitively how it could have happened while his mother continued to insist it just happened. His confusion was not resolved, he remained very agitated, and he became increasingly inaccessible.

To illustrate a child's fear and defensive withdrawal in response to confusion, another critical anecdote is taken from observation of Joey who repeatedly found himself unable to understand his mother's cues.

At a therapeutic meeting with the entire family, the mother sat with a fixed rigidly unvarying grin. Joey, a schizophrenic child, stared at his mother's face perplexedly and suddenly asked rather anxiously, "What's wrong? That look on your face." His mother said there was no special look on her face and that he was always asking her the same question. In response, he became markedly withdrawn and showed very reduced initiative in further interaction and communication.

Consistent with our more general conceptualization of childhood schizophrenia and its developmental features, we approach the analysis of every communication interaction of the schizophrenic child and his mother with the following theoretic propositions pertaining to the mother:

(1) In her verbal responses, the mother of the schizophrenic child weakens rather than strengthens positive growth of adaptive function. Her support and her direction of the child, and the reinforcements she provides in response to his behavior are either absent, attentuated, excessive, or distorted so as to be confusing.

(2) Related to proposition (1), the mother of the schizophrenic child does not assist the child sufficiently to overcome his bewilderment regarding reality. We have suggested that the generalization and categorization of perceptual information which a child must exercise in order to resolve the many confusions of his existence are dependent on outer cues from his human environment as well

as on inner capacities.[9] The mother of the schizophrenic child does not provide the requisite number and quality of such external cues.

In applying these propositions to the study of verbal interchanges between a schizophrenic child and his mother, we have assumed that in addition to attachment to the nurturing person for security the normal child ultimately requires a degree of distance or separateness from the nurturing person in order to develop those inner representations and images which are so characteristically human. Such separateness becomes feasible in the context of a continuing connection to the mother through the distance bridging function of communication. We examine in a detailed fashion, therefore, how the mother deals with and maintains the essential distance between herself and her child in the course of their relational activities. Though helping the child to separate physically from herself, does she encourage a warm relationship? To achieve such warmth, there is a necessity for mutual visual regard, auditory interchange, and physical contact and cuddling—administered in proper doses and appropriately spaced. Or does she create and maintain a very impersonal relationship? This would be expressed in communicative interactions which are devoid of visual, auditory, and physical contact and in which the mother diverts the child away from herself, and towards other objects in the environment.

As we have already suggested, the mother of a schizophrenic child has to cope with the child's deviance, even where she may be properly motivated in her efforts to provide sustenance to the child.* The aspects of ego deviance in the child which particularly challenge the mothers of schizophrenic children include their receptor aberrations, their deficiencies in affectional response, their overriding deficiencies in the immediate skills of communication, and their weakness in awareness of self and non-self.

The mother must overcome the schizophrenic child's avoidance of distance receptors. This pre-relational problem of the schizophrenic child hinders the total process of learning and ego maturation, since it interferes with informational input, active organization of experience, monitoring of functional expression, and the utilization of the human being as a reinforcing agent. Apart from this, it hinders the development of affectional relationships.

---

*This kind of normal maternal behavior has been found chiefly among the mothers of the "organic" children.

Every mother of a schizophrenic child also has to contend with the child's aberrations in attachment behavior. These deviances in the social responses of the child are diversified. The child may not recognize or distinguish the mother from others; and, indeed, he may not have an image of other persons as continuing, unified objects. Or the child may recognize the mother but elude her. Or the child may want only partial contact with the mother. For example the child may want body contact but no eye or auditory contact. The child may also want to contact the mother but may desire the privileges of "primary process" expression in which very primitive demands are made on the mother. These unusual attachment behaviors challenge the mother, and at best have an abrasive effect.

It is obvious, too, that the child's lack of acceptable speech skills has the effect of diminishing the possibilities for mutual comprehension. The mother has to work harder than the mother of a normal child to understand the child and to give him cues which he can understand. We would propose that where clarity in communication is lacking the use of verbal devices to assure clarity is an essential constituent of all communicative interchanges; but they are even more essential in the interchanges between the schizophrenic mother and her child.

Aside from the greater difficulty in attaining mutual communicative clarity, the mother of the schizophrenic child must employ the very instrument of communication to assist the child in overcoming his disordered construction of reality. This, of course, is the crux of the therapeutic problem as well. In therapy, as in mothering, the task is the corrective stimulation and maintenance of the many areas of purposeful function in which the schizophrenic child is lacking. All therapists are sensitive to their own inclinations to respond to the ego deficiencies of the schizophrenic child and the terrifying demands of primary process expression by counter-hostility, or detachment, or passivity, or even by guilty, depressed, hopeless feelings. We are not surprised that the mothers have comparable reactions when they attempt corrective stimulation.

In evaluating a schizophrenic child's verbal exchanges with his mother, the central questions for us thus refer to the mother's effectiveness in responding to the child in a way that weakens aberrant response and strengthens acceptable and normal response. Does the mother stimulate and sustain visual and auditory engagement? Does she enhance the child's experience and expression of affection? Does she improve the child's communications? Does she utilize all her behaviors in the service of assisting the child to build an orderly schematization of reality?

## STUDYING THE MOTHER–CHILD VERBAL ENCOUNTER AS A UNITARY ACT

Every verbal encounter between mother and child may be viewed as a unitary act with a beginning, a middle and an end; and with connections to the past and to the future. This simple model of the verbal encounter as an act facilitates the operational analysis of the mother's behavior in her role as mother. For example, the mother's attachment enhancing function is reflected in her management of the beginning which is the greeting phase, and of the ending which is the leave-taking phase. We presume that the universal rituals of greeting and leave-taking are essential exercises in relationship. They encourage affectional response and attachment as well as the acceptance of separation. They help define the permanence and continuity of the relationship when separation is anticipated. The pleasurable aspects of the relationship are enriched.

The mother's ego-enhancing responses to the child for the purpose of improving the child's construction of reality are represented in every phase of the mother–child encounter. These refer to the mother's reinforcing behavior, noted above, through which she rewards (approves), punishes (disapproves), sets limits and establishes the range of acceptable behavior; buttresses and teaches. The mother's commitment to the task of dispelling the child's confusion and the child's unclear or distorted perception is universal among all mothers, whether the children be normal or abnormal. However, this commitment is a primary and pervasive focus of interest in the case of mothers of schizophrenic children who are impaired in orientative and receptor behavior and in the organization of reality. Throughout the encounter we ask the general questions: Does the mother of the schizophrenic child support the child's efforts to perceive reality clearly and sharply? Are her verbal constructions clear to the child? Does she improve the very unclear verbal constructions of the child? Does she answer the child's questions adequately?

With the above in mind, our standardized mother–child meeting, to be described, will ultimately be analyzed with reference to the special requirements of the beginning, the middle and the end of each unitary encounter. The beginning of the encounter represents the greeting phase.

The greeting has features derived from its significance as the opening phase of an act—in this case an act of human engagement. Since it is the beginning of an encounter between two individuals, it assumes that each participant perceives and recognizes the other. It further requires that both participants agree to engage with each other. Further this agreement must embody the intention to engage in a verbal and gestural manner, utilizing the acceptable symbols of communication.

The greeting has another set of characteristics, specifically derived from the relationships and respective role of the participants. In the experiment to be described greetings are exchanged between mother and the child who does not anticipate the visit. The greeting thus contains a mutual recognition of their past separation and present reunion, references to their mutual love in terms of warmth and reciprocating need, and a consideration of the child's surprise. We expect that the mother always anticipates a greeting. She desires a "good" greeting, that is, more than a token "Hello," adequately extended, and with full expression of attachment. Finally, we expect that the mother always anticipates surprise and puzzlement in view of the unexpected nature of the visit.

The mother is thus first challenged to foster attachment by encouraging the child to participate fully in the greeting ritual. The details of this ritual include efforts on the part of the mother to explain or rationalize the separation and to seek expressions of renewed togetherness. Even in the greeting the child is prepared for impending separation. The clear expression of the beginning and the avoidance of ambiguity and blurring increases the experience of attachment and the awareness of the rhythmic recurrence and continuity of relationship. The child is provided with the intellectual and emotional cues for attachment and separation; and he is encouraged to communicate through the use of these cues.

The second important task of the mother during the greeting phase is the dissipation of the child's confusion and attendant anxiety about the unexpected nature of the visit. The mother is sensitive to the element of surprise as the most immediate source of puzzlement, anticipates it and tries to give the child understanding to cope with it.

In every encounter, one may observe whether there is a greeting at all. If there is, one may observe how it is expressed. What are its verbal, visual and somatic constituents? Who initiates the greeting and does the other person respond? Is it a "good" greeting? If the greeting is attenuated, is there an effort on the part of each communicant to extend, enlarge and strengthen the greeting? One may observe if the child expresses surprise, if the mother anticipates surprise, and if the mother explains the unexpected character of the visit in a way that is meaningful and satisfying to the child.

In the middle phase, the mother is occupied with maintaining the child's interest and attention, and with sustaining the child's agreement to communicate. In this phase she may also establish the temporal and spatial bounds of the visit. Here too she is required to counter the child's deviance, to reinforce acceptable expression and behavior and to support verbal clarity. Therefore, in examining the middle phase, we ask: Does the mother frustrate the child's deviance, maintain his attention, support clarity of communication?

In the end phase, the mother and child become involved in the leave-taking. Here the mother teaches the ritual of leave-taking. More profoundly, however, she attempts to diminish the anxiety of separation. She does do by defining quite carefully the duration of the impending separation, by supporting the child in his distress and augmenting the sense of trust in the re-establishment of their connection. Here we evaluate the mother's effectiveness in assisting the child to define and cope with the separation, to express his grief over the approaching separation and to experience a predominant attitude of hope and trust in the continuity of their relationship.

## EXPERIMENT TO STUDY MOTHER–CHILD COMMUNICATION

The encounter which we fashioned to observe the mother–child interaction and to obtain the data of communication was similar for all the children. Yet it was only semi-structured in that it did not restrict the child and mother to a limited number of response choices. Rather it permitted completely free interactive expression within an established framework of space, time and physical surrounding. The general clinical circumstance for the study was that these psychiatrically most disordered of children had all been separated from their families at an early age (about 6 to 7 years of age) and were in residence at the Ittleson Center for Child Research. The specific experiment circumstance was a surprise visit by the mothers to the children. Though in residence, the children were accustomed to regular weekends at home or regular visits from their parents at the Center. However, in accord with therapeutic purpose contacts with parents were always planned ahead with the children and expected by them. For the purpose of the experiment, however, the visit of the mother to the child was so structured as to be off schedule and thus unexpected. Early in our pilot studies, we found that this aspect of the experiment evoked substantial puzzlement in most of the children. On the basis of more total clinical understanding, it seemed to us that this experience of puzzlement in the experiment had links to the child's deepest problems of attachment and self-awareness, as well as to his more general problems of confusion and attendant anxiety.

The simple standardized procedure has been applied to diagnosed schizophrenic children, after varying periods (but more than two months) of residence in the Ittleson Center for Child Research. The mother is asked to visit her child at a time when he is not generally visited. In addition, the visit is arranged to take place in the observation room where they have not met each other before. The mother is informed that she and her child are to be observed, although emphasis is placed on the child as the object of interest. The child is not told of the mother's impending visit until immediately before the visit, so that it is unexpected and potentially puzzling to the child. The child does not know he is being observed. The physical arrangement of the observation room is the same for each visit. There is a small table in the center of the room with two chairs for the subjects facing a one-way mirror. On one side of the table is a small bookcase containing toys, books, games and a plate of cookies. On the other side is a bench. The child is brought to the room by a research assistant. After 20 minutes, the visit is terminated by the assistant who takes the child back to the activity from which he had come. The visit is recorded on sound movie film and on audio tape.

After the child leaves, the mother is interviewed by the research psychiatrist. In this open-ended interview, she is encouraged to describe her impressions and reactions. She is asked how the interaction compares with the conduct of a meeting with her child under more usual and ordinary circumstances. She is also asked to describe her reactions to being observed. Though not used directly in our analysis, this information has supported the assumption that the interactional behavior during the experiment is consistent with the usual behavior.

A verbatim, typewritten transcript of the verbal interaction is derived from the tape recording of the visit. Then, the sound motion pictures are studied intensively to obtain a description of all relevant non-verbal behavior. The latter description is integrated with the verbal productions. Changes in facial expression, gestures, and body motion are noted as they are linked to the spoken words. The transcript of the mother–child 20 minute interaction is arranged so that the child's responses are on one side of the transcript and the mother's responses on the other side, both recorded in the sequence of occurrence. Pauses between verbal responses of more than two and a half seconds are noted.

The verbal and behavioral productions are divided into the smallest meaningful units of relational response. These records then serve as the raw data for our communication analysis.

The experiment has definite limitations. However, the experiment is one of a variety of studies in childhood schizophrenia in progress at the Ittleson Center. Hopefully, these will correct the limitations of the present investigation. For example, the present experimental study of the interactional behavior of the schizophrenic child and his mother casts light on one special instance of all the interlocking relationships which contribute to the development of the schizophrenic child. Therapeutic investigation and direct observation of the family as a whole[2,3,5,7] support the very important role of the father in the development of the schizophrenic child. The father may exercise his influence directly on the child or indirectly by affecting the behavior of the mother or the entire family as a unit. Similarly the mother may exert her influence through the father. Concentration of attention on the mother–child dyad is an artificial maneuver to reduce the enormous complexity of the observational data. Though the observation and analysis thereby becomes more feasible, the view afforded by this method is obviously a partial and, therefore, imprecise reflection of the conduct of the entire family.

There are other obvious limitations or, if you will, weaknesses in the design. The mother knows she is being observed. Does her self-consciousness alter her usual pattern of response to her child, so that what we observe may have little bearing on her historical influence on the schizophrenic child? Are we relying too heavily on a single and all too brief specimen of the interactional relationship between mother and child?

Nevertheless, the standardized character of the observation enables us to compare the observed dyads among themselves. Beyond this, however, all of the mothers have been interviewed extensively, they have become familiar to us in treatment and they have been visited at home. To an even greater degree, the children have been observed and treated individually as well as in milieu. In every case, therefore, we possess information far beyond the single visits in the laboratory and, as a matter of fact, in our early experiments, we used such clinical data to determine that the observed gestures and the relational behavior were consistent with our supplemental information.

Our method was derived from Levy's method of behavioral analysis—a method he exemplified in his observations of mothers and their babies during the act of nursing.[17,18] This method concentrates attention on small specimens of behavioral interaction and tries to exhaust their possibilities as independent sources of information. We have also utilized other data as a final resort when they are available. Such data have been used to answer questions when information beyond that supplied by the interactions have been required. For example, it has sometimes been necessary to know the child's functioning intelligence and verbal comprehension in order to evaluate the mother's communication behavior with the child.

Up to now, we have been systematically analyzing the written records of the verbal transaction, and in so doing, we have precluded, for the present, additional conclusions that might be drawn from listening to the tape or looking at the movies. We know already that the reference only to the written record has limited our analysis of affect. The muted, flattened voice of a mother, or any other unusual speech patterns, can be fully appreciated only by listening and looking. However, we do plan in the future an analysis of the acoustic and gestural aspects of the data.

In the analysis of the written record, we have been conscious of the hazard of overstressing a conclusion based on an insufficient number of communication units. This error is easily corrected in our records, however, because a 20-minute communication ordinarily contains many, many units of interchange. (Using our present designation of communication units, the mean number of units per record is 168.) It is always possible, therefore, to check the validity and consistency of an interpretation regarding communication trend by searching the transcript for similar or identical units of interaction.

In our analysis of the 20-minute interaction, we have restricted our attention to the pattern of intercommunication under immediate view, that is, to the special way the mother and schizophrenic child stimulate each other by reciprocating signals of meaning and feeling. Even so, we have been stunned by the extreme complexity of the data which emerge and need to be taken into account. The procedure for assay of communication which we shall be describing has developed very gradually indeed over the past ten years, for we have discovered that communication evaluation requires an attitude of patience and regard for detail far beyond our early anticipation.

The emphasis on the unique aspects of adaptation of the child and mother to each other and on intimate and detailed linkage between specific phenomena and the preceding and later relational responses, encouraged an interest in larger, meaningful units of response. In the earliest phase of our interactional and communication studies we sought a few rigorously defined "pure" variables. However, it quickly became clear to us that certainly in the initial trajectory of research we ought not to limit ourselves to a few simple dimensions merely for the sake of methodological rigor. Such an approach would be precise, reliable and methodologically manageable to be sure. However, it could only lead to theoretic propositions of limited practical value because the data would be necessity be so restricted that they would be unrevealing of the true and essential significance of the interaction. To illustrate, one can and should count the number of words in each record. However, such a word count has seemed less pertinent to us as a basis for understanding the aberrant responses of schizophrenic children than evidence of stimulus confusion in the environment or evidence of lack of clarity in the family transmission of information. Yet the evaluation of complex phenomena such as stimulus confusion or lack of clarity is a far more involved and more easily contaminated operation than counting words. Or, as another example, consider the asking of questions, a common enough communicative gesture by the mothers of schizophrenic children. We could simply count maternal questions, and impute a simple or single meaning to the question asking, and thereby seek to explain the failures of the schizophrenic child. However, it was apparent to us that question asking varied in import as a function of the changing social context and individually unique intrapsychic processes. For example, the mothers occasionally used questions to stimulate the impoverished verbal responses of the children—a natural response on the part of any adult in the presence of a non-communicative child. On one occasion, the three observers were looking at a movie of mother–schizophrenic child interaction. The child had just been asked a question by his mother. He responded by a long period of meditative silence. The movie was stopped; and the three observers considered what their own inclination was in response to the child's silence. All agreed that they had the impulse to ask a leading question. (Later that week, the same observers had an opportunity to listen to a structured psychiatric interview of the mother. To their amazement, she manifested the same periods of long silence. Again during a very long moment of delay in the mother's response to a question, each of the observers spontaneously announced his own inclination to goad the mother on by questions. The interviewer responsible for the unstructured interview felt he had been more impelled to ask questions to prod this mother than he had with any other mother whom he had interviewed.) On the other hand, our records included a number of mothers who asked questions to divert the child from emotional issues absorbing the child. Thus in Example 5, pages 154–157, the mother did not acknowledge the child's cues referring to an aggrieved state, and arrested his communicative efforts by asking questions. The mother's questions represented response avoidance. In answer to the child's crying over his separation from home, the mother's only reaction was to ask repeatedly "How are you?" In the same way it has been possible to show that the mother's initiation of topics may be stimulated by the child's inactivity in regard to verbalizing. Or the initiation of new topics may be an instrument for hindering, diverting, or controlling the child's expression. Thus, one mother employed many unrelated topics to avoid dealing with her child's anger.

This kind of observation repeatedly supported the conviction that discrete and particularized occurrences were always explained in part by larger communication goals and contexts which were the framework for the smaller events. We determined, therefore, to study each mother–child interaction as a unique case in all its complexity; and to do so with a level of exactness which was consistent with individual case analysis.

We developed a set of presumptions and definitions pertinent for communication description, which enabled us to link our broad theoretic propositions and the observable, ostensive data of the unique verbal encounter. All case inferences were constantly checked by reference to the specific communication. Thus, in one case, we inferred that a child asked questions merely for the sake of asking questions. He seemed to enjoy being in the role of questioner rather than in the role of a child being asked questions. We made this interpretation since in repeated verbal interchanges his question asking had no relation to the mother's responses. Question asking in itself without regard to its information seeking function had become a re-enforced, gratifying form of social response for him.

In coding the relational responses and the errors in clarity of communication of mother and child, the assumption that each unit of communication could be understood best in terms of the total context improved the precision with which we applied our definitions and also the agreement among observers. In general, we decided that our definitions would stress objective description, and yet would be broad enough to represent the transactional significance of each interactional episode. The definitions would be expressed in ordinary language, that is the language any person might commonly use to describe the episode under view.

Judgments regarding failures in communication have been based on the use of the presumptive norm. In other words, we have proposed that these failures are grossly aberrant communications that are not found among normals. This would be comparable to the pediatrician observing a rash and concluding without recourses to statistics that the rash is an abnormality. Illustrations of such communication failures will be presented with the summary of maternal failures to follow.

We recognize that some judgments of communication error may be more open to question. This would be exemplified in the judgment that a mother's language level is incomprehensible to her child because it is too complex for a child to grasp and more suitable for an adult. Such a judgment would be assisted by studies of normal development in which the language exposure of normal children and mothers would be explored. We do know, after all, that mothers occasionally use words and phrases beyond the understanding of their children. The absorption by the child of words that are "beyond" him is a normal process of enlarging his vocabulary. What safeguards do normal mothers employ to assure adequate understanding? At what point and under what circumstances does the incomprehensibility of the mother's language fail outside the range of the normal?

Apart from the gross communication errors which we may immediately and safely describe as failures in communication, we are often assisted in our judgments by the confirmatory impact of convergent data in the transcript. As an illustration, in Example 6, the mother's major failure is her inability to perceive the emotional cues of her child. This is observed in the brief sample presented on pages 159–163 of the present report but is confirmed again and again throughout the 20-minute meeting. The mother misses her child's initial desire for approval and for recognition of his positive school accomplishments; and the absence of her approval bothers the child throughout the meeting. The mother also misses all anxiety cues, including the intense anxiety and distress which the child obviously manifests in later meeting in connection with his separation from her and his placement in the Center.

As previously mentioned, we are occasionally assisted in our judgments of communication error by using the extensive information available to us in a clinical program of comprehensive treatment of children and parents. Thus in the case noted above, the child enters the room and after a brief limp greeting says "Combien?" Within the context of the greeting, his mother obviously cannot grasp this strange question. On investigating his experiences during the day, we discovered that on that day his class had had a French lesson and had learned to greet each other in French. His incomprehensible question "Combien?" was an error since he had been meaning to ask "Comment allez-vouz?" In any case, he was pleased and wanted his mother's recognition which she frustrated in her dry remark "Are you speaking French already? Oh, you couldn't have learned it all in a couple of days. There must be some still left to do." Not only can she not grasp his "Combien?" without further information, she also misses entirely his displeasure and his puzzlement at her retort which he misinterprets to mean that she feels he has not studied. He says "I did really my studies." And the mother replies "You did?"

Undoubtedly the method of the present study falls short of strict precision—in part because of our previously stated belief that excessive rigidity of definition and assumption could hide the true complexity and meaning of that interaction. But we have, on other occasions, tested postulates regarding the parental speech and communication in what might be regarded a more precisely scientific fashion. Thus, as already reported, we have been able to demonstrate in a carefully controlled experiment and by completely blind speech analysis that the speech of mothers of a group of schizophrenic children is far inferior to that of mothers of a matched group of normal children in capacity to communicate meaning and emotion and as a speech model for the children to emulate.[15] What we are attempting to do in the presently reported analysis of mother–child communication is a far more difficult task than that exemplified in the above noted highly controlled comparison of normal and schizophrenic children. We are now attempting to illuminate the detailed and dynamic way in which the verbal cues and behavior of the mother and child influence each other. For example, if the mother communicates poorly or offers a vague or contradictory verbal cue, how does she affect the child? Do the data demonstrate how she weakens the child's adaptive behavior? This strategy, perhaps, is crude in its assumptions and definitions, but it is appropriate at this point for the complex data at hand and likely to be of particular significance to those who are interested in therapeutic alterations of the disabilities of schizophrenic children.

The material is being codified for quantitative analysis. Measures such as the Clarity Score to be described and other scores representing calibration of interactive response will assist us ultimately in demonstrating relationships between the schizophrenic child's aberrations and his interactional experiences. However, there is also a unique validity in a clinical approach which regards each case as an experiment and attempts to delineate the crucial communicative and interactional parameters in the case. This clinical approach can be followed if errors in each unit of communication are described in very simple, objective terms and in ordinary language and with an eye on the small details of context and sequential response. In doing so, the communication sources of the deviancies in the child's world seem to emerge.

## THE ANALYSIS OF CLARITY OF COMMUNICATION

We have been impressed with the possibility that the social environment of schizophrenic children has had the general effect of weakening their responses, and, particularly, of attenuating their construction of reality. We have studied communication between schizophrenic children and their mothers with particular focus on communicative clarity at each phase of the interactional encounter, because we have assumed that the mother is able to strengthen her child's effectiveness in functions involved in the orderly and consistent construction of reality only to the extent that her own communications are clear.

In evaluating the mother's part in the communications with her child therefore, we have up to now emphasized the clarity of her communcations.*[20] In accord with our discussion, in order to evaluate the clarity of her communication it has been necessary first to define the specific communicative task she has had to perform in the verbal encounter with her child. In arriving at such a specification of her problem in each interaction, we have considered a number of factors. As stated, her task has been determined in part by the special demands placed on her by the facts of her child's deviance in level and quality of adaptive response and, more particularly, in communication behavior. In part it has been determined by the historical fact of the child's placement at the Center, his separation from her, and the unexpected nature of the visit. And in part it has been determined by the different requirements of the beginning, middle and end phases of the encounter. Keeping her task in mind, it has been feasible to arrive at an assay of the clarity in her communcations.

To evaluate clarity of a message, we arrived at an empirical description of clarity and its requirements following a naturalistic study of communications of manifestly clear and unclear communications of mother–child pairs.[20] Our description of clarity follows:

> In order for a message to be considered clear, the words that are used must be distinctly expressed; that is, the pronunciation must be clear. The intended meaning must be comprehensible to the listener with relative ease; or within the listener's potential for new learning. The vocabulary and form of expression should approximate the level of understanding of the recipient. The feelings must be clearly expressed. The feelings must be appropriate to the words that are used; that is, there should be no contradiction between affect and idea. The implications must be clear. The message must be logical; that is, it must not contain ideas that contradict each other or that are in contradiction to the context or facts. The message must be relevant; that is, it must have the right place in the context.

*The many other facets of communication will be analyzed ultimately.

In addition to clear message context, it is evident that clear dyadic communication requires a structural form and integrity. Thus, each of the topics must be adequately elaborated, with clear beginning and ending, and they must be logically connected to previous and subsequent topics except where intervening needs or situational interferences occur. There should be a back-and-forth reciprocity in which each communication response becomes a stimulus to the other person.

As noted in our general discussion of communication, the communication interchange generally contains built-in maneuvers for assuring mutuality of understanding. The mother uses a variety of clarity aids—statements or questions which add to the clarity of the message. Clarity aids which may be noted include repetitions, confirmatory questions, synonyms, simplifications, definitions, redefinitions, descriptions, qualifications, modifications and elaborations. However, we have further assumed that in any encounter between mother and child, the mother ordinarily has an extraordinary investment in ascertaining that each message, whether she be sending it or receiving it, is entirely clear. In this experiment of a 20-minute communication, we expect her, therefore, to accept the continuing task of correcting all communication errors, whether these are reflected in the child's misunderstanding of the mother's communications or his own inappropriate and unacceptable verbal and gestural responses. We regard any instance of maternal failure to correct an error of the child as an error in the mother's communication, except in those circumstances where the child simultaneously presents the mother with a more overriding alternative demand. (Such, for example would be represented in the impulsive move by the child to leave the situation so as to require most of all a maternal response of restraint.)

Chart 1 summarizes errors in clarity of communication which may be applied to the analysis of the verbal communications in the experimental mother–child encounter. These errors include those actively made by the speaker, that is, errors of commission. As noted, however, among the errors which directly have the effect of diminishing clarity, we have also included the failure to correct the errors of the other participant; that is, errors of omission.

## CHART 1
## MAJOR CLARITY ERRORS*

I.  COM—*The Errors of Commission:* This major classification includes all errors actively made by mother and child. This is in contrast to those errors which occur by default; such as the mother's failure to correct or attempt to correct the communication errors made by herself or the child, or the mother's failure to clarify or attempt to clarify unclear aspects of the situation.

A)  LDC—*Lack of Denotative Clarity:* The explicit aspects of a message are unclear. The literal expressions of ideas, facts, and references to emotions that are conveyed by words (such as "I am sad.") are unclear. This category is intended to define problems in conceptualization or formulation of ideas as well as problems in the clear expression of ideas. It includes incoherence; incomplete, fragmented or fractional responses; awkward or idosyncratic use of language symbols; grammatical errors resulting in ambiguity; vagueness,** unclear pronunciation, and messages that, although otherwise clear, are beyond the comprehension of the listener because of the intellectual limitations of the latter. (These latter errors are represented by the designation LDC-BC, Lack of Denotative Clarity—Beyond Comprehension.)

B)  LCC—*Lack of Connotative Clarity:* The implicit aspects of a message are unclear. Both ideas and emotions communicated by implication are unclear. For purposes of classification and coding all non-verbal aspects of communication are considered to be "connotative." The means commonly used for this aspect of communication are: vocal inflection, amplitude, rate, rhythm and tone of speech; facial expression, body movement and posture. Words can also have strong connotative function, such as represented by figures of speech. The words in metaphorical expression, in similies and in expressions of humor and sarcasm often communicate implied meanings in addition to the accom-

---

*A more extensive exposition of this classification with examples is presented in a report to be published by The New York Academy of Sciences. As noted, the classification of errors in clarity which was developed at the Ittleson Center, was derived following a detailed analysis of the communications of mothers known to be highly "perplexed" in their interactions with their schizophrenic children. To describe the errors, we used conventional psychiatric terms which were defined with particular clarity by Bleuler. Recent workers who have also focussed systematically on illogical, amorphorus, fragmented and incongruent styles of communication in families with seriously disordered offspring include Wynne, Singer, Bateson, Jackson, Weakland, Riskin, and Satir.[22,23,26,1,16]

**Those forms of illogical expression and vagueness that represent introduction of irrelevant content or distortions of reality are classified under category D, *Irrelevance,* category H, *Reality Distortions* and category I, *Misrepresentation of Other Participant.*

panying non-verbal and connotative cues.* An example of the difference between the connotations supplied by words; the conventional second meanings of idiomatic, symbolic or meta-phorical statements; and the non-verbal connotations which are supplied by vocal and body cues is as follows: "You are a rock of Gibraltar." In its verbal connotations this means, "You are a strong person—impregnable." But this same statement said with a questioning inflection of the voice and raised eyebrows implies the opposite.

C) INC—*Inconsistency:* Contradictory or incongruent ideas or feelings are presented by a participant. The inconsistency may be between two or more aspects of a single response given by the partic-ipant or between the current and previous responses. Verbal content may contradict non-verbal behavior; the words may contradict the feelings; denotations may be inconsistent with connotations; or there may be contradictions between two or more denotations or between two or more connotations.

D) IR—*Irrelevance:* The content of the message is not totally related to the context.

    a) IRT—*Total Irrelevance:* The content of the message has no relationship at all to the context.

    b) IRP—*Partial Irrelevance:* The content of the message is only loosely, tangentially or obliquely related to the context. It lacks, in various degrees, pertinence. A partially irrelevant response may result from a misunderstanding of the other's message by the sender or may result from inattention or evasiveness on the part of the sender.

E) LE—*Lack of Elaboration:* The message is lacking in richness and/or in its value as a stimulus for elaboration of a topic. This category particularly applies to the superficial, terse or "token-like" comment.

F) DNR—*Lack of Response to Statement of Other (Does Not Respond):* A participant fails to respond to the statement by the other where a response is appropriate.

G) DNA—*Lack of Response to Question of Other (Does Not Answer Ques-tion):* A participant fails to respond to a question by the other where a response is appropriate.

H) RD—*Reality Distortion:* External reality is misinterpreted or misrepre-sented by a participant. Descriptions of objects, events, situa-tions and persons—including the person who is speaking—are

---

*In the current study the coding of errors is limited to the typewritten transcripts rather than the sound motion pictures. The analysis of errors in connotative clarity, therefore, is limited by the absence of the subtle changes in speech quality and non-verbal behavior contained in the films of the interaction.

distorted. This category includes delusions, grandiosity and magical ideas as well as less bizarre misrepresentations or contradictions of reality.

I) RDMO—*Misrepresentation of the Other Participant:* One participant misinterprets or misrepresents the message coming from the other person. He mislabels cues. Or he distorts, contradicts or incorrectly describes the other person's behavior aside from that person's formal communication.

J) INT—*Interruption of the Other:* One person begins to speak while the other is still speaking and has not as yet finished his message. The other person may or may not stop speaking at this point. Interruption of the other in situations where this is appropriate is not considered a clarity error.

K) SS—*Simultaneous Speech:* Both persons speak at the same time. This may occur with interruptions or when both people begin to speak simultaneously.

L) MUT—*Multiple Unrelated Topics:* A participant includes several unrelated topics in a single response.

M) MR—*Multiple Response:* In a single response the participant includes several topics or subtopics which are related to each other directly or by the situational context, but which represent excessive elaboration, use of unnecessary detail, or circumstantiality.

N) IS—*Indistinct Speech:* A participant does not clearly pronounce his words or says them too softly to be heard. Mumbled, unintelligible responses fall into this category. (Speech which is clear to the other communicant but is unclear to the observer is not a clarity error; but speech which is unclear for both observer and other participant is a clarity error.)

O) TTD—*Topic Transition Deviations:* This group of categories includes a variety of violations of topical integrity. For example, topics are not "completed" or are reintroduced repeatedly even if "completed."* Transitions from topic to topic are awkward or abrupt without apparent associative links to the previous topic or apparent relation to other situational or contextual stimuli.

    1) PTC—*Premature Topic Change:* A participant interrupts or switches to a new topic before there is adequate termination or closure of the topic being discussed.

    2) PTP—*Premature Change to a Previous Topic:* A participant interrupts or switches to a previously introduced topic before there is adequate termination or closure of the topic being discussed. If this previous topic has al-

---

*For comprehensive discussion of the importance of the act as a unit with clear beginnings and endings, see David M. Levy.[19]

ready been adequately discussed and terminated, its repetition is considered an additional error. (The latter situation is represented by the designation PTP-T, Premature Change to a Previous Topic Already Terminated.)

3) ATC—*Abrupt or Awkward Topic Change:* The topic change occurs without apparent associative links to the previous topic or apparent relation to situational stimuli. This is seen particularly with the introduction of irrelevant content and also often occurs in conjunction with PTC and PTP.

4) TP—*Change to Previous Topic:* This designation may or may not represent a clarity error. If the change is to a previous topic which has not been adequately discussed and terminated it is not considered an error. If the change is to a previous topic which has been adequately discussed and terminated then it is considered an unnecessary and irrelevant repetition, and therefore a clarity error. (The latter situation is represented by the designation TP-T, Change to Topic Previously Terminated.)

II. FC—*The Errors of Omission or Failures to Correct Clarity Errors or Confusion:* This major classification includes all failures by the mother to correct or to attempt to correct communication errors made by the child or herself, or her failure to attempt to clarify, and, where it is possible, to clarify any other unclear or confusing aspects of the environment.

A) FCLCM—*Failure to Correct Message Lack of Clarity:* This category covers the mother's failure to use appropriate aids to clarify messages (CA) such as repetition, modification, explanation, elaboration, and questioning of child as to his understanding of messages where appropriate. The mother's failure may be in clarifying her own statements or in helping child clarify his own messages. This failure may be in relation to any of the errors listed in Group 1, committed by either mother or child, e.g., FCLDC, FCIRP.

B) FCLCS—*Failure to Correct Situational Lack of Clarity:* Failure to use appropriate aids to increase situational clarity (CA-SIT) such as explanation in regard to confusing or potentially confusing situations. A lack of situational clarity (LCS) refers to the confusing impact of environmental circumstances which are not well defined or are too complex for the child experiencing them. It does not include confusing or unclear communication by the other participant. A source of LCS in this study is the unusual, surprise nature of the visit. When the mother fails to clarify the situation for the child, this is considered a FCLCS.

Each unit of communication is appraised and rated with regard to clarity as follows:

4. Unequivocally clear.
3. Predominantly clear, in spite of elements of lack of clarity.
2. Predominantly unclear, in spite of elements of clarity.
1. Unequivocally unclear; obscure.
U. Unscorable.

In addition, the kind of error is recorded. On this basis it is possible to obtain a summed score, termed the Clarity Score,* and to formulate a description of the major errors in communication for each participant.

For present discussion, we have appraised the first 20 units of communication in each of 25 records of interaction between schizophrenic child and mother. This appraisal, therefore, is based on a very small part of the total record and refers to a portion of the beginning or greeting phase. In all but two cases, the 20 communication units were transacted within the first two minutes or less. Even so we have been struck by how much is revealed in this brief period of interaction.

## PATTERNS OF COMMUNICATIVE FAILURE
## OF THE MOTHERS

In reviewing our 25 records of mother–child interaction for purposes of classifying the maternal failures in communication, we have considered first the nature of the communication challenge which each of the children had represented to his mother in our experiment. With this in mind the children may be categorized with regard to motivation and capacity to communicate as follows:

1. Children who withdraw from communication, either partially or entirely; and who may have an essential capacity to communicate, although they vary widely in this respect. These children may avoid relational response and communication entirely so that they are completely mute. Or they may be selectively mute. Or they may be reluctant to initiate or to attend to partial components of communication such as visual engagement with others. Or

*Rank order correlation of summed Clarity Scores based on scores provided by two raters for the first ten units of communication of 16 mother–child interactions was .88 significant at < .005 level, 1-tailed test). We can assume a higher level of reliability for the larger number of communication units used in the present study.

they may be able to respond to a verbal interchange only if the mother initiates speech. These children require assistance to develop more complete interest in and attention to the elements of communication.

2. Children who do not possess the full capacity to communicate effectively. Their disabilities vary widely. Thus the disabilities may range from total incapacity to communicate to partial incapacity. The children's errors may represent retarded intellect, and related limitations in comprehension, vocabulary and the speech with which they are able to conceptualize. Deficiencies in emotional awareness also limit the capacity to communicate since feeling states are not distinguished and labelled. Finally, there are impairments in any or all the expressive aspects of speech and communication. Here, the children require corrective education to improve their communication response. Of course, the primary incapacity to communicate may be complicated by the withdrawal from communication. (A dramatic example of how such incapacity is improved by the mother's response occurs when the mother overcomes the child's confusion and improves the child's communication by speaking at the child's level and tempo of understanding.)

3. Children who do not withdraw from communicating and are able to communicate. They have active interest in talking. Their communication adequacy is simply and easily maintained by affective and cognitive clarity in the communication messages from the environment. One does, of course, observe impoverished affect, concretistic and awkward forms of expression, symbolic errors, and the underlying deficiencies in self-awareness and the construction of reality. In these instances of affective and cognitive confusion or impoverishment, primary responsibility for the communication error in the mother–child interaction may be assigned to the mother.

Because of the above noted communication deficiencies, in order to communicate effectively with her schizophrenic child, to a varying degree each mother needs to: 1) attract the attention of the child and stimulate his interest in talking to her, 2) maintain the flow of talk and interchange of communication, 3) understand the child and teach him to talk with conventional phonation, rhythm and articulation, and 4) teach him to express his thoughts logically, coherently and with appropriate affect. In the latter regard she must teach the child what should not be talked about.

On the basis of these maternal responsibilities, considered in terms of the mother's communication interaction with her child, we may state that an analysis of the 25 records reveals a variety of patterns of failure in communication on the part of the mothers. We define failure to mean any shortcoming on the part of the mother in fulfilling her communication objectives, as described. As noted the errors may be of commission. Here the mother makes errors of her own in denotative and connotative expression, in relevance, in congruence and in suitable topic elaboration. She is unclear. Her errors actively diminish the child's communication response, his relational and affectional behavior and his schematization of reality. The errors may also be of omission in which the mother's errors consist of instances when she does not correct the communication errors made by the child and when she does not act to explain and illuminate those aspects of the encounter which are obviously confusing to the child. (Poor explanation of the surprise visit is an example.) In other words, the mother fails to respond to the deviant verbalizations and interactional responses of the child. Under such circumstances, she fails by default to facilitate correction of the child's errors and fails to stimulate and maintain effective communication, warm affiliative response, and orderly construction of reality.

The over-all patterns of failure in communication of the 25 mothers to be described overlap but are arbitrarily presented as separate varieties of failure for purposes of discussion. In brief, these patterns of failure are as follows:

1. Failure to stimulate the child's interest in active communication.
2. Failure to maintain the continuous flow of communication with the child.
3. Failure to reinforce normal and acceptable speech and communication in the children.
4. Active confounding of the child in regard to his construction of reality.
5. Missing or not responding to the child's communicative cues.
6. Failure to cope with the child's unusual deviances in communication.

We shall enlarge on our definition of each of these maternal failures in communication and illustrate the failures with samples, chiefly of the first 20 units of communication in the mother–child encounter.* (The same samples will illustrate failures 1 and 2.)

---

*In one of the examples (Example 4, pages 145 to 153) we are presenting communication samples which did not appear in the first 20 units in order to provide unusually sharp demonstration of the mother's errors.

The following symbols are used in the transcripts:

----- Indistinct Speech

—— Simultaneous Speech (Those parts of the response of one participant which are underlined are said at the same time as those parts of response of the other participant which are underlined and on the same line in the transcript. See example, page 145.)

. . . Pause less than $2\frac{1}{2}$ seconds

## MATERNAL FAILURES IN COMMUNICATION

I. *The mothers do not stimulate their children's interest in talking and in the components of the act of talking together. In this group of mothers is the mother who does not try to overcome the child's avoidance of visual and auditory engagement. She does not actively strengthen engagement and weaken withdrawal. She is passive and removed from social contact; or she responds to the child's behavior in a manner which is very vague or uninvolved. What the child perceives is poorly articulated, difficult to discriminate and ofttimes confusing in its lack of purpose and direction. The child's behavior, so to speak, does not result in consequences from the mother which are potentially effective in altering the child's disposition to non-communication and social isolation.\**

II. *The mothers do not maintain the children's communication and the continuing flow of communication. This group of mothers includes the mother who finds being with the child and the process of connecting with the child by talk very burdensome. The talk lags and the mother prefers to divert the child's attention from herself to a magazine or a child's book. Or she remains passive and withdrawn while the child engages in restless, goalless, self-stimulating behavior. Empirically, this kind of failure in the communication behavior of the mother of a schizophrenic child usually parallels the first failure noted, that is, the mother's failure to improve the child's interest in initiating talk and communication. The specific errors in clarity which contribute to these two overlapping patterns of maternal failure include any failure to correct the child's errors, e.g., irrelevancy, idiosyncratic speech, and disruption of topical continuity. The child darts from topic to topic and the mother does not assist him in maintaining continuity. The mother fails to elaborate topics sufficiently and also fails to promote it in the child. The interactions between the children and their mothers in Examples 1 and 2 illustrate these first two patterns of maternal failure.*

### EXAMPLE 1

In this sample of mother–child interaction, the child presents no problem in communication. She gives no unclear responses and the content of her responses is not bizarre. In her responses to the child, the mother makes a number of errors of a subtle variety. On the surface, few of the mother's responses are dramatically deviant as regards clarity. However, her over-all communication behavior reveals a superficial kind of offhand engagement with the child until she becomes involved in the "Pick-up-Sticks" game. The mother is vague in response to the child's puzzlement

---

*This type of maternal failure is akin to the kind of maternal passivity and neglect described by Sobel in his study of schizophrenic mothers and their babies.[24]

over the off-schedule, surprise visit (M3, M9.*) She gives misinformation which the child knows to be wrong (C8, M9, C9, M10). Her answer to a question by the child is tangential or partially irrelevant (M11). She gives terse or insufficiently elaborated answers where more detailed answers would be more appropriate to the child's need to define the situation (M5, M9). More than the average mother in our group, she relies on direct non-verbal communicative signals (signals which convey the whole meaning without accompanying words) and accepts this tendency in the child (C13, M14, M19, M22). Her terse response, use of non-verbal cues and her tangentiality contribute to poor elaboration of topics. The slowness and meagerness of the verbal interaction is indicated by the fact that it took over four minutes to obtain twenty verbal responses. The average time in our twenty-five excerpts is less than two minutes. Her passivity is further underlined by the fact that all topics are initiated by the child and not by the mother. She puts the responsibility for structuring the visit on the child (M3) but then ignores the child's request for direction (C20) and then she asks the child if she wants to do something the child has already asked to do. (C20 and M23; see also milder example of this at C3, M4 and M5.) She generally seems to avoid the directing, clarifying maternal role except when she is instructing the child in the "Pick-up-Sticks" game. Then she seems overly concerned with defining the game.

There are no significant topic-transition deviations or violations of topical integrity in this record; but there is a skimpy, impoverished quality to the interchange. The over-all effect of the mother's approach to the child is to discourage any richness in communication.

## EXAMPLE 1
Age of child—8 yrs. 11 mos.

| (CHILD) | (MOTHER) |
|---|---|
| | 1. She hears the outer door opening, looks at it and walks to the door. She helps open the inner door. She smiles at her daughter, puts her arm around the child. |
| 1. "Ma?" Child enters room, looks at mother and smiles. | |
| | 2. "What do you want, Dear?" As she leads daughter toward bench. |

*These refer to the numbered responses of the mother in the transcript. The numbered references to the child's responses begin with C.

| (CHILD) | (MOTHER) |
|---|---|
| 2. "What are we gonna do in here?" As she sits down on bench next to mother. She smiles at mother and looks toward bookcase. | |
| | 3. "Anything you want. What would you like to do?" As she nods and looks at bookcase. |
| 3. "Can I have a cookie?" | |
| | 4. "Um hm." |
| 4. "Who brought these cookies?"* As she stands up. | |
| | 5. "I don't know. I came in here and they were here. Would you like a cookie?" As they both walk to bookcase.(5 sec. pause) |
| 5. She takes a cookie from plate on top of bookcase and takes a bite of it. | |
| | 6. She takes the plate of cookies from bookcase and places it on center table as she mumbles something indistinctly. |
| 6. "All right. Here." As she offers mother a cookie. | |
| | 7. "Oh, thank you." As she takes cookie and puts it in her mouth. "What would you like to do." |
| 7. "Ma?" She is standing next to and looking into bookcase. | |
| | 8. "What?" |
| 8. "Did you just come to see me?" As she walks to end of bench next to bookcase, leans on it, looks at mother and smiles. | |
| | 9. "Um hmm."** She is standing by bookcase, facing daughter. |
| 9. "Mrs. Lucas, too?" She is smiling and leaning on bench. | |

*Cookies put there by staff.
**Mother regularly visits social worker, Mrs. Lucas, on this day.

(CHILD)

(MOTHER)

10. "Oh, I saw Mrs. Lucas for a few minutes."

10. "What did you say to her?"

11. "She told me to come on Friday and pick you up at one o'clock."

11. "One o'clock? That's when you are going to pick me up?"

12. "Um hmm."

12. "Are you going to pick me up, or Daddy?" She is smiling.

13. "Me." As she nods and then sits down on chair near center table. (24 sec. pause to next verbalization at C14.)

13. She looks around room. Then picks up childrens' book from top of bookcase and hands it to mother. And finishes eating the cookie she has in her hand.

14. She takes book and places it on table. She finishes eating cookie she holds in her hand. She moves closer to table to prepare to read book.

14. She walks to center table and mumbles something indistinctly. "-----"*

15. She gets up and sits down on bench.

15. She slides chair mother has been sitting in closer to table and comes toward mother who is sitting on bench, looks at mother's pocketbook and says, "What's in that bag?"

16. "Oh, this is my pocketbook, and a book, my eyeglass case, and I have my lunch." As she opens pocketbook.

---

*"-----" indicates speech which is unintelligible on tape recording.

|                    (CHILD)                    |                    (MOTHER)                    |

(CHILD)

16. She says something indistinctly and is standing over mother, looking at her. "-----"

17. "Oh." (9 sec. pause)** Said with a chuckle. She walks to bookcase and picks up Pick-up-Sticks game and says, "How do we do this?" As she walks back to mother.
(2 minutes)
18. "How do you open it?" As she tries unsuccessfuly to open box.

19. She takes a cookie from the place on the table, and smiles. And steps back to bench.

20. "-----. Can I take and pick some up?" (5 sec. pause) As she takes box and empties it on table.

(MOTHER)

17. "Oh." (9 sec. pause)* Said As she smiles.

18. "It's Pick-up-Stick."

19. She takes box from child's hand, puts childrens' book down on table and opens box.

20. She gets up from bench, goes to table, takes stick magnet out of Pick-up-Sticks box and says, "Um, this is the stick that has the magnet. -----"

21. She spreads out sticks on table, picks them up and drops them again. She sits down at table, picks up stick magnet from table, and says, "See, this is a magnet. Where do you want me to put it? (4 sec. pause) What color do you want me to pick up?" (8 sec. pause) She begins to pick up the sticks.

*Time in brackets indicates time between immediately preceeding and subsequent verbalization.

(CHILD)                                          (MOTHER)

21. She takes another cookie, starts
eating it and watches mother
work. "Cookie. Look, it
dropped." (4 sec. pause) As
she drops part of cookie on
floor. She gets up and picks
cookie up from floor.

22. She motions to daughter to put
cookie in ashtray on table.

22. She puts cookie in ashtray. She
takes another cookie. She then
comes around table to sit down
again.

23. "Don't you want to pick up
some sticks?"

23. "Yeah." As she picks up sticks
and mother gives her the stick
magnet.

24. "Let's see what the score is.
One black stick . . ." (11 sec.
pause)

24. "What was that lady's name
who brought me here."

25. "I don't know. I never saw her
before. Who is she?" She is
reading instructions on box and
says, "All right, now it says if
you pick up five blue sticks you
get 50 points. No, one at a
time, Dear. I'm sorry. Ten red
sticks, 25 points. But you're not
supposed to move the other
ones." (7 sec. pause)

25. She is standing over table,
picking up the sticks and following the mother's instructions. She makes a motion
toward the cookie plate.

26. Mother nods.

26. She takes cookie from plate
and then continues to pick up
sticks.

|                                      (CHILD)                                      |                                  (MOTHER)                                  |
|-----------------------------------------------------------------------------------|----------------------------------------------------------------------------|

(CHILD)                                                     (MOTHER)

27. Continuing, says, "If you take
the one outside, Dear, you'd be
better off. Take one that's on
top." (15 sec. pause) As she
watches daughter pick up sticks
while she sits on chair.

(4 minutes)
27. "Now how much?" As she
smiles.

## EXAMPLE 2

This sample of mother–child communication demonstrates a lack of substantial engagement and a superficiality of communicative interchange. Although the passivity and intellectual limitations of the child herself contribute to the meagerness of the interchange, the primary responsibility for the impoverished communication seems to lie with the mother.

The child is passive, gives simple, terse responses. In the main, her responses although brief are appropriate, with few exceptions (C14, C15, C16). These exceptions suggest retardation in level and speed of comprehension. A similar inference is drawn from the lack of elaboration in her responses. Her impoverished verbal responses and engagement may also be due to a distracting puzzlement over this surprise visit (C11, C12).

The mother fails in dealing with the above communication problems and the implicit confusion of the child. She offers no direct explanation for this off-schedule visit. She does not fulfill her task of actively engaging the child. At best, her attempts are feeble. She introduces topics which do not lend themselves to elaboration by the child. She fails to elaborate topics sufficiently and does not encourage the child to do so. Evidence for the communicative impoverishment are the frequent topic changes and the many brief topics, with only about two units to a topic. The result is a superficial, tentative engagement of the child. There are frequent long pauses as though the mother is at a loss as to what to say. The mother seems to lack communicative resources.

## EXAMPLE 2

Age of child—7 yrs., 11 mos.

(CHILD)                                                     (MOTHER)

1. "Hi, Mommy." As she looks at
mother, enters room and walks
rapidly to mother.

(CHILD)

(MOTHER)

1. "Hi, Darling, what you doing? Huh?" As she smiles, then puts arms out toward child.

2. "Nothing." And then she jumps in mother's lap.

2. "Well."

3. "-----" As she puts finger in her mouth momentarily and looks at mother.

3. "Do I get a kiss?" As she moves her face closer to child.

4. She kisses mother quickly on lips.

4. "That's a girl. What did you do just come from school?"

5. "Yeah."

5. "How nice."

6. She walks to other end of bench, sits down and looks at mother.

6. "I see that you have your barrettes in your hair today. Huh?"

7. "Yeah." (6 sec. pause) Looking straight ahead.

7. "Have you ever been in this room before, Janey?" As she leans toward her and looks at her. It is to be noted that the mother looks at child when she speaks to her, unless otherwise noted.

8. "Yeah." As she looks at ashtray. It is to be noted that child does not look at mother, unless otherwise noted.

8. "Oh, you got dungarees on today, huh?"

9. "Yeah."

9. "Do you wear them to school too, Jane?"

10. "No." As she picks up ashtray.

10. "Uh huh."

(CHILD)                                  (MOTHER)

11. She gets up, walks to mother without looking at her, and then walks back to her seat on the bench, sits down and says, "Where's Daddy?"

11. "He went to work, Sweetheart."

12. "Where's Johnny?"* As she fingers mother's pocketbook.

12. "Johnny's in school, Darling. (3 sec. pause) I came up to see Miss Lucas."** As she touches child's arm momentarily with her hand.

13. "Yeah."

13. "Yes. What did you learn in school today, huh?"

14. She gets up, looks about quickly, and then sits down on bench again.

14. "What are you looking for?" (8 sec. pause)

15. She picks up and fingers pocketbook, and says, "Hi, Mommy."

15. "Hi, Sweetie." As she pats her hair.

16. "I like these barretts in my hair." (5 sec. pause) As she looks into the pocketbook.

16. "What are you looking for." As she holds part of bag and looks into it also."

17. She takes a package of Charms out of pocketbook.

17. "Do you want them to take back for tonight, huh?"

18. "Yeah, yeah." As she nods and continues looking into the pocketbook.

18. "Okay."

*Child's brother.
**Social worker.

| (CHILD) | (MOTHER) |
|---|---|
| 19. "This yours, Mommy?" | |
| | 19. "No, there's gum in there, Sweetheart. There's gum in there." |
| 20. "Empty." | |
| | 20. "No, I think there's a piece in there, too. Do you want?" She looks into pocketbook and says, "Want a piece of gum?" |

III. *The mothers fail to reinforce normal and acceptable speech patterns in the children. This is a large group of mothers of schizophrenic children who fail to encourage communicative clarity, relevance and logic. They do not teach rhe proper sequence of responses between the communicants, the importance of clear beginnings and endings, the avoidance of perseveration, the avoidance of unnecessary elaboration. They fail to correct bizarre or primitive expression.*

## EXAMPLE 3

The immediate problem the mother faces is that of dealing with the bizarre content of the child's communication. Included in the child's deviant responses are bizarre repetition (C1, C5, C10, C13, C16, C18, C2 and C6), illogical or magical expectations of mother (C3), other reality distortions (C7 to C9), abrupt topic changes and irrelevancies. The mother deals inadequately with these gross communication errors of the child. She either connects feebly (M18) or not at all (C9, M10).

## EXAMPLE 3

Age of child—9 yrs., 6 mos.

| (CHILD) | (MOTHER) |
|---|---|
| | 1. There is a noise at the door. She looks at door as it opens. |
| 1. She is smiling broadly, as she enters room, saying, "Like me?" (3 sec. pause) She runs to mother who remains seated at table, and repeats, "Like me?" As she joins her right hand to mother's left hand. | |

(CHILD)

(MOTHER)

2. "Like you." As she smiles at child and puts her right hand about child's waist. It is to be noted that mother looks at child during all conversation unless otherwise noted.

2. "Did you get my letter today?" As she holds mother's right hand. She looks at mother and it is to be noted that child looks at mother during all conversation unless otherwise noted. She speaks with a lisp, with much affect in her voice, especially as contrasted with mother.

3. "No, I didn't." Mother's voice is controlled and flat.

3. "Why?" As she smiles and whines.

4. "I didn't open the mailbox." As she drops child's right hand. "Because I was in such a hurry to get here."

4. "Where's Daddy?" As she smiles at mother.

5. "He's at the office. How are you? -----." As she pats daughter's cheek.

5. Smiling, she says, "Like me?"

6. "I love you." ($3\frac{1}{2}$ sec. pause) As she crosses her arms in her lap.

6. "Did you get my letter?" As she continues smiling.

7. "I did not."

7. "Finger." As she smiles and motions to her finger.

8. "What's that?" (6 sec. pause) As she looks at child's finger.

8. "Finger." As she smiles broadly.

| (CHILD) | (MOTHER) |
|---|---|
|  | 9. "What is it?" |
| 9. "I love finger." As she smiles. |  |
|  | 10. She adjusts child's sweater. |
| 10. "Like me?" As she smiles, and is standing next to mother at the table. |  |
|  | 11. "Love you." (5 sec. pause) As she adjusts child's sweater. "Did you like school today?" And quickly brushes hand over child's hair. |
| 11. "Miss Silver got sick." As she smiles. |  |
|  | 12. "Miss Silver got sick? Who was teaching you today?" |
| 12. "-----" As she smiles and moves finger diagonally in front of face. |  |
|  | 13. "Who?" |
| 13. She crosses finger horizontally in front of her neck and says, "Like me?" |  |
|  | 14. "Love you." |
| 13. She crosses finger horizontally in front of her neck and says, "Like me?" |  |
|  | 14. "Love you." |
| 14. "Did you bring me candy?" |  |
|  | 15. She looks into pocketbook, then into bookcase; takes paper bag from bookcase to table, opens it and says, "Yes. (13 sec. pause) Which would you like?" |
| 15. "This." As she takes out a cellophane bag of chocolate "kisses," and smiles. |  |
|  | 16. "May I have one?" |
| 16. "Like me?" As she smiles, and has her fingers in the cellophane bag of chocolates. |  |

|                (CHILD)                |                (MOTHER)                |
|---------------------------------------|----------------------------------------|
|                                       | 17. "I love you."                      |
| 17. She gives mother a candy, then places bag on table. |                                        |
|                                       | 18. She takes candy and says, "What did you think? Do I like you? What do you think?" As she puts her right hand on child's back. |
| 18. "Like me?" As she smiles and opens candy. |                                |
|                                       | 19. "What did you think?" (4 sec. pause) |
| 19. (No response)                     |                                        |
|                                       | 20. "You look very nice today." As she brushes child's hair with her right hand. |
| 20. "Why didn't you write me a letter?" |                                      |
|                                       | 21. Smiling, she says, "I came in person, so I didn't have to write you. Did you know yesterday that I was seeing you today?" As she gives child a gentle push toward chair. |

## EXAMPLE 4

In the following interaction the mother allows and even participates in frequent disruptions of the normally expected form of two-party communication. She does not help the child to recognize and accept the need for clear beginnings and endings of topical units. Indeed, she actively contributes to this lack of adequate structuring.

The mother has at least three alternatives in dealing with the child's frequent interruptions: (1) She can interrupt her own message when the child breaks in and tell the child not to interrupt her. She may then return to what she, the mother, was saying and complete her message. (2) She can interrupt her own message and yield to the child's interruption. (3) She can continue talking despite the child's simultaneous speech.

This mother at no time uses the first technique but rather yields to the child or continues speaking simultaneously with the child. The frequency of simultaneous talking is graphically portrayed by the frequent underlining in the transcript of parts of messages. In several instances the mother herself interrupts and commences to speak simultaneously with the child (M4, M7, M12).

Often the mother and the child are talking simultaneously without apparent interest in or awareness of the content of each other's messages. There are, however, some occasions when, although they may be talking simultaneously, the mother's subsequent response indicates that she has heard what the child said.

In many instances the mother allows the child to introduce different unrelated topics in such rapid succession that the mother has no time to adequately respond to each topic (C1, C2, C2.1). The mother frequently allows or introduces abrupt transition (M32–C33, M37–C38, and C37–M38) from topic to topic, further leading to a fragmentation of the interaction. She does not impose topic closure nor does she insist on appropriate transitional techniques. The mother further allows repeated reintroduction by the child of previously discussed and apparently terminated topics (C2, C6 and C40). The mother's passivity in imposing order on the interaction is further manifested by the way she allows the child's physical manipulation of her (C6, C8, C34). Lack of clarity in content, such as sequential inconsistencies or contradictions by the child, is also allowed by the mother. Compare C18.3, C22 and C29 with C30, C31, C32 and C38, and C41 and C54 where there is a back-and-forth sequential contradiction by the child of her stated desire to go to the movies. In this situation the mother ineffectively attempts to point out this contradiction (M30 and M31).

Both mother and child on occasion do not specify antecedents of the pronouns they use [C3, C22, C27, M47 ("he").] The child's confusion is manifested in her use of a clarity aid in C49 ("Who?"). However, even here we are not sure whether she is attempting to get clarification about M47 ("he") or M49 ("them").

The result of these above defects in communication is a fragmented, discontinuous verbal interaction.

## EXAMPLE 4

Age of child—8 yrs., 7 mos.

| (CHILD) | (MOTHER) |
|---|---|
| 1. Child interrupts mother's previous statement. "I wanna wear the rings, Mommy." Child sits on mother's lap. | |

(CHILD)

(MOTHER)

1. "We have them home . . . I put them right back in the little jewelry box -----"*

2. "Please can I say* hello ----- to Phillip.** How come you . . . How come Daddy can't come?"

2. "Well, Daddy can't take the time off from work; that's what it is. See!"

3. "Uhm. I . . . She didn't even tell me you're here, Mommy." As she hugs mother.

3. "----- Yeah I know she didn't. Ooh, I've never been in this room before. Have you ever been in this room?" "-----"

4. "Oh, when I was playing with Mary I was in here, Mommy." As she crawls off mother's lap and sits beside her.

4. "Oh, was this the room that Dr. White had you come in with Mary to play Pabloo and Pablish?"***

5. 'Um hm. Uh.

Yeah."

5. "Oh, I see."

6. "Oh, please can I say hello . . .to Phillip?" As she gets up, takes mother's hand. Mother rises and follows.

6. "We'll see him after . . . if they say it's all right."

*Underlining indicates simultaneous talking. "-----" indicates speech which is not intelligible on the tape because of simultaneous talking or mumbling.
**Child's brother who is in waiting room.
***"Pabloo and Pablish" is an imaginary game child played with another psychotic child.

| (CHILD) | (MOTHER) |
|---|---|

7. "Now
we'll see
him."

              7. "No.
              not now; now we will not see

8. "How               him."
come Phillip couldn't come in
here?" Child pulls mother to
bookcase. Pushes mother back.
Mother shows no resistance.

              8. "Because you know Phillip
              would make a big mess in here.
              He'd throw down all the toys

8.1 "Uh."*           . . .*
              and everything."

9. "What about

  -----"           9. "Look
              at those nice books over there.
              What kind of books do they
              have here

9.1 "I . . . don't . . ."    . . .
              I never saw these books

10. "I don't          before.
know Mommy." As they walk
hand in hand to bookcase.

             10. "I never saw these books . . .

11. "Mommy, please, I want to go  or this room before."
home, Mommy."

             11. "You go home Friday, Darling."

12. "Mommy,
please . . . . ."**      12. "Friday
              you'll go home."

13. "Um."

             13. "See."

14. "Sunday did you know you
were coming, Mommy?" Pull-
ing and pushing mother who
offers no resistance.

             14. "Oh, sure."

---

*Presence of "uh" on same line with ". . ." indicates that this was interjected during a pause, contained within the mother's response.

**Presence of ". . . . ." at end of line indicates statement which has been broken off.

| (CHILD) | (MOTHER) |
|---|---|

15. "Hm Um?"

16. *"Who told you that? Did Dr. White tell you . . ."

        15. *"----- tell you anything."

        16. "No, Dr. Wilkinson told me about it."

17. "Who's Dr. Wilk?" child shouts.

        17. Mother is holding child's hand. "You never saw Dr. Wilkinson before? Ah! Gee, I thought you did."

18. "Who's Dr. Wilk?"

18.1 "Yes."

        18. "Dr. Wilkinson?

        Well, he's in the research department and he wanted us to . . . me be with you today,

18.2 "Um hm."

18.3 "Mommy, let's go. I'll show you the movies." As she pulls mother to couch and the two sit.

        you see, and I was not to tell you ----- surprise."

19. "What's Mr. Carino doing with Phillip?"

        19. "I think he's reading to him. I brought two books along."

19.1 "Uh."

        'Ho Hum The Monkey' book and what was the other one . . . 'Johnny Go Round.'"

20. "Mmm Hmm."

21. "Mommy, I love you."

        20. "So he's reading to him."

        21. Mother is smiling as she talks. She is still holding Janet on her lap. "I love you too, Sweetheart."

---

*Both begin speaking simultaneously.

| (CHILD) | (MOTHER) |
|---|---|

22. "Please
go down to movies to see
them."

    22. "Well, I can't until Dr. Wil-
    kinson tells us that a
    -----."

23. "No, no
ask the lady, the lady."

    23. "Oh yeah, well, when she
    tells us."

24. "Mmm Hmm."

24.1 "Mm."

    24. "Well, we have some time

    just you and I together this
    time . . . See?"

25. "And Daddy and Phillip."

    25. "And Daddy and Phil . . . no
    Daddy's not here; Daddy's
    working . . ."

26. "Hmmm."

    26. "Gimbels . . . and Mr. Carino
    came promptly one thirty and
    Phillip and I got all ready
    to go . . .

27. "Did you tell
him you were going to see
sister or wha
-----."

    and . . ."

    27. "I said I
    had . . . no, I didn't."

28. "What did you say to him?"

    28. "I told him I have to speak to
    someone at the Center. So . . .
    I thought we were going to
    have a lot of trouble having
    him stay with Mr. Carino.

28.1 "Um Hm."

    but then he got interested in
    the station wagon. Maybe he's
    gonna drive the station wag-
    on." Mother laughs. "So then
    he'll stay . . . see?" Mother
    is chuckling as she speaks.

| (CHILD) | (MOTHER) |
|---|---|

29. "Mmm Hmm. . . . Please can I . . . can you see the movies, Mommy? . . ."

    29. "Hmmm, what kind of movies do they have? What have they been showing?"

30. "Luckily, I'm glad I'm gonna miss it; I'm gonna miss movies." As she claps hands. "Yeah, I'm gonna miss movies. Good, good, good."
31. "No, no."

    30. "You don't like movies?"

    31. "You don't like . . . oh, I thought you did like the movies."

32. "I don't like it, Mommy. . . . I'm gonna miss it . . . I'm happy I'm gonna miss it."

    32. "Ah. What time did the movies start, just before? Right after . . ." Mother chuckles as she speaks.

33. "You know what . . .

you know what, Mommy. Friday's Mary's birthday."

    33. "This coming Friday's Mary's birthday? It really is?"

34. "Ya." Child is leaning back on mother's lap, playing with mother's hands. Mother does not participate in play but does not resist.

    34. "Remember you told me that I should write you a letter on Sunday and I didn't say anything. I figured, well, I gotta have some more news for you."

35. "Yeah."

    35. "And I'm gonna see you Tuesday so I might as well not write on Monday.

| (CHILD) | (MOTHER) |
|---|---|
| 35.1 "Umm" | |
| | Wasn't that a good surprise, Janet? |
| 36. "Yeah, but the lady | And nobody told anybody." Mother speaks in a chuckling voice. |
| said that um I want you to do something with me." | |
| | 36. "Oooh . . ." |
| 36. "Why'd she say that to me?" | |
| | ----- and you were so surprised when you walked in, weren't you?" |
| 37. "Yes, Mommy." | |
| | 37. "You were so surprised."* |
| 38. "I'm happy I'm gonna miss movies."* | |
| | 38. "And you know, Uncle Bobby told Grandma how nice you looked that day. Oh, he thought you looked wonderful."* |
| 39. "When could Grandma Rock come over?" | |
| | 39. "Well, I don't know whether she'll be able to come to the Center or not; |
| 39.1 "Uh." | |
| | she can't take time off from the office. |
| 39.2 "Uh." | |
| | But, she's coming over on . . . When is she coming? . . . Saturday, |
| 40. "Mommy" Child speaks in a whisper. "Call the lady and let's go to see Philip." | this Saturday -----" |
| | 40. "No, I can't go see Phillip now." |

*Note the three topic changes, each topic being unrelated to the previous one, within this three-response segment of interaction (C37–M38).

(CHILD)                                                    (MOTHER)

41. "Yeah, go to the
movies also . . .                      41. "No, no."
and you can see . . . I just
wanted to show you what it
. . . what the movie is about
and ta (sic) and for them to
see you."

42. "It's hard to be with Mary,
too?"

42. "Mmm Hmm."

43. "Oh, I thought you liked
Mary?"

43. "But it's very hard to be . . ."

44. "Well, when you leave the
Center

44. "Mommy, I told them about my        -----"
friends, Doris, Dolly and
Daisy."

45. "Oh, you did. Well, maybe
you'll see

44.1 "-----"

45. "Hmmm."                            them on Saturday."

46. "You know what I'll do if I see
Catherine, I don't know whether I'll see her or not, but if I see
her I'll ask her how to get up to
her house and maybe we can
go up there on Saturday; say
hello to the three little girls . . .

45.1 "Yes."

if they're home. Up um, then
you can play with them because they're lovely children;
they're very nice and they
always ask about you all the
time."

46. "What's their last names?"

(CHILD)          EXCERPT D      (MOTHER)

47. "That I don't know; I didn't know what their last name . . .

46.1 "I told her."

he always climbs up to the hill all the time."

47. "Hmmm!"

48. "He always climbs up those big steps on the hill in back by the machine, you know?"

48. "Mmm Hmm."

49. "But we never see them; I haven't seen them all week long."

49. "Who?"

50. "Doris, Dolly and Daisy.

49.1 "Sh. sh. sh."

But if I do see them, I'll ask them if they're going to be home on Saturday and if they will be then maybe you can arrange to play with them for a little. We can arrange a date that you can play with them outside, . . .

50. "And you, you can talk to Catherine?"

and go out."

51. "Yes, that's right."

51. "How old

51.1 "Ah."

is Catherine look?"

52. "How old does she look?"

52. "Mmm Hmm."

53. "Oh, I would say about 22."

53. "Mommy, you're more beautiful than Mrs. Berg."

54. *"I'll say that

54. *"Oh, yeah."

when you go down to movies that you're more . . .

55. "Oh, no."

55. "Yes, I will."

*Both begin to speak simultaneously.

| (CHILD) | (MOTHER) |
|---|---|
| | 56. Mother laughs. |
| 56. "I'll say you're more, Mommy's more beautiful than you Mrs. Berg. See what she says. No, you are more beautiful than Mary?" Claps hands on mother's cheeks. | 57. "No one is more, everyone's the same ----" |
| 57. "And more beautiful than everyone in the Center." | 57.1 "I'm more beautiful than Mary?" |
| | 58. Mother speaks very softly. "Well, I'm glad you think that. I'm very happy that you think that |
| 57.1 "Um Hm." | . . . and I think you're the most beautiful girl in the world." |
| 58. "What time did you arrive here, Mommy?" | 59. "Well, I got here about five to two and then I had to wait for a little while, but I want . . . see Mr. Carino came just promptly 1:30, |
| 58.1 "Mmm Hmm." | and took us down." |

IV. The mothers communicate with the children but in a manner which actively confuses the child. Not only do the mothers' communications fail to explain and convey reasonable constructions of reality to the child but they may more directly confound the child by a variety of evasions, distortions and incongruencies. This type of mother frequently also misses her child's cues (failure 5).

## EXAMPLE 5

In this interaction the child is clear in his communication. The mother actively confuses the child and discourages communication of his own feelings by imposing a barrage of topics (M4, M11, M18) which do not interest him. Her avoidance or missing of his cues results in the attachment of the wrong word symbols to his meanings or an imposed misinterpretation or misrepresentation of his feelings and behavior. During the greeting phase, she is apparently trying to avoid and deny

his unhappiness, tries to divert him from his crying and impose a happier
facade. (See C1 to C6 and M1 to M7). In the context of the child crying
and saying he wants to go home, mother asks three times, "How are you?"
or "How are you doing?" and child responds twice with "Fine," although
he is in tears. The mother not only faisl to define or explain the unusual,
surprise visit but, despite the fact that she was told that the child would
not be informed about her visit beforehand, asks him, "What are you
doing here?" and "You came to see me?" as if he is supposed to know
the reasons for the visit and had a determining role in its occurrence
(see M8 and M9).

At another point (M19 to M21 and C20 to C22) she appears not to
be listening and asks the same question repeatedly after child has
answered it repeatedly. This interchange resembles her repetitious "How
are you?" during the greeting. Another less dramatic example of her
behaving as if he had not answered her is seen at M12, C13, M13 and
C14.*

**EXAMPLE 5**

Age of child—6 yrs., 4 mos.

| (CHILD) | (MOTHER) |
|---|---|
| 1. He enters room, looks at mother. | |
| | 1. "Hello." As she looks at him and smiles. |
| 2. "Ma." He walks toward mother. | |
| | 2. "How are you, Jimmy?" She is smiling and puts her hands about him as he approaches her. |
| 3. In a crying voice he says, "Mommy, I want to go home." As he looks at mother and moves closer to her. | |
| | 3. "You want to go home?" She puts his arms around her, draws him close and embraces him. |

*She may have been trying to get a more elaborate response in this and the other two
examples of repeated questioning. However, if this were her intent she would have had
more chance of success by more explicitly asking for elaboration.

| (CHILD) | (MOTHER) |
|---|---|
| 4. "I want to go home." He speaks in a crying voice. |  |
|  | 4. "Tomorrow is your day to go home, Sweetheart. Don't cry. Tomorrow you know that I will come and pick you up. I came to see you today. How are you, Sweetie Pie?" As she releases him and kisses his hand. |
| 5. "Fine." As he stands next to her. |  |
|  | 5. "Hmmm? Sit down with me a little bit, okay?" She smiles, draws him to bench and sits him down on it. |
| 6. He is crying, and puts several fingers into his mouth as he sits down on bench. |  |
|  | 6. "Jimmy, how are you doing, Honey?" As she embraces him. |
| 7. "Fine." He looks straight ahead. |  |
|  | 7. "Well, give me a hug and a kiss, -----." |
| 8. He kisses her on cheek after taking his fingers from his mouth. |  |
|  | 8. "Oh, are you a nice boy, James. What are you doing here, James?" She has one hand on his shoulder and one hand on his chest. |
| 9. "-----" As he moves away from her. |  |
|  | 9. "You came to see me?" |
| 10. "I came to see you." He moves to edge of bench, momentarily puts finger in mouth and looks straight ahead. |  |

(CHILD)

(MOTHER)

10. "Tell me, what did you -----"
She bends toward him and
pushes his hair back from
forehead.

11. He murmurs, "-----" As he looks
at door.

11. "You look so nice, Sweetheart.
You're such a doll. You are
going to come home tomorrow
and do you know what I'm
going to make for you? Tomorrow when you come home? A
swimming pool." As she is
bending over him.

12. "Aw." As he cries.

12. "You like the swimming pool?"
As she rubs his arm.

13. "Yes." He speaks in a whining
voice.

13. "You want it or you don't
want it?"

14. "I want it." As he looks at door.

14. "And what else do you want
me to prepare for you when
you come?" As she rubs his
right arm.

15. "French fries and hamburgers."
His crying has stopped and he
looks toward bookcase.

15. "Yes, and what else? And who
should wait for you? When
you come home?" She con-
tinues to bend toward him.

16. "Granny."

16. "Granny?"

17. "And Mommy." He smiles and
continues to look straight
ahead.

17. "And Mommy. And what about
Bobby? Do you want Bobby?"

18. "Yes."

(CHILD) | (MOTHER)

(MOTHER)

18. "He was asking about you. Bobby was asking about you and he said 'I want Jimmy to come home so I can stay with and play with him.' What do you have yellow on your face here, all around?" She puts her finger on his face. "That's lipstick? That's not lipstick, lipstick is red. Did you eat lunch?"

(CHILD)

19. He rubs part of face that she touched, looks at her briefly and says, "Some of it." He gets up and walks to bookcase.

19. "What did you have for lunch, Jimmy, hmm?"

20. "Fish." He speaks in a quiet voice as he picks up cookie.

20. "Jimmy, what did you have for lunch, Honey, hm?"

21. "Fish." As he puts cookie in mouth and walks back to bench.

21. "Tell Mommy, what did you have for lunch, Sweetheart."

22. "Fish." As he stands in front of her and looks at her.

V. *The mothers do not grasp or they ignore the children's communication cues, either intellectual or affective or both. Such a mother does not recognize her child's feelings or meanings; or if she does recognize his intended meanings, she does not acknowledge them. The mother's imperviousness applies to all varieties of feeling, whether derived from love (pride, sympathy, joy) or whether from the emergency emotions of fear and anger. Of particular importance in this regard is her insensitivity to the child's difficulties in generalizing about reality and his expressions of anxious puzzlement. The mothers in this category frequently do not anticipate or recognize the child's confusions and his related fears.*

## EXAMPLE 6

This interaction sample is offered to demonstrate both the mother's avoidance or missing of the connotations of the child's message as well as the mother's difficulty in clearly communicating connotations. This latter difficulty is shown in her poor communication of emotion through speech intonation and gestures and in her use of humorous and sarcastic implications that are beyond the child's capacity.

These failures occur early in the greeting phase of the visit when the child is attempting to show off newly learned French words by greeting her, albeit incorrectly, in French (C6).

Instead of responding to the praise-seeking implications of the child's attempt to greet her in French, the mother responds in a controlled, flat voice with no change in facial expression and no body movement other than a mechanical head shake (C7). The sarcastic, humorous implications, which may be paraphrased as "Don't be such a big shot, a show-off!" in her statement, "Ah, you couldn't have learned it all in a couple of days." are judged unclear because of the muting or lack of non-verbal components of affective expression. In addition, this type of sarcastic humor, even if more clearly defined by these non-verbal metacommunicative or connotative cues, is beyond the capacity of this child. This judgment is supported by the child's subsequent responses. His immediate response is a constricted or token one, "Yes." Because of his misunderstanding of his mother's statement, his subsequent response is partially irrelevant. He indicates that he understood her remarks as a criticism about not doing sufficient studying rather than an attempt to accuse him of being a "show-off" (see C8 and C9). Further data in the transcript which is consistent with our judgment that he did not understand her remark occurs ten minutes later when the child directly asks, "Mommy, how come you said I couldn't learn it all yet?" Another example of the mother's problem in communicating humor occurs at M16, C16, M17. Another instance where the child and mother partially avoid or miss each other's cues, resulting in a kind of "parallel" communication in which they connect only tangentially, occurs when the mother attempts to introduce a personal, mutual trend by saying she also studied French (M10 to M15 and C10 to C14). They both then become preoccupied with excessive, concrete detail.

## EXAMPLE 6
Age of child—8 yrs., 10 mos.

(CHILD)

(MOTHER)

(The mother remains fairly immobile and speaks, throughout interview, in a rather flat, controlled, colorless voice unless otherwise noted. There is often a brief waiting period of several seconds before she speaks. She looks at him when speaking unless otherwise noted.)

1. There is a noise at the door and she slowly looks half around. As the door opens she looks at the child who enters, smiles, puts pocketbook on bench beside her and says, "Hi, Bobby."

1. He enters, smiles at mother. Walks toward her and says, "Hi."

2. She gets up from bench, puts arms around him and smiles.

2. He puts his arms about her, limply turning his head away as she hugs him.

3. She kisses him on the back of neck.

3. He walks away from her with a half smile on his face.

4. "How are you?" (5 sec. pause) She is smiling and sits down on red bench.

4. No response.

5. "Well?" As she continues smiling at him.

(CHILD)                                    (MOTHER)

5. He has walked to side of room
and is standing 6 feet away
from mother with back toward
a wooden bench which is
turned toward wall near the
mirror. He is looking at her
and smiling slightly.

                                           6. "Well, how are you?" As she
                                           continues smiling.

6. Looking at her and holding
bench with hand he answers,
"Combien." (4½ sec. pause.)

                                           7. "Are you speaking French al-
                                           ready?" She sits quite stiffly on
                                           bench with arms crossed and
                                           legs crossed and shakes her
                                           head as she says, "Ah, you
                                           couldn't have learned it all in
                                           a couple of days. There must
                                           be some still left to do."

7. "Yes." (4 sec. pause)

                                           8. "How do you like it?"

8. "Fine. We did Page 2 and Page
3 already.

                                           9. "You did?" As she smiles
                                           slightly.

9. "I did really my studies. I just
looked through the book on
the other days. I-I did real,
I did really most of my studies
today."

                                           10. "You did? (4½ sec. pause)
                                           You know, I took French for a
                                           few years in high school."

10. "And what happened?"

(CHILD)                                          (MOTHER)

11. "What happened? Oh, I went to, you know, a regular, ah, classroom with teachers. I had a different teacher each term but each term I got harder and harder work to do. And we even had, ah, books written in the original, ah, French that had been translated into English. That was nice reading it the way it really was written."

11. "What do you mean?" As he continues to stand near wooden bench maintaining his distance. His voice generally has more color and animation than his mother's voice.

15. "What do I mean? There are some famous books written by French authors and they have been translated into English but when I went to school, well, I wasn't the only one. The whole class, ah, had the assignment of reading it in French. You know, a little bit each day."

(2 minutes)
12. He walks to center table, 3 feet to the side of where mother is sitting, puts one leg up on lower support of table, looks sideways at mother and says, "How come, how come they couldn't read the whole thing?"

13. "The whole thing? Because that was our assignment." (3 sec. pause) As she remains in the same immobile position.

13. "Oh. How thick was it about?"

| (CHILD) | (MOTHER) |
|---|---|
|  | 14. "Oh, about that thick." As she smiles in a controlled fashion and uncrosses her arms, putting fingers about an inch apart to demonstrate. She quickly resumes former position of having arms crossed in front of her. |
| 14. "How many pages about?" ($3\frac{1}{2}$ sec. pause) |  |
|  | 15. "Hm, a couple of hundred." (6 sec. pause) She half smiles in a perfunctory manner. |
| 15. No response. |  |
|  | 16. "Are you studying this because you like the language or because you want to hear what they say when they, ah, speak in, ah, French when they have the hockey games? (6 sec. pause) |
| 16. He looks away from her as she talks and then glances at her and he says, "I think for all kinds of reasons." |  |
|  | 17. "Ahum." |
| 17. He takes his foot from table support, faces mother and says, "Mommy, how come in the thing they don't really explain the sounds of the letters? It just says some letters. How come it doesn't say all of them?" (4 sec. pause) |  |
|  | 18. "There's probably a reason for it. You bring it home the weekend, you could show me what you mean and I'll explain it to you." |
| 18. "All right." |  |

|         (CHILD)          |        (MOTHER)          |
|--------------------------|--------------------------|

                     19. "Okay?" and smiles slightly. "You know your team, the Red Sox, seem to be doing pretty well the last couple of weeks. Have you been following up on them?"

19. "Yeah," and turns away.

                     20. "What's the latest? I haven't noticed for the last day or so." (4 sec. pause)

20. His back is half toward her as he answers, "-----. They, they, they did Tuesday but, but I won Monday."

                     21. "Yes, I know they won Monday." (6 sec. pause)

21. No response.

                     22. "You know, I think I once saw a ball game with Grandpa many, many years ago. I forgot just where it was. It was a lot of fun."

22. He faces her, leaning on table, as she talks and he asks, "Who was playing?"

VI. The mothers may be well intentioned, strongly committed to communicating with the children, warm in their emotional responses and disposed to assist the children in their efforts to construct reality. However, the mothers are not entirely equipped to cope with the severe communication deficiencies of the children and they commit some errors which augment the child's communication aberrations. Typical of such errors would be the mother's inability to find a simple enough or suitably concrete vocabulary which the child might understand. Another example would be the tendency to speak at a pace that is too rapid for the child to comprehend. In this category, the mothers' errors most nearly approximate errors that might be found in mothers of psychiatrically normal though cognitively impaired children. Conceivably a good mother with strong maternal drives could make such errors with a very deviant child.

## EXAMPLE 7

In this sample of interaction the mother's task is to deal with a low order, intellectually impaired child. Her over-all handling of the communication is good. She immediately defines the surprise nature of the visit. She actively engages the child. She frequently takes an appropriate teaching approach. Although she has some difficulty gearing her communication to the child's level she is generally adequate as compared with other mothers who must deal with the children who have gross conceptual deficits. She frequently tries to clarify by using repetition and questions and is careful to define the situation. The difficulties which she manifests are due to her presentation of concepts beyond child's capacity, and to some excessive shifting of topics with premature topic changes. This creates an over-stimulating situation for the child. In addition, she allows the child to change topics prematurely and abruptly.

## EXAMPLE 7

Age of child—10 yrs., 6 mos.

| (CHILD) | (MOTHER) |
|---|---|
| | 1. Mother turns around on the couch to greet child. "Joyce! Hi! Surprise!" |
| 1. "How are you?" | |
| | 2. "Fine. How are you doing, girl?" |
| 2. "Fine." | |
| | 3. "Who gave you that jacket?" |
| 3. Child has walked into the room and has stood several feet from mother, not facing her. Now she faces mother. "Ah, ah <u>ah, ah, ah, the Ittleson."</u> | <u>Mother laughs.</u> |
| | 4. Mother goes to child and begins unbuttoning her coat. "Ittleson? Oh. (3 sec. pause) Let's see. Take your jacket off. You surprised to see Momma?" |
| 4. "Yes." | |
| | 5. "Kiss Mommy. Kiss Momma. Kiss me." |
| 5. Child kisses mother. | |
| | 6. "Good. So were you in school? In the classroom?" |
| 6. "Yes." Child removes her hat and resumes standing facing away from her mother. | |

|  (CHILD) | (MOTHER) |
|---|---|

7. "What were you doing?"

7. "I went downstairs this morning. You was, I was, I was here here this morning in school."

8. "Oh you were in school. Oh. What happened to your hair? What's wrong?"

8. Child puts her hands on her head. "Ah, ah."

9. "Are you surprised? You so surprised you can't speak?"

9. "Ah."

10. Mother combs child's hair. "You stunned?" Laughs. "Let me comb your hair ($4\frac{1}{2}$ sec. pause) Mommy just came to stay with you a few minutes."

10. "All right."

11. "Then you can go back. Who did your hair?"

11. "Um Miss Irene."

12. "Miss Irene? Ooh, Miss Irene is nice counselor. She did the girls' hair. Oh, it's nice, hmm. ($3\frac{1}{2}$ sec. pause) You got a cold?" As child walks to bookcase, mother follows her combing child's hair.

12. Child walks to bookcase and takes a book. "Umm Hmm!"

13. "Huh?"

13. "Mmm Hmm. I got a cold."

14. "Yeah? Ooooh. It's not too bad, is it?"

14. Child looks at cover of book she is holding and says, "What's this? 'Ah How <u>The</u>

15. " '<u>The</u>
Clown Got.

Got His"

| (CHILD) | (MOTHER) |
|---|---|
| | 15. What's that? S-M-I-L-E (Mother spells "smile") What is he . . ." <u>"Smile, yes.</u> Let me hear you read some of that." |
| 15. <u>"Smile."</u> | |
| 16. "Okay." | |
| | 17. "Did you see that book before?" |
| 17. "Yes." | |
| | 18. "Oh, you had that book. Oh, let me see you read something. Hmm?" |
| 18. "Okay. 'There was a clown name'" (2 sec. pause) | |
| | 19. "Now what was the cow, clown's name?" |
| 19. "Bussi." | |
| | 20. "No, Bosco." |
| 20. "'Bosco who was different from all the other clowns in the circus. The puffy orange'" (3 sec. pause) (2 minutes) | |

This last pattern of maternal failure is found in the present study only in the case of our children with evidence of cerebral dysfunction. Here the children have primary limitations in their abilities for cognitive and communicative response. The mothers may achieve a high degree of skill in their efforts to stimulate and maintain adaptive and communicative response in the children. Indeed, we have studied one case in detail for techniques for managing and stimulating children with expressions of cerebral limitations and attendant behavior compensations. Nevertheless, these children are difficult to manage and the mothers have made errors which, we propose, have contributed to the childrens' symptoms and particularly those which account for his placement in the class of childhood schizophrenia. Of these 25 cases, three cases are examples of such mother–child interaction. In each of these cases, residential treatment has been successful in reversing the uniquely psychotic features of the children's responses and the children then present pictures of simple mental retardation.

## APPLICATION OF CLARITY DATA
## TO TEST A THEORY OF ETIOLOGY

We have already explained that the present study of communicative interaction between schizophrenic children and their mothers does not propose a single and unequivocal causal factor in childhood schizophrenia. Rather it directs our attention to what is in all likelihood an important facet of environmental influence in the development of the children. Beyond this, we can use some of our communication data to test postulates that may be derived from our theory of etiology in childhood schizophrenia. Thus, in brief, we have maintained that the adaptive aberrations of schizophrenic children are the final outcome of a complex chain of transactions in which two classes of influence on the children play a part. One class of influence refers to intrinsic somatic deficits within the child, particularly as manifested in cerebral dysfunction. The other class of influence refers to disorders in the psychosocial conduct of the family, particularly as reflected in its insufficient provision of experiences for stimulating and strengthening ego functions in the child. We have further proposed the hypothetical model in which both intrinsic factors in the child and extrinsic factors in the environment operate in varying proportions in the schizophrenic child.

For practical purposes in treatment and in research, we have termed "organic" all schizophrenic children who give any evidence of neurological aberration in their histories or neurological examinations. All other schizophrenic children have been labelled "non-organic." In addition to searching for evidence of "organicity," we have included in our clinical diagnosis a psychiatric judgment of the contribution of aberrant family influence to the behavioral deviations of the schizophrenic children on the basis of observation of the children themselves, their parents and their siblings in the course of their treatment.

The hypothesis of varying combinations of intrinsic factors (such as cerebral dysfunction) and extrinsic factors (such as family dysfunction) contributing to the ego deficiencies of schizophrenic children implies that some of the children come from families within the normal range. We would anticipate consistent evidence of the factor of cerebral dysfunction in the schizophrenic child, in the circumstance of a "normal" family climate. The hypothesis further implies that some schizophrenic children are free of all evidence of "organicity." In this latter event we would anticipate evidence of a low level of familial competence in enhancing growth of the child. This is not to say that the families of "organic" schizophrenic children have not contributed to the deviancies of the children. Indeed, in the rearing of these children, the unusual demand of an aberrant child on the parents, regardless of competence, may cause these parents to commit errors. Such "organic" children are difficult to rear; and the errors that the parents make—regardless of the best will—produce confusion in the children of the type noted in childhood schizophrenia. Some of the families of the "organic" schizophrenic children should be expected to overlap with the families of "non-organic" children in family adequacy.

This conceptual model of etiology has already received support from previous studies. Thus, there is evidence pointing to neurological deficits and attendant signs of cerebral dysfunction in one subgroup of schizophrenic children.[5,25] Our clinical experience confirms that while deviations in family climate are not infrequently found among these children who are restricted in cerebral function, some of the children do come from families which are well within the normal range of family adequacy. Indeed, as a group, the families of "organic" schizophrenic children have not been differentiated from families of normal children.

What light, then, can our communication data shed on our theory of etiology? We assume that the communication behavior of the mother and, more particularly, those characteristics of the communication behavior embodied in our definition of communicative clarity are potent environmental influences on the schizophrenic child.* With this assumption, we may draw the following postulates pertaining to communicative clarity of the mothers from our general theory of etiological influences in childhood schizophrenia:

(1) As a group, mothers of schizophrenic children show greater defficiency in clarity of communication than mothers of normal children. We shall test this postulate in another study by data from the interactions of normal children and their mothers.

(2) Mothers of "organic" schizophrenic children overlap with but show a higher level of communicative clarity than mothers of "non-organic" schizophrenic children. The highest levels of communicative clarity are attained by a subgroup of mothers of the "organic" schizophrenic children.

*Obviously, although clarity is only one aspect of communication influencing the effectiveness of the mother's conduct with her child, it is a basic factor in communication. We presume that absence of clarity is a barrier which narrows the bounds of communication and its utilization in social relationships.

To test these propositions, we make use of the following appraisals of the children:

(1) *The Communicative Clarity Score:* Each communication unit of the mother is scored as described from 1 to 4. (See page 128.) Since there are 20 communication units in our sample and complete clarity is scored 4, the maximum score each mother can attain is 80.

(2) *Neurological Appraisal:* This is an independent assay by a child neurologist. If positive findings in either neurological examination or history are found, the child is placed in the "organic" group, (O). If such findings are not noted, the child is placed in the "non-organic" group, (NO).

Sixteen of the children in this study fall into the "organic" subgroup and nine of the children are in the "non-organic" subgroup. As hypothesized, the mothers of the two subgroups do indeed differ in average level of communicative clarity. As a whole, the mothers of "organic" children show higher level of communicative clarity than the mothers of "non-organic" children (significant at .025 level, by Mann-Whitney U Test, 1-tailed test). The Communicative Clarity Scores of the mothers of "organic" children range from 58 to 76 while the Communicative Clarity Scores of mothers of "non-organic" children range from 54 to 69. Six of the 16 mothers of "organic" children have Communicative Clarity Scores above the highest Clarity Score, that is 69, obtained by any of the mothers of "non-organic" children.

We are in possession of other systematically gathered information regarding the families that help to cast light on the significance of our communicative clarity data. We are particularly interested in the psychiatric judgment of the contribution of the family of the schizophrenic child to the child's deviancy. As noted, this judgment is made on the basis of therapeutic experience with the child and his various family members as individuals. Ratings of the family contribution to the child's deviancy range from 1 to 5 as follows:

(1) *very marked,* (3) *much,* (5) *slight.*

In Table 1, the children are classified first in "organic" and "non-organic" subgroups. The children are classified on the basis of the psychiatric assay of the contribution of the family to the deviancy of the schizophrenic child. The Communicative Clarity Score of each mother is included.

As one might anticipate all "non-organic" children fall in the category of score (1) in the psychiatric assay, designating the most deviant families

**TABLE 1**

COMMUNICATIVE CLARITY SCORES OF MOTHERS OF INDIVIDUAL SCHIZOPHRENIC
CHILDREN GROUPED BY NEUROLOGICAL EXAMINATION AND BY PSYCHIATRIC
ASSAY OF THE PATHOGENIC INFLUENCE OF THE FAMILIES

ORGANIC CHILDREN*

| Case # | Psychiatric Assay of Family Influence | Family Adequacy Score | Mothers' Clarity Score |
|---|---|---|---|
| 2 | 5 (minimal) | 213 | 73 |
| 7 | 5 | 248 | 71 |
| 21 | 5 | 236 | 76 |
| 9 | 4 | 203 | 71 |
| 23 | 4 | 216 | 70 |
| 4 | 3 (much) | 195 | 70 |
| 12 | 3 | — | 60 |
| 15 | 3 | 188 | 65 |
| 17 | 3 | 201 | 62 |
| 8 | 2 | 181 | 60 |
| 19 | 2 | 196 | 58 |
| 11 | 1 (very marked) | 124 | 63 |
| 16 | 1 | — | 63 |
| 18 | 1 | 148 | 58 |
| 24 | 1 | 149 | 67 |
| 25 | 1 | 129 | 67 |

NON-ORGANIC CHILDREN**

| Case # | Psychiatric Assay of Family Influence | Family Adequacy Score | Mothers' Clarity Score |
|---|---|---|---|
| 1 | 1 | 179 | 58 |
| 3 | 1 | 110 | 58 |
| 5 | 1 | 194 | 65 |
| 20 | 1 | 142 | 62 |
| 22 | 1 | 152 | 60 |
| 14 | 1 | 159 | 63 |
| 6 | 1 | 169 | 69 |
| 10 | 1 | 109 | 54 |
| 13 | 1 | 142 | 61 |

*Children who manifest positive neurological findings either in history or in neurological examination.
**Children who do not manifest positive neurological findings either in history or in neurological examination.

with most pathogenic influence on the child. In contrast, families of "organic" children are distributed among all five categories of scores by psychiatric judgment. Here, too, however, a large number of children fall in the score (1) category referring to the most deviant families.

The rank order correlation between the psychiatric appraisal of family influence and the Communicative Clarity Scores of the mothers of the "organic" children is .67 (significant at .005 level, 1-tailed test). The rank order correlation cannot be computed between the psychiatric appraisals and Communicative Clarity Scores of mothers of "non-organic" children because there is no variation in psychiatric rating in the "non-organic" group. However, the rank correlation between the two measures for the entire group of 25 children is .58 (significant at .005 level, 1-tailed test). The psychiatric judgment of family influence based on psychiatric observation of the individual schizophrenic child and each of the members of his family correlates significantly, therefore, with our measure of clarity of the mother's communication.

To explain these significant correlations, it is helpful to examine the distributions of individual psychiatric ratings of the family influence and of mothers' Communicative Clarity Scores for each child recorded in Table 1. Three children are rated in category 5 by psychiatric appraisal. These are the three children who most unequivocally show deviancies which are judged to be minimally related to family aberration. This group contains three of the four mothers with highest Communicative Clarity Scores. To enlarge this group of children with least deviancy in family background, we may add the two children in psychiatric category 4 to the three children in category 5. Further, since category 3 refers to considerable pathogenic influence in the family, we may treat all children in categories 1 to 3 of the "organic" group as one group of eleven "organic" children with very deviant family background. The former group of mothers shows a median Communicative Clarity Score of 71 and a range of scores from 70 to 76. The latter group of mothers show a median Communicative Clarity Score of 63 and a range of scores from 58 to 70. The two groups of mothers of "organic" children overlap in only one case in communicative clarity. From the Mann-Whitney U Test, it is clear that mothers of "organic" children in psychiatric family assay categories 4 and 5 show higher level of communicative clarity than the mothers of "organic" children in psychiatric categories 1 to 3 (significant at .001 level, 1-tailed test).

Similarly, the five "organic" schizophrenic children in psychiatric categories 4 and 5 may be compared with the nine children in the "non-organic" subgroup of schizophrenic children. In contrast to the mothers of the "organic" children in categories 4 and 5 (with median Communicative Clarity Score of 71 and a range of 70 to 76), the mothers of the "non-organic" children show a median Communicative Clarity Score of 61 and a range of scores between 54 and 69. These two groups of mothers show no overlap at all in Communicative Clarity Scores. From the Mann-Whitney U Test, it is clear that the mothers of the five "organic" schizophrenic children in psychiatric categories 4 and 5 show higher Communicative Clarity Scores than the mothers of the nine "non-organic" children (significant at .001 level, 1-tailed test).

The Communicative Clarity Scores of the mothers may also be correlated with a measure of family behavior based on direct participant observation of family interactional conduct by a trained family observer.[2,3,7] This measure, termed the *Family Adequacy Score*, measures the behavior of the family as a unit. The entire family is viewed for three hours, including a meal time; and ratings of the interactions among the family members in their various family roles (for example, interactions of father and mother as marital partners and again as parents; or interactions of children with the parents) and of the family as a total functional unit are made. The Family Adequacy Score sums all the ratings. We have employed the single summed score as a measure of the family's capacity to meet the child's growth needs.[5] This score, then, reflects the judgment of a non-psychiatric observer who directly observes and appraises the family in the process of its operations as a unit.

Family Adequacy Scores were available on all the children but two children in the "organic" subgroup. Rank order correlation between Family Adequacy Scores and Communicative Clarity Scores is .65 for the "organic" children (significant at .01 level, 1-tailed test) and .63 for the combined group of "organic" and "non-organic" children (significant at .005 level, 1-tailed test). Again, therefore, we have evidence of a significant correlation between two independently derived measures, one a measure of interactional conduct of the entire family and the other a measure of the mother's clarity of communication. The correlation between these two measures is approximately similar to that between Communicative Clarity Scores of the mothers and the psychiatric appraisal of the family as a pathogenic influence. We are not surprised, even though the psychiatric judgments and the Family Adequacy Scores are based on different observations made by different observers, inasmuch as the psychiatric judgment of the families as pathogenic influences on the child and the Family Adequacy Scores of the 23 children show a rank order correlation of .88 (significant at .005 level, 1-tailed test).

The results thus show consistency among maternal Communicative Clarity Scores, psychiatric rating of the family as a factor in the deviancy of the schizophrenic child, and Family Adequacy Scores. One may interpret these relationships to show that communicative clarity of the mothers is an important facet of family conduct. Since the data are in accord with the postulates regarding communication which we derived from our hypothesis of the etiological spectrum in childhood schizophrenia, communicative clarity may be an important factor contributing to atypical development of schizophrenic children.

It is reasonable to assume that the clarity of the mother's communication has an impact on the schizophrenic child. We would speculate that the degree of impact of this quality of maternal communication varies from one schizophrenic child to another. In the case of the "non-organic" children the mothers are at the lower end of the scale in order of communicative clarity, but the children themselves, to all appearances, are physically and neurologically equipped to grow and respond to environmental and relational influence. Might it not be, therefore, that the communication failures of the mothers are an important factor in the aberrant development of these children? On the other hand, among the "organic" schizophrenic children, with evidence of neurological and cerebral dysfunction, there are some children whose mothers are high in communicative clarity and whose families, as entities, give evidence of normal behavior. Might we not, therefore, infer that these children are impaired in self-regulative functions and in construction of reality for reasons other than maternal failure in communicative clarity? Finally, in the case of "organic" children with deviant families and with mothers lacking in communicative clarity, might we not interpret that their adaptive restrictions reflect the communication limitations of their mothers as well as their own deficits?

## A RECAPITULATION

The present report has described the initial phase of an investigation of the interactions of schizophrenic children and their mothers. Since we have assumed the key significance of verbal communication in human interaction and social organization, their interactions have been appraised by an assay of their verbal patterns. Similarly, we have assumed that every mother has a determining role in stimulating and maintaining the growth of her child's adaptive functions. In defining the mother's role, we have stressed her use of communication to enhance her child's attachment responses and to strengthen and maintain a meaningful and stable organization of reality by the child, assuming there is genuine warmth of relationship. We have reasoned that failures in communication between mother and child will impede the child's development of adaptive functions, human warmth and attachment response and construction of reality. We have, therefore, asked what are the errors in communication that stand out in the verbal encounter between the schizophrenic child and his mother and how can these communication failures be linked to those key functional impairments which themselves determine the diagnosis of the child as being schizophrenic or psychotic. Among the major errors in communication which we link to the adaptive deficiencies of schizoprhenic children are gaps in clarity.

Clarity refers to all those attributes of the communication message which enable the listener to understand the intended meaning. Clarity is thus a complex concept which refers to many qualities of speech including level of word difficulty, appropriateness of words, congruence between ideas and emotion, logic, relevance and the comprehensibility of all the metacommunicative implications beyond the mere referential significance of the words. Coding for clarity of the message requires an understanding of the over-all purpose of each encounter. We have proceeded on a case basis to analyze first the challenge posed for each participant in the communication interactions between schizophrenic child and mother and then the clarity of the verbal communication in the light of this challenge. The standardization of the encounter in the context of an unexpected visit has made the element of surprise a dominant challenge to almost all the mothers and children. The communications lend themselves to analysis in terms of the special pressures and demands of surprise.

Our study has pinpointed errors in maternal communication in the verbal encounter between mother and child—errors which we assume have influenced the schizophrenic child's relationships to reality. Although we propose that such errors in maternal communication are likely to be of greater dimension in the experiences of schizophrenic children, some or all of these problems may be found to some degree in the lives of normal children who have not followed the same pathogenic course as schizophrenic children. The bewilderment of the schizophrenic child in his efforts to organize reality would seem to be a function of the reverberating feedback between the responses of the child which are colored by his dispositions, and those of his environment. It is possible to study these interactions in the child's verbal encounter with his mother.

## Bibliography

1. Bateson, G., Jackson, D. D., Haley, J., and Weakland, J.: Toward a Theory of Schizophrenia. *Behav. Sci.*, 1:251–264, 1965.
2. Behrens, M., and Goldfarb, W.: Study of Patterns of Interactions of Families of Schizophrenic Children in Residential Treatment, *Amer. J. Orthopsychiat.* 28: 300–312, 1958.
3. Behrens, M., and Sherman, A.: Observations of Family Interaction in the Home, *Amer. J. Orthopsychiat.* 29: 243–248, 1959.
4. Goldfarb, W.: Receptor Preferences in Schizophrenic Children, *AMA Arch. Neurol. Psychiat.*, 76: 643–652, 1956.
5. Goldfarb, W.: Childhood Schizophrenia, Cambridge, Mass.: Harvard University Press for the Commonwealth Fund, 1961.
6. Goldfarb, W.: The Mutual Impact of Mother and Child in Childhood Schizophrenia, *Amer. J. Orthopsychiat.*, 31: 738–747, 1961.
7. Goldfarb, W.: "Families of Schizophrenic Children," in Mental Retardation, Baltimore: The Williams & Wilkins Co., 1962.
8. Goldfarb, W.: Self Awareness in Schizophrenic Children, *Arch. of Gen. Psychiat.*, Vol. 8: 47–60, Jan. 1963.
9. Goldfarb, W.: An Investigation of Childhood Schizophrenia, The 1964 Lasker Lecture; *Arch. of Gen. Psychiat.*, Vol. 2: 619–634, Dec. 1964.
10. Goldfarb, W.: Corrective Socialization: A Rationale For the Treatment of Schizophrenic Children, The 1965 Saul Albert Lecture, McGill University. To be published in the *Canadian Psychiatric Association Journal*.
11. Goldfarb, W., et al.: "Parental Perplexity and Childhood Confusion," in A. H. Essman: New Frontiers in Child Guidance, New York: International Universities Press, 1958.
12. Goldfarb, W., and Braunstein, P.: "Reactions to Delayed Auditory Feedback Among Group of Schizophrenic Children: in P. H. Hoch and J. Zubin: *Psychopathology of Communication*, New York: Grune & Stratton, Inc., 1958.
13. Goldfarb, W., Braunstein, P., and Lorge, I.: Study of Speech Patterns in Group of Schizophrenic Children, *Amer. J. Orthopsychiat.*, 26: 544–555, 1956.

14. Goldfarb, W., Braunstein, P., and Scholl, H.: An Approach to the Investigation of Childhood Schizophrenia: The Speech of Schizophrenic Children and Their Parents, *Amer. J. Orthopsychiat.*, 29: 481–489, 1959.

15. Goldfarb, W., and Scholl, H.: Speech of Mothers of Schizophrenic Children. Presented at the Annual Meeting of the American Psychiatric Association, New York City, May, 1965.

16. Jackson, D. D., Riskin, J., and Satir, V.: A Method of Analysis of a Family Interview, *Arch. of Gen. Psychiat.*, Vol. 5: 321–339, 1961.

17. Levy, D. M.: Psychosomatic Studies of Some Aspects of Maternal Behavior, *Psychosom. Med.*, 4: 223–227, 1942.

18. Levy, D. M.: Behavioral Analysis, Springfield, Ill.: Charles C. Thomas, Publisher, 1958.

19. Levy, D. M.: The Act as Unit of Behavior, The Fifth Annual Sandor Rado Lecture, *Psychiatry*, Vol. 25: 295–314, 1962.

20. Levy, D. M., Meyers, D. I., and Goldfarb, W.: Relational Behavior of Schizophrenic Children and Their Mothers: A Methodological Study. Presented at the Annual Meeting of the American Orthopsychiatric Association, March, 1962.

21. Meyers, D. I., and Goldfarb, W.: Studies of Perplexity in Mothers of Schizophrenic Children, *Amer. J. Orthopsychiat.*, 3: 551–564, 1961.

22. Morris, G. O., and Wynne, L. C.: Schizophrenic Offspring and Parental Styles of Communication, *Psychiatry*, Vol. 28: 19–44, 1965.

23. Singer, M. T., and Wynne, L. C.: Thought Disorder and Family Relations of Schizophrenics. *Arch. of Gen. Psychiat.*, Vol. 12: 187–212, 1965.

24. Sobel, D. E.: The Mothering Process in Schizophrenia, *Inter. Psychiatry Clinics*, Vol. 1: 847–861, 1964.

25. Taft, L. T., and Goldfarb, W.: Prenatal and Perinatal Factors in Childhood Schizophrenia. *Develop. Med. Child Neurol.*, 6:32–43, 1964.

26. Wynne, L. C., and Singer, M. T.: Thought Disorder and Family Relations of Schizophrenics. *Arch. of Gen. Psychiat.*, Vol. 9, 191–206, 1963.

# Discussion: The Verbal Encounter Between the Schizophrenic Child and his Mother (Goldfarb et al.)

by Lyman C. Wynne, M.D., Ph.D.

Dr. Klein, Dr. Goldfarb, ladies and gentlemen: The Columbia Psycho-analytic Clinic is to be congratulated, not only for reaching chronologically its twentieth year, but more so for producing evidence that a distinctive level of developmental maturity has been reached. The papers we have been hearing today constitute such evidence, particularly through their display of vigor and thoughtfulness in diverse and differentiated ways. The work of Drs. Goldfarb, Levy, and Meyers has long provided an especially brilliant instance of these characteristics. Their studies manifest thinking that makes use of psychoanalytic understanding in a central way but does not defensively or self-righteously exclude other avenues of understanding.

The paper presented by Dr. Goldfarb illustrates something I especially value and have struggled to include in my own research: the use of specific and systematic research design which grows out of, and remains linked to, clinical, therapeutic work. The data Dr. Goldfarb has presented today are mostly based on a particular structured experimental technique which he has used to tease out and study specific variables and dimensions, especially clarity of communication. However, this approach remains related to the context of both the broad clinical program at the Ittleson Center and the other research conducted there. The result in this study is the selection of a method which is standardized but at the same time involves a ''natural'' kind of transaction between mother and child.

Without attempting here a critique of this method, I should like to note just three features concerning it. First, the method lends itself to the study of the *form*, manner, and sequential patterning of the mother–child transactions. Everyone, with and without a schizophrenic child, has great difficulty in describing *formal* characteristics of his or her own communication. These formal characteristics include the degree of clarity of communication and how clearly communication is organized. We have been impressed in our family studies at NIMH that direct history-taking and individual psychotherapy with parents provides us with considerable *content* about the parent–child relationships, but remarkably little about the *form* of parent–child communication, which needs to be studied with other methods. As Dr. Margaret Thaler Singer and I have emphasized repeatedly, these formal, stylistic aspects of communication are much more central than content in the evaluation of both the ego defects of schizophrenics and disorders of intrafamilial relationships. Dr. Goldfarb's method thus has the important merit of sampling the forms of parent–child communication directly and in detail.

I might mention in passing that there is a rapidly enlarging array of methods of studying family transactions directly. These include the use of excerpts of tape-recorded conjoint family therapy, structured and "programmed" research interviews with two or more family members together, and special techniques, such as the Family Rorschach and the Revealed Differences technique.

Second, these methods of sampling transactions directly do not rely upon the reconstruction of the transactional patterns between mother and child from transference-countertransference data seen in individual treatment relationships with a therapist. Such reconstructions, of course, run into the many problems of getting data evaluated for research purposes by persons other than the therapist, of distinguishing what is transference from what are new modes of behavior, and of distinguishing what is derived from the mother–child relationship from what is derived from other relationships. On the other hand, there are certainly pitfalls in assuming that a representative sample of mother–child communication is obtained in visits such as those set up by Dr. Goldfarb. However, I quite strongly suspect (though I cannot prove it), that formal, stylistic features of communication, such as clarity, are highly characterologic and tend to be sampled similarly with a variety of methods. This is not true with content, but does seem to hold, in our NIMH research, for such differing ways of sampling speech as clinical interviews, the individual and Family Rorschach, and the Object Sorting test.

Third, Dr. Goldfarb's method provides a fresh, standardized, emotionally meaningful starting point for the mother–child transaction, all features which greatly facilitate the research comparison of different kinds of mother–child pairs. So far, Dr. Goldfarb has selected out one aspect (communicative clarity) of the mothers' behavior in this situation. Obviously, the child's communicative clarity could be similarly scored, and still more interestingly, though with more methodologic difficulty, the sequential patterning of the communication in both directions could be studied with computer programming of the scores. Many of the examples recorded in the paper, and the narrative comments about them, suggest that a systematic analysis of the sequential deterioration of clarity would be highly revealing, particularly on the question of who initiates and augments communicative irrelevance *prior* to gross symptomatic manifestations.

Dr. Goldfarb has made a special point of showing that the clarity of mothers of children with positive neurological findings is generally higher than the mothers of children who are negative neurologically. I would find this comparison easier to interpret if the children in the two groups were matched in severity of impairment. This control seems desirable because of the frequent question that it may be the impact of the child's symptoms upon the mother or both parents which may cause the parents to show communicational and other disorders. Presumably, neurological signs which are often quite esoteric are going to have less direct impact upon the mothers than gross psychotic symptomatology; therefore, severity measures, which I understand Dr. Goldfarb has available, as well as the organicity which he has reported, might help clarify difficulties of this kind in the understanding of these patients and families.

Also, I feel that the present work will be easier to interpret when comparison studies are done with non-schizophrenic children and their mothers. This may require some ingenuity to carry off, but I think it is possible, for example, by having children who are medical patients on a chronic medical or surgical service have surprise visits from their mothers. In these visits, as in the present study, the initial focus is how the mother and child deal with the meaning of the surprise visit. Do they deny that it is a surprise, or do they talk about it? Does the mother orient the child in terms understandable to him or does she mystify him? By study of such a comparison sample, some questions about the distinctiveness of the patterns which Dr. Goldfarb has illustrated might be illuminated.*

Turning from methodologic to conceptual matters, I would like, in a very shorthand, schematic way, to suggest an alternative model for thinking about the data that Dr. Goldfarb has outlined, one which may be consistent and compatible with the one he has presented but which differs somewhat in emphasis. Dr. Goldfarb has mentioned that clarity of communication is just one aspect of these mother–child transactions and that many other facets of communication will be analyzed ultimately. Dr. Goldfarb makes an assumption about the significance of communicative clarity which is certainly plausible: "that the mother is able to strengthen her child's effectiveness in functions involved in the orderly and congruous construction of reality only to the extent that her own communications are clear." On the other hand, the mother's clarity probably cannot contribute very much to such a complex ego function as the "construction of reality" unless this builds upon at least two other ingredients in the mother–child relationship: (1) affiliation versus disaffiliation, and (2) orientation or establishing a shared focus of attention versus failure to do so. Affiliation or attachment involves a positive emotional tie which is lacking or actively repudiated in disaffiliation. There are, of course, many non-verbal components to affiliation and disaffiliation. These include, in settings such as the visits of the present study, approaching, smiling, frowning, averting visual contact, reaching out, holding or caressing, etc. On the verbal side, there are comparable intonational and content indications of engagement or disengagement, empathy or rebuff. Such features are, to be sure, aspects of communication and can be scored, as Dr. Goldfarb has done, in terms of their "clarity." But it seems to me an issue different from clarity, whether or not affiliation or disaffiliation, and orientation or its lack, are manifest.

Just as I feel that Dr. Goldfarb's own case descriptions emphasize failures of engagement and orientation even more strikingly than shortcomings in clarity of communication, I feel that examples in the present

---

*After this discussion, I was informed by Dr. Goldfarb that his group has arranged for precisely this kind of control-group study—with child orthopedic patients visited by their mothers.

report, as well as case descriptions in his earlier writing, suggest that the concept of parental "perplexity" is perhaps not the most apt feature to emphasize about the behavior of these parents. I rather prefer a term that Dr. Goldfarb has used repeatedly in describing the phenomena of parental "perplexity," namely, parental *paralysis*. In his case examples, perplexity seems to come when the parent has given up and turns to the psychiatrist and says, "What should I do now?" In point of fact, there does not seem to be much *subjective* perplexity when the parent is dealing with the child. There is a kind of blankness, a kind of paralysis, some omnipotent magical kind of thinking, and so on, but really very little perplexity until they turn in despair to another person, namely the psychiatrist. This paralysis is associated with inactivity in affiliating with, or engaging the child and with a striking tendency to let the child structure the situation and give orientation, rather than providing orientation for the child. I think that Dr. Goldfarb and I are noticing and describing the same phenomena here; I am simply expressing a preference for a somewhat different conceptual emphasis.

I am struck by the similarities in some respects between the parents of Dr. Goldfarb's childhood schizophrenics and the parents of a subgroup of adolescent schizophrenics. These patients have had an insidious onset, are so-called "process schizophrenics," and generally are what I have called schizophrenics with amorphous forms of thinking. The parents of these patients, like the parents Dr. Goldfarb describes, provide a markedly undifferentiated, amorphous, psychological environment, with lack of structuring, a lack of landmarks, and a lack of intonational orienting cues. I suspect that there is a considerable overlap between these parents and some parents of the childhood schizophrenics with whom the Ittleson group has worked, namely, those who do establish some sort of affiliative bond with their children, but break down at the stage of orientation and focusing attention. It is my impression that these children are not quite so severely disturbed nor so autistically isolated as the children of parents who more actively disaffiliate (like the very severely ill, mostly autistic, Langley Porter children mentioned above).

Both of these varieties of schizophrenics can be contrasted to a third group, who by and large have often been called "reactive schizophrenics," "schizo-affective schizophrenics," etc., who have gone further in ego development before breakdown. These patients generally have parents who, again, are rather different: they are more clear, better differentiated, in their thinking than the parents of the "amorphous" schizophrenics. They do provide structure and orientation, but often in a shifting fashion with bizarre twists of reasoning used in relation to the child. Thus, this involves a different pattern on the communicational level.

I wish to stress in these synoptic remarks that, by making distinctions both between kinds of patients and kinds of families, one can perhaps work gradually to a more comprehensive theory of individual developmental processes and their relation to transactions in the family.

I want to express appreciation for having the opportunity to study Dr. Goldfarb's paper and I hope that it will be read both for itself and in the context of his other writings. I hope that I have conveyed that I feel this work is richly provocative and stimulating and that it opens up a treasury of ideas which deserve intensive exploration, both at the Ittleson Center and elsewhere. Thank you very much.

# The Adaptive Balance Profile and Prediction of Early Treatment Behavior

*by Arnold M. Cooper, M.D., Aaron Karush, M.D.,*
*B. Ruth Easser, M.D., Bluma Swerdloff, D.S.W.*

## I. INTRODUCTION

For some years now the authors, joined later by Drs. Max Cohen, H. Lee Hall and Stanley R. Lesser, have been working on the development of a technique which would bring some increased measure of objectivity to the procedures which psychoanalysts use in making assessments of the patient's psychological strengths and weaknesses, particularly with regard to his suitability for various kinds of treatment. Psychoanalysts who have been charged with the task of making prognostic assessments on the basis of one or two initial interviews—a situation which occurs, for example, if one is an admitting psychoanalyst for a treatment center—have had the impression that their clinical judgment is often reliable, but that it is difficult for them to know precisely either the basis for their evaluation or the reasons why in particular instances the evaluation is incorrect.

As psychoanalysts, we are comfortable with the use of an educated intuition and we train our students as best we can to develop similar talents. We know that into this final intuitive judgment goes an enormous complexity of raw data gleaned during the course even of a single interview. We use a complex mode of reworking this data in accord with principles of psychoanalytic theory. It would seem to be of quite obvious usefulness if we were able to define and particularize some of the data and the mental data-processing which enter into our global decision. The Adaptive Balance Profile which we devised is an attempt to do this.

In a previous publication we have reviewed the literature and described our own theoretical position in some detail.[7] We have defined ego strength in accord with the general view in the psychoanalytic literature as the capacity for psychological adaptation.

To assess the adaptive capacity of the ego we have devised rating scales for each of nine significant areas of the ego's integrative functioning. We call each of these scales a *balance* for reasons stated below and the nine balances are Dependency, General Pleasure-Frustration, Sexual Pleasure-Frustration, Affectivity, Defense, Emergency Emotion, Guilt, Pathology and Social Integration. The combination of scores of each of the nine balances comprises an Adaptive Balance Profile, which we hope will be able to convey significant data about the quality and quantity of strength or weakness of the ego.

Our scales run from 0—the ideal functioning of the ego in the area of question, to 4—which represents maximum weakness. Half-points are used so that we have a nine-point scale. In addition to this ordinal ranking there is for each balance a polar rating: plus or minus. Plus represents tendencies towards defensive or reparative assertion and minus represents tendencies towards inhibition of function. The term balance indicates the continuum from plus to minus. Each balance schedule thus has ratings of plus one to four and minus one to four, making a total of 17 possible scores for each balance.

In devising our schedules we have leaned heavily on psychoanalytic theory and have avoided detailed behavioral descriptions. Some examples from the schedule for Balance III, Sexual Pleasure-Frustration, will help clarify this description.

On the plus side, the side of defensive pursuit of sexual pleasure, plus 1 is described as follows: "Sexual activity tends periodically to be over-estimated in lieu of other sources of pleasure. Pleasure is preserved as a rule but affective ties to a particular partner may be damaged when frustration occurs. Variety in sexual partners is given exaggerated importance especially during a crisis of frustration or failure, in sex or another area of behavior. Sexual pleasure is positively anticipated and is usually followed by pleasurable recollection. It is accompanied both by relaxation of inner tensions and by toleration of the sexual pleasure needs of sexual partners." That describes relatively mild deviation from the ideal.

In contrast, plus 4—maximum weakness—is described this way: "Pathological sexual pleasure pursuit is at times carried out in overt anti-social acts (bigamy, seduction of children, rape, etc.), unaccompanied by guilt. There is no tender feeling for the sexual partner nor is there sexual pleasure in the act. There is no pleasurable anticipation or recollection. Fixation on overt perverse sexual behavior is common."

Minus 4—maximum weakness—on the side of inhibited pursuit of pleasure is described in the following: "Sexual anhedonia (lack of pleasure) prevails. Perverse fantasies are common and are preferred to coitus. Sexual performance may be possible but with no gratification. There may be complete inhibition of sexual executive behavior with or without phantasies of sex. There is no pleasurable anticipation or recol-lection. Fixation on perverse sexual behavior in passive roles is common, especially in fantasy."

We have tried to frame our items in a combination of clinical and theoretical terms which we hope combine the virtues of the flexibility and depth of analytic interviewing and the precision required for accurate rating. We have not wished to dissect psychoanalytic thinking into other terms, but rather to describe more precisely particular areas of ego function which we believe to be of prime importance for an assessment of ego strength. The complete schedule of all nine balances is shown as an appendix in charts 1–9.

In using the Adaptive Balance Profile, the rater collects his information from one or two open-end or 'psychoanalytically oriented' interviews with the patient, assigns a score for each of the nine balances, and will obtain a profile which might look like Figure I. This was the rating of a single woman of 40 who had for several years been a nun, lived a self-sufficient isolated life with few pleasure resources or affective ties, but worked effectively as a teacher and was respected by her peers. All her ratings are on the side of inhibition, and her deviation is particularly severe in the areas of sex and guilt. Figure II is a rating of a man showing a mixed pattern of aggression and inhibition. General and sexual pleasure are inhibited in pursuit and expression and his symptomatology tended towards phobia formation. His relationships are characterized by an aggressive outlook, rage is expressed openly, and he tends to be a leader in groups. The extent of his deviation is moderately severe, all of his scores being between two and three.

The over-all goal of our project is to draw Adaptive Balance Profiles on a group of people before going into treatment as well as on a group who will have a period of time without treatment. A second team of observers will again interview and draw profiles on the group of patients who have waited a year before beginning treatment and on all patients as they finish treatment. We hope to be able to correlate treatment results and the nature of the treatment process in each case with the type of profile. In the best of all possible worlds, certain types of profile would be predictive of certain treatment events and outcomes. This paper is a report on some preliminary work with a method for correlating different Adaptive Balance Profiles with differences in patients' behavior in treatment during the first six to nine months.

## II. RELIABILITY

Thirty-five cases were used in working out the reliability of our Adaptive Balance Profile. All judgments were made by individual observers without consultation among observers. Interviews, with a few exceptions, were conducted throughout by only one person with the other raters present in the room but not participating in any way in the interview. After the original group of analysts was trained in the use of the Profile, a second group was trained with the intention that this would be the group which would do the follow-up interviews. Tests for reliability were carried out using usual statistical methods.

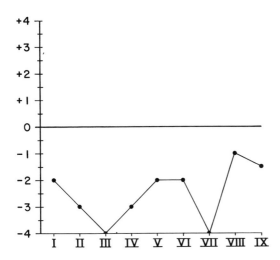

Figure 1. Adaptive Profile Balance.

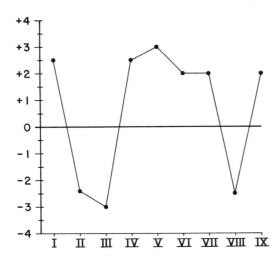

Figure 2. Adaptive Profile Balance.

Under our experimental conditions of using teams of three raters, all of whom were trained together, our method has been sufficiently reliable to permit us to proceed with evaluation of tests results. Statistical tests revealed the observers were within one-fourth of a balance value 68% of the time and within one-half of a balance value 95% of the time. None of the balances was significantly out of agreement and no observer significantly differed from the others.

## III. EXPERIMENTAL DESIGN

As a preliminary test of the validity of the Adaptive Balance Profile we have studied aspects of the behavior of the patients we rated, during their first six to nine months in treatment, both reparative psychotherapy (two times per week) and reconstructive psychoanalysis (four times per week). We attempted to make assessments of a group of treatment variables. For our purposes at this time, the evaluation of the patient's treatment behavior was made from the records. This is clearly subject to certain kinds of error and distortion, but so are attempts to obtain evaluation directly from the therapist or from the supervisor. The record does provide certain built-in checks upon itself. Every record contains some verbatim material and some statements concerning both the therapist's and supervisor's opinion of what is happening in the important trends in treatment, and there is a six-month summary in which the therapist attempts to restate his view of the major events and characteristics of the therapy. Finally, in choosing characteristics for study we have tried to limit ourselves to those which would be more readily determinable because their manifestations would be fairly direct and overt. Included in our study are the following:

1. *Predominant emotional attitude towards the therapist*—positive or negative. The attempt here is to discern whether the tone of the treatment situation is primarily friendly, or distrustful and guarded. We are interested in the desire of the patient to gain the approval of the therapist, the ability to maintain friendly feelings towards the therapist despite the vicissitudes of treatment, and the degree to which the patient is able to view the relationship with the therapist as one he desires and about which he has positive expectations and a sense of satisfaction.

2. *Capacity for Therapeutic Alliance*—The therapeutic alliance is generally defined in the literature as the relatively non-neurotic rational rapport between patient and doctor. A good therapeutic

alliance requires that the patient be able to communicate, listen to the therapist, observe himself, report his observations, accept fantasies and feelings and make useful identifications with the therapist. The working alliance is distinct from the emotional attitude towards the doctor in that, for example, the patient may have warm and friendly feelings to the doctor but be unable to engage in introspection or meaningfully communicate feelings or fantasies to the doctor. Similarly, the patient, even when angry, may be quite capable of carrying on constructive therapeutic work simultaneously. Trust in the procedure of treatment itself, which is separate from the trust in the doctor, is an important factor in the therapeutic alliance. The capacity to join with the therapist in sharing common goals and a sense of understanding one another are essential parts of the therapeutic alliance.

3. *Capacity for Psychological Insight*—Insight involves several things.
   A. The ability to synthesize information from several disparate sources and perceive a common element in the data. The patient who has the conceptual capacity to see that his behavior has a common characteristic in widely different situations has the possibility of obtaining insight.
   B. A capacity for self-observation. This capacity for self-observation must be sufficiently free of inhibition so that the patient is capable at some points of responding emotionally to his own behavior as he might to viewing the behavior of another. This involves:
   C. An ability to tolerate new observations about oneself which were not previously part of the self-image, and to incorporate them into a revised self-image.
   D. Implied in this is a capacity for abstraction which permits one to change observations pertaining to simple behaviors into matters of feeling and motivation. The ability to perceive behavior in terms of feeling and motivation is an essential for the achievement of insight.
   E. The final bridge to psychological insight is the translation of new understanding to new forms of behavior. It is only this experience which supplies conviction.

   Psychological insight, then, can be described as the synthesis of new knowledge about oneself into motivational and emotional terms and the incorporation of this synthesis into a newly revised self-image, which expresses itself in new behavior.

4. *Acting Out*—When unconscious conflicts or wishes are heightened by the patient's relationship in the transference and the treatment situation, patients will sometimes attempt the resolution of these conflicts by carrying out real actions in the real world rather than simply remembering, reflecting and experiencing feeling without

action. While the term acting out is somewhat loosely used in psychoanalytic literature, we have attempted to confine it here to the more limited situation where the actions carried out are related to particular treatment events rather than reflecting general sources of conflict. Defined in this way, acting out is relatively easy to detect from clinic records. As an example, the patient who fails to apply for the residency he wanted and which would enable him to continue his analysis, and instead must accept an out-of-state residency which terminates his treatment is obviously acting out.

5. *Overt Resistance*—While bearing some relation to acting out, overt resistance as we have defined it constitutes a separate behavior pattern in treatment which ought to be relatively easy to detect. We mean such things as failure to keep appointments, frequent lateness for appointments, conscious withholding and lying, and so forth.

6. *Tendency to Disorganize*—These are the patients who in the analytic situation of free fantasy, diminished stimulus input, poverty of affective responsiveness and loosened ego controls develop some signs of disruption of ego integrative functions. Some of these patients begin to develop severe and intolerable anxiety which begins to disorganize thought processes. Some show severe blocking. Some exhibit tendencies to depersonalize. Others are flooded by fantasy with diminished reality testing and tendencies towards illusion formation and even hallucination can occur.

7. *Affectivity*—This is an assessment of the capacity to form emotional ties which are characterized by some stability, affectionate and tender feeling, a sense of pleasure given and received.

8. *Prognosis*—This is an attempt, based on what has occurred in treatment during the first six months, to make a prediction concerning ultimate outcome.

The items chosen for evaluation at this time are obviously of several different kinds. Some of them ought clearly to be of prognostic significance. Capacity for a therapeutic alliance, capacity for psychological insight, capacity for forming affective ties are certainly important determiners of the ultimate outcome of any therapy. Similarly, in a negative sense, the tendency to disorganize is certainly an indicator of therapeutic outcome. The questions of acting out, overt resistance, and positive or negative feelings towards the doctor during the initial period of treatment are perhaps not directly related to therapeutic outcome per se, but are more importantly indicators of special problems arising in the course of treatment concerning which it is well for the therapist to be forewarned. A method allowing prediction of such treatment events would clearly be useful. Other aspects of treatment behavior such as tendencies towards passivity, the ability to work with anamnestic material, the attitudes elicted in the therapist by the patient, capacity for constructive use of interpretations, and others are currently under examination in this preliminary study.

## IV. METHODS

Thirty-seven patient records were evaluated for the eight treatment variables described. We attempted to correlate the nature of the Adaptive Balance Profile of the patient with the presence or absence of each of the characteristics being studied. Because so many of our balance values lie within a relatively small range of two to three on the scale, attempts to make a correlation of the kind of profile and treatment behavior by simple visual inspection of the profiles proved unsuccessful.

Instead the technique of discriminant analysis using regression-type equations was used. For each characteristic under consideration—for example, therapeutic alliance—a discriminant analysis using a regression-type equation is done. This equation describes the interrelations of the balances in the profiles of those patients rated high or low in the characteristic. Patients rated positive for the characteristic are designated "1" in the formation of the equation and patients rated negative are designated "0." If the clinical ratings—for example, good or poor therapeutic alliance—do differentiate groups with two different types of profiles, then in the solution of the equation those patients rated positive for this characteristic will have values around 1 and those patients rated negative will have values around 0. Should this not be the case then the Adaptive Balance Profile has failed to distinguish those patients possessing a characteristic from those who do not.

The hazard in this technique lies in the power of the mathematical equations involving multiple measurements and their interrelations to sort groups on the basis of insignificant differences. The equations can, however, be verified by testing their ability properly to classify as "1" or "0"—positive or negative for the characteristic—patients whose clinical characteristic is known but who were *not* used in developing the equation. This verification technique has been regarded as a severe and effective test of the value of discriminant analysis equations.[1] Because our samples were small, leaving only 2 to 7 patients in each category who were not used in developing the equations, we "pooled" those results for the eight characteristics.

By this method we determined that of forty instances of clinical classification not used in the development of the equations, the Adaptive Balance Profile, as determined by the discriminant analysis, correctly sorted the presence or absence of a characteristic 75% of the time on average. In this manner it is possible to show that the discriminant analysis equations are significant at a 95% level of significance on average for the eight characteristics studied. The significance of the equation for each individual characteristic could not be determined because of the small sample size. If this technique is capable of defining the distinction of presence or absence of a characteristic with a high statistical probability, then for any new patient whose Adaptive Balance Profile is determined a meaningful prediction can be made of his treatment behavior in the areas studied. We are indebted to Mr. Robert Winter for carrying out the statistical treatment of our data.

Some of our results at this time have been worked out using only five of the nine Balances in our equations, attempting to pick five which would likely be most significant. This is simply a labor-saving device since the computation involved in using all nine Balances is large. Using more Balances in the equation can only improve the results but cannot make them worse, since it is possible that we will find additional correlations but we cannot find fewer correlations. It should be noted that we were not able to rate every patient in every characteristic under study.

## V. RESULTS

Results of the correlations, thus far, are depicted in Table 1. Thirteen patients were rated for their predominant emotional attitude toward the therapist; four rated positive and nine rated negative. Five balances—dependency, affect, defense, emergency emotion and guilt—were used in setting up the equation. Of the thirteen patients, ten of their profiles were within the limits set by the equation. We suspect that the balances for affectivity and general pleasure are significant for rating the predominant emotional attitude towards the therapist, and if this is so our result may be improved when the nine-balance equation is completed.

Fourteen patients were rated on capacity for therapeutic alliance; five were rated positive and nine were rated negative. Here, using all nine balances thirteen of fourteen cases correlated correctly.

**TABLE 1**

Correlation of Ratings of Variables with Adaptive Balance Profiles

| CHARACTERISTIC ASSESSED | NUMBER PATIENTS RATED | NUMBER RATINGS CORRELATED WITH ABP | % CORRECT |
|---|---|---|---|
| EMOTIONAL ATTITUDE TO THERAPIST | 13 | 10 | 77% |
| THERAPEUTIC ALLIANCE | 14 | 13 | 93% |
| PSYCHOLOGICAL INSIGHT | 10 | 9 | 90% |
| ACTING OUT | 17 | 13 | 77% |
| OVERT RESISTANCE | 15 | 12 | 80% |
| TENDENCY TO DISORGANIZE | 19 | 11 | 58% |
| AFFECTIVITY | 14 | 11 | 79% |
| PROGNOSIS | 14 | 10 | 71% |
| TOTALS: | 116 | 89 | 78% |

Ten patients were rated for capacity for psychological insight; four were rated positive and six were rated negative. Using five balances in the equation nine of the ten profiles correlated correctly.

For acting out we rated seventeen patients; nine were considered positive and eight negative. Using all nine balances in the equation we correctly correlated thirteen of seventeen patients.

Fifteen patients were classified for overt resistance; six positive and nine negative. Twelve of the fifteen were correctly correlated, using nine balances in the equation. To illustrate the magnitude of difference that may be involved, a previous result using five balances in the equation correctly correlated only nine of fifteen patients.

Our poorest result was obtained in the attempts to rate the tendency to disorganize. Of nineteen rated patients, eight positive and eleven negative, eleven were correctly correlated.

The results on affectivity again illustrate the importance of using all nine balances in drawing the equations or making a correct selection among the balances used. A first run using the balances for dependency, affectivity, defense, guilt and pathology, yielded seven of fourteen correct correlations. Using the five balances, dependency, general pleasure, sexual pleasure, affectivity and social integration, the results were correct in eleven of fourteen cases, and using all nine balances did not further improve this result. These results indicate that no one balance determines the result but an interrelation among several balances is decisive.

For prognosis based on the judgment of initial interviewer, therapist, and authors, the patients were correctly correlated in ten cases of fourteen.

While it must be emphasized that this data is preliminary, and the number of cases reported for each category is not high enough for us to claim statistical significance, the correlations in most instances are encouraging.

## VI. DISCUSSION

Of interest is the apparent failure of our balances to correlate with disorganization of the patient in the treatment situation. Disorganization is a behavioral characteristic which is probably reported in the records quite accurately since it disrupts the treatment process and requires the immediate attention of the therapist. Since it is a characteristic involving rather discrete behaviors its detection from the charts ought to be relatively simple and sure and this is our impression in reading the charts. One possible explanation of our failure is that our balances lack sufficiently sensitive indicators of the quantity of anxiety which may be aroused by the threat of actualization of unconscious fantasy. This seems unlikely in view of the seeming sensitivity of the balances in other areas studied. Another possibility is that the appearance of disorganization is particularly sensitive to the interventions of the therapist, and its appearance may within wide limits be an indicator of therapeutic skill rather than a simple function of the patient's ego. Finally there is some evidence to indicate that the patients who disorganize in therapy are of two distinct types and that we are presented here with a statistical artifact because we drew our equations representing only one of these groups. This possibility is at present being explored.

It is of some interest to note that although we define therapeutic alliance and predominant emotional attitude towards the therapist as different characteristics, we find that while the patient population groups for the two characteristics do differ, there are no patients who show a positive therapeutic alliance and negative affective attitude towards the therapist nor are there any with positive affective attitude toward the therapist and a negative therapeutic alliance. Warning once again, of course, that our sample is small, it suggests that these two qualities may not be entirely separate.

Similarly, the correlation between emotional attitude towards the therapist and the presence or absence of psychological insight is extremely high. The population groups rated as being high or low in psychological insight are nearly identical to the groups rating positive or negative in their emotional reaction to the therapist. These correlations certainly are not surprising and are clinically well known. The capacity for psychological insight very likely is a key factor in determining the amount of pleasure or pain associated with the treatment process and in determining the patient's ability to identify with the therapist.

It is again not surprising that the prognostic statements arrived at correlate very highly with the presence of psychological aptitude, positive affective capacity and so on. Since these are the clinical bases for arriving at the prognosis, one can only say that the balance equations derived are in agreement with the clinical observations.

## VII. SUMMARY

We have reported some preliminary attempts to establish the validity of the Adaptive Balance Profile as an instrument for distinguishing different patient populations among people applying for psychiatric treatment, and for making predictions about the responses to treatment. Of the treatment characteristics studied so far—the predominant emotional attitude towards the therapist, capacity for therapeutic alliance, capacity for psychological insight, appearance of acting out and overt resistance, tendency to disorganize, affective capacity, and the overall prognosis—the results encourage us to believe that the profiles may be a useful, objective, and repeatable indicator of significant areas of the patient's behavior in treatment.

Our sample is yet too small for definitive statistical assessment. It does appear, however, that the possibility exists of mathematically describing the shapes of Adaptive Balance Profiles which correlate with certain specific treatment behaviors. If this technique proves valid, the resulting equations would then permit a prediction of the statistical likelihood that a particular patient will show a particular characteristic in treatment. A predictive tool of this type would be of considerable assistance in making appropriate treatment decisions for each patient regarding the kind and goals of treatment. Since the patient's capacities are not the only factor in determinging treatment outcome, we recognize that no predictive tool can be used as the sole arbiter of treatment decisions. We expect that further work over the next few years will yield enough data to understand better the range of usefulness of the Adaptive Balance Profile.

## Bibilography

1. Frank, R. E., et al. Bias in multiple discriminant analysis. *J. Marketing Res.,* August, 1965.
2. Karush, A., Easser, B. R., Cooper, A., and Swerdloff, B. The evaluation of ego strength. I: a profile of adaptive balance. *J. Nerv. Ment. Dis.* 139: 332–349, 1964.

## APPENDIX: ADAPTIVE BALANCES

### Chart 1. Dependency Balance

Ideal Balance Range (Scale—0)

Responses to changing environmental demands reflect accurate perceptions of the situation and of the person's resources. The resultant behavior is either effective in coping with the new stress or challenge or seeks out a socially acceptable alternative when the obstacle to any given achievement of a goal cannot be overcome by independent behavior. The new alternative allows pleasure, security and self-esteem. The hallmark of the ideal balance of adaptation that maintains the social self-image is elasticity without regression. Dependence upon others may be utilized in a cooperative fashion as a temporary means to an end. It is not a preferred way of life. Dependency objects are neither clung to as parent-substitutes nor rejected for unrealistic independence.

| Range of Predominant Defensive Aggressivity | Range of Predominant Inhibition |
|---|---|

(The essential differences between "+" and "−" ratings are in the ways in which dependency objects are sought and in the reactions to frustrations of dependency needs.)

| Scale: $(+1) \rightarrow (+4)$ | Scale: $(-1) \rightarrow (-4)$ |
|---|---|

(Rating "1" is reserved for those whose life performance on the whole remains adequate and appropriate to their resources but who periodically suffer a loss of self-esteem and self-confidence unless approval from a particular external object is forthcoming. This approval gives reassurance that the expectations of the ego-ideal (which may be excessively high) are being successfully met.)

+1. Failure to live up to the ego-ideal leads to diminishing self-esteem rather than an objective reappraisal by the person of his goals and resources. He then tries aggressively and even exhibitionistically to gain external validation of his ability and worth from one or more objects. This intensified, active search for attachment to an approving object occurs intermittently. Despite the acted-out craving for recognition, effective life performance continues although it is not as gratifying or reassuring as is overt approval and applause from a dependency object.

−1. Failure to live up to the ego-ideal leads to diminishing self-esteem rather than an objective reappraisal by the person of his goals and resources. He then turns to wishing for external validation of his ability and worth from one or more objects. The wish for attachment is essentially passive and there is an inhibition of overt demands for applause. Instead there ensues an intensified striving for superior accomplishment with intermittent self-criticism and feelings of inadequacy. Actual accomplishment is usually adequate or even superior but is not as gratifying or reassuring as overt approval and applause from a dependency object.

+2. Self-esteem tends to be based on success in getting others to give applause, guidance and even protection from failure and disappointment as well as help in gratifying needs. Object relationships are featured by unconsciously delegating one or more chosen objects to perform with omnipotence, as if they were parents. Dependence upon such objects is not however constant or generalized to all areas of behavior, although dependence often seems to be of primary importance to the person's security. Dependency needs are usually aroused by failures to achieve a desired goal whether because of inadequate efforts or of insufficient resources. The person reacts to his dependency needs actively and aggressively and often makes coercive demands for care and love upon the depen-

−2. Self-esteem tends to be based on success in getting others to give applause, guidance and even protection from failure and disappointment as well as help in gratifying needs. Object relationships are featured by unconsciously delegating one or more objects to perform with omnipotence, as if they were parents. Dependence upon such objects is not constant or generalized to all areas of behavior, although dependence often seems to be of primary importance to the person's security. Dependency needs are aroused by failures to achieve a desired goal whether because of inadequate efforts or of insufficient resources. The person reacts to his dependency needs with passive expectations and yearnings for care and support from a chosen object. At the same time, efforts are made to deserve

dency object. At the same time, efforts are made to deserve the desired support by trying to satsify the real or imagined standards of the dependency object (by appearing to be strong and even tyrannical, e.g.). Affection is usually expressed for the giving dependency object. Frustration of dependency wishes causes a loss of self-esteem which results often in a tendency to complaints and even accusations of bad faith against the disappointing object. However, the person generally turns to other objects whom he endows with delegated omnipotence and seeks their reassurance after such disappointments. During this preoccupation with obtaining dependency gratification, the person continues to use his skills and abilities but derives little pleasure from accomplishment unless noticed and applauded by the dependency object.

the desired support by trying to satisfy the real or imagined standards of the dependency object (by appearing uncomplaining and even abused, e.g.). Affection is usually expressed for the giving dependency object. Frustration of dependency wishes causes loss of self-esteem which leads to depressive reactions and even a tendency to pain-dependent (masochistic) phantasies or overt acts of unconscious self-punishment may occur. Ultimately if the dependency object continues to be frustrating, the person generally turns in the same passively hopeful way to other objects whom he endows with delegated omnipotence and seeks their reassurance and support. During this preoccupation with obtaining dependency gratification, the person continues to use his skills and abilities but derives little pleasure from accomplishment unless noticed and applauded by the dependency object.

(Ratings "3" and "4" are reserved for more obvious infantile distortions of dependency needs in object relationships. In "3" the object begins to lose significance as a special person and becomes a vehicle of gratification and security. As means of supply, objects become more and more easily interchangeable. Object-directed behavior may become indiscriminate so that all or nearly all important goal-directed activities ultimately hinge on establishment of a dependent tie to an ad-hoc parent surrogate. In "3," omnipotence is still delegated to the object but there is limited capacity or interest in living up to the standards, real or imagined, of the dependency object. In "4," the person functions more closely to the narcissistic level of infantile omnipotence where objects are controlled by the magic of wishful thinking without regard for the needs or limitations of the object.)

+3. Self-esteem depends largely on the ease of getting immediate recognition, applause and approval. The overt demands for care and service tend to force the object into a submissive role. The aggressive acting-out may be childishly exhibionistic. Affectionate ties to giving dependency objects are superficial, inconstant and carry little conviction. On the other hand, where the dependency object makes some reciprocal demand for love, it tends to be experienced as a demand which threatens depletion. Anger and coercive expectations of the object are intensified. Continual frustration results in increasing aggression toward the object, blame and even accusa-

−3. Self-esteem depends largely on the ease of getting recognition, applause and approval. The demands for care and service are hidden behind a facade of helplessness, failure and apparent suffering. Passivity is usually a way of life. Helplessness is used as an integrating instrument to wring care and service from the dependency object. Affection for the object is superficial, inconstant and carries little conviction. On the other hand, reciprocal demands for love by the dependency object are experienced as an exhausting threat of depletion. Passivity increases and there tends to be an increasing affective withdrawal from the object. Continued frustration results in increased

tions. Paranoid trends with occasional grandiosity to justify the demands may appear but do not have a delusional organization. Ultimately the inability of one object to give what is expected is followed by a shift of dependency attachment to another object.

+4. Infantile omnipotence is expressed in efforts to control objects by constant and insistent demands for their availability and service. These persons tend to repel others by their self-centered voraciousness. The oral aggression invades most relationships. They thus create their own affective isolation despite the apparent wish for close contact implied by their sometimes frantic efforts to compel objects to give care and services. There is little sustained affection for objects with frequent shifts in attachments from one object to another. The frustrating dependency object often arouses persecutory anxiety followed by defensive rage and paranoid attack against the object.

anxiety and periodic moderate-to-severe depression. Aggression tends to be repressed and may be turned against the self in obvious masochistic behavior. Sooner or later, the person turns to other objects whom he endows with delegated omnipotence and repeats his infantile passive dependent attitudes.

−4. Infantile omnipotence is expressed in fantasies of wishful control of objects who will gratify every desire and willingly enslave themselves. Their voracious phantasies about dependency objects are often accompanied by anxiety and withdrawal. The danger of "closeness" comes from the threatened annihilation of the object and the fear of retaliatory destruction. There may be compensatory grandiose phantasies carried on in isolation. Overtly they appear as passive, unrelated and even helpless people who are in apparent constant need of care and support, but who are unresponsive to the needs of others. Oral receptivity governs most of their relationships. They show little sustained affection for objects with frequent shifts from one object to another. Frustration may lead to severe depression; persecutory anxiety may appear but leads to flight from the threatening situation and withdrawal.

## Chart II. General Pleasure-Frustration Balance

### Ideal Balance Range (Scale − 0)

Pleasure sources are varied in range and include all areas of behavior. They are not pain-dependent (masochistic) or primarily infantile (perverse). Frustration is tolerated as an inevitable part of living. It does not lead to perceptual distortions by anxiety, rage and guilt which may make a given source of socially acceptable pleasure permanently unavailable. Frustration in one area that requires renunciation of pleasure does not affect the positive anticipation of pleasure from other sources. Sublimated displacements are a prominent feature of growth to maturity.

### Range of Defensive Pursuit of Pleasure

Scale: (+1) ⟶ (+4)

+1. Pleasure is actively pursued. It is obtained from several areas of behavior

### Range of Inhibited Pursuit of Pleasure

Scale: (−1) ⟶ (−4)

−1. Pleasure in the passive role tends to be preferred. It is obtained from several

(e.g., work, family, marriage, etc.). It is positively anticipated and is usually followed by pleasurable recollection. It is accompanied both by relaxation of inner tension and by toleration of the pleasurable needs of others. Frustration tolerance may be temporarily diminished resulting in compensatory self-indulgence and an exaggerated pursuit of pleasure from other sources. Infantile pleasure sources may be used at such times but are not the rule.

+2. Pleasure tends to be restricted to one or a very few areas of behavior and is actively sought. It is usually, but not always, positively anticipated. Recollection is often tinged with disappointment. Relaxation of inner tension after pleasure is inconsistent. There is periodic overt anger at having to tolerate the pleasure needs of others. Frustration is tolerated with difficulty and leads to recurrent overt efforts to replace unavailable pleasure sources. These efforts may be impulsively carried out. Regression to infantile pleasure sources may occur periodically.

+3. Pleasure is obtained from one or a few highly specific activities but is of limited duration. Ostensible pleasure-seeking behavior may periodically become a compulsive preoccupation that dominates the picture. Infantile modes of gratification are common and may include sadistic pain-dependence. Anticipation of pleasure often has an anxious quality that leads to a hurried engagement in the activity, with or without expectation of real enjoyment. Recollection is usually disappointing. Inner tensions are not relaxed after presumed gratification. There is active hostility toward the pleasure needs of others when directed toward himself.

+4. Anhedonia is extreme but is often marked by the compulsive pleasure-seeking that is more ostensible than real. The seeking of pleasure may dominate behavior with poor regard for reality. It often takes on a

areas of behavior (e.g., work, family, marriage, etc.). It is positively anticipated and is usually followed by pleasurable recollection. It is accompanied both by relaxation of the inner tension and by toleration of the pleasure needs of others. Frustration tolerance may be temporarily diminished resulting in the spread of inhibition of of pleasure from the original area of frustration. Infantile forms of gratification may appear in fantasy but are not the rule.

−2. Pleasure tends to be restricted to passive gratification in one or a very few areas of behavior. It is usually, but not always, positively anticipated. Recollection is often tinged with disappointment. Relaxation of inner tension after pleasure is inconsistent. There is periodic suppressed resentment at having to tolerate the pleasure needs of others. There may be a tendency to postpone pleasure using the excuse that no further pleasure could compare with a real or fantasied pleasure of the past. Frustration is tolerated with difficulty. Regressive passive and infantile fantasies of gratification occur periodically.

−3. Pleasure is limited largely to fantasy or to one of a few passive activities of a highly specific nature but of limited duration. It is enjoyed, if at all, primarily in the passive recipient role, although fantasies may be aggressive. Pleasure sources are constricted. Masochistic pain-dependence and other infantile modes of gratification are common. There is little anticipation of of actual pleasure. Recollection is usually disappointing. Inner tensions are not relaxed after presumed gratification. There is repressed hostility toward or lack of awareness of the pleasure needs of others when directed toward himself.

−4. Anhedonia in fantasy or action is extreme. There is a general withdrawal from all overt pleasure pursuits, even those passively received. Fantasies of pleasure may occur but are structured largely in

quality of desperation. It is usually infantile and may be anti-social in character. Resort to drugs, alcohol, sexual perversion, etc. may be attempted. There is no pleasurable anticipation or recollection.

infantile oral terms. There is no pleasurable anticipation or recollection.

## Chart III. Sexual Pleasure-Frustration Balance

### Ideal Balance Range (Scale −0)

This balance refers to genital sexuality. Sexual pleasure is sought and enjoyed through coital patterns that are acceptable to the socio-cultural group with which the person identifies. This may not necessarily be the whole society of which he is a part. So-called "perverse" stimulations may be enjoyed to increase pre-coital excitement but are not essential to sexual pleasure. It never includes infliction of pain upon the partner, absorption of pain or adult homsexuality. Sexual frustration is tolerated. It is regarded as a postponement of gratification and is not perceived as a threat or damage that arouses emergency emotions of anxiety or rage. Sexual needs tend to be effectively combined with the affective needs to receive and give love.

### Range of Defensive Pursuit of Pleasure

#### Scale: $(+1) \rightarrow (+4)$

+1. Sexual activity tends periodically to be overestimated in lieu of other sources of pleasure. Pleasure is preserved as a rule but affective ties to a particular partner may be damaged when frustration occurs. Variety in sexual partners is given exaggerated importance, especially during a crisis of frustration or failure in sex or another area of behavior. Sexual pleasure is positively anticipated and is usually followed by pleasurable recollection. It is accompanied both by relaxation of inner tensions and by toleration of the sexual pleasure needs of sexual partners.

+2. Sexual frustration is experienced as a threat or damage to security. It is remedied by periodic indiscriminate sexuality that tends to be used as an instrument of aggression. Promiscuity and Don Juanism then become prominent but affective ties to an object may still be maintained. Substitute fantasies play a more important role at the same time. Pleasure is usually, but not always, positively anticipated. Recollection is often tinged with disappointment. Relaxation of inner tension, after sex, is inconsis-

### Range of Inhibited Pursuit of Pleasure

#### Scale: $(-1) \rightarrow (-4)$

−1. Sexual pleasure and activity are temporarily diminished in response to frustration regardless of whether the frustration is induced by reality or unconscious sexual inhibitions. Periodic anxiety which may arise in the sexual or other areas of behavior may produce a reduction in sexual pleasure and in sexual activity. During such temporary periods of inhibition, there is a preference for a constricted type and source of sexual experience in which the unfamiliar is avoided. Sexual pleasure is positively anticipated and is usually followed by pleasure needs of sexual partners.

−2. To function effectively in sex, a partner is sought with highly specific attributes that are necessary to facilitate potency. As a result, rigidity in sexual choice periodically becomes the rule. Affective ties to the chosen sexual object are generally maintained. Sexual pleasure needs tend to be combined in fantasy with other needs, e.g., for omnipotence and aggression. Potency disorders and frigidity are common. Sexual fantasies without much overt action begin to play an important role. Pleasure is usual-

tent. There is periodically overt anger at having to tolerate the sexual pleasure needs of sexual partners.

ly, but not always, positively anticipated. Recollection is often tinged with disappointment. Relaxation of inner tension, after sex, is inconsistent. There is periodic suppressed resentment at having to tolerate the sexual pleasure needs of sexual partners.

+3. Sexual pleasure is separated from affective ties to the objects. It tends to be pursued by a regressive revival of polymorphous perverse patterns. The latter are mutually replaceable in pleasure value with socially acceptable patterns of coitus. These perverse preferences may be defensive in purpose but arouse little or no conscious shame or guilt. Aggressive perverse sexual fantasy is compulsively pursued and tends to replace overt sexual behavior. Anticipation of sexual pleasure often has an anxious quality that leads to a hurried engagement in sexual activity, with or without expectation of real enjoyment. Recollection is usually disappointing. Inner tension is not relaxed after sex, and may be intensified. There is active hostility toward the sexual pleasure needs of sexual partners.

−3. Sexual pleasure is separated from affective ties to objects. (That is, sex and love are combined with difficulty. Sexual need may in fact be the only basis for an object attachment.) Pain-dependent (masochistic sexual perversion may be present. Passivity predominates in overt behavior and in fantasy. Sexual masochistic or passive fantasy is compulsively pursued and tends to replace action. There is little anticipation of actual pleasure in sex. Recollection is usually disappointing. Inner tension is not relaxed after sex, and may be intensified. There is repressed hostility toward, or lack of awareness of, the sexual pleasure needs of sexual partners.

+4. Excessive sexual pleasure pursuit is at times carried out in overt anti-social acts (bigamy, seduction of children, rape, etc.) unaccompanied by guilt. There is no tender feeling for the sexual partner nor is there sexual pleasure in the act. There is no pleasurable anticipation or recollection. Fixation on overt perverse sexual behavior is common.

−4. Sexual anhedonia (lack of pleasure) prevails. Perverse fantasies are common and are preferred to coitus. Sexual performance may be possible but with no gratification. There may be complete inhibition of sexual executive behavior with or without fantasies of sex. There is no pleasurable anticipation or recollection. Fixation on perverse sexual behavior in passive role is common—especially in fantasy.

## Chart IV. Affective Balance

### Ideal Balance Range (Scale − 0)

There is free formation of ties of affection, friendship and love to objects. The objects that inspire affectivity are not chosen primarily because they can be identified with the Self or because they represent parental surrogates and are therefore dependency objects. Sexualized love is directed toward one heterosexual object although there may be more than one such object in a lifetime. Self-esteem is maintained primarily through independent and self-reliant activity. The giving of affection and care to other objects is as important to self-esteem as is receiving it.

## Range of Excessive Display of Affect

Scale: $(+1) \longrightarrow (+4)$

+1. Affective ties to sexual objects are easily established. More than one sexual object tends to be sought. The affective ties to the primary object continue although impaired in intensity and duration. Non-sexual affective relationships usually are well established and maintained.

+2. Seductiveness is an aggressive way of life in which the goal is to extract love from many objects. Return of affection to such objects lasts as long as the flow of love and service from the object continues without interruption. Projection and anxiety periodically become prominent features of object relationships and tend to arouse defensive hostility to non-giving objects.

+3. Pseudo-affectivity predominates in object attachments. Such persons act as if they desired love and were able to give love. Under the guise of affective closeness, however, the goal is to dominate and control the object. The tie to such objects is often cruel and pain-inflicting (sadistic).

+4. Intense efforts to feel love and to receive love fail to work. The purpose of the frantic involvements is to deny an emptiness of affective experience. The behavior has an as-if quality in which imitative expressions of feeling cover a narcissistic desire to achieve omnipotent control of other objects without regard for their needs.

## Range of Affect Deficiency

Scale: $(-1) \longrightarrow (-4)$

−1. Affective ties to sexual objects are easily established. However, substitutions are made with difficulty when the preferred object is unavailable. The result is a periodic inhibition and rigidity in object choice because of the need to combine affective and sexual gratification. Affective ties to non-sexual objects are usually well maintained.

−2. Affective ties are established with one or a very few objects. Love and affection are given to the object only if affection and services are first received. Passivity is therefore the preferred mode of obtaining love. If rejected or if love is not constantly forthcoming mild to moderate depression and persecutory anxiety become prominent features of object relations.

−3. Affective ties are limited to the passive reception of affection and interest from another object. Giving affection and care is, however, insignificant or absent. The tie to objects is often submissive and pain-dependent (masochistic).

−4. Affection and love are neither enjoyed passively nor given to other objects. Instead, no affectional attachments are sought or formed. Such persons seem to be indifferent to other objects and remain affectively isolated.

## Chart V. Defense Balance

Ideal Balance Range (Scale −0)

Defenses against conscious anxiety and guilt are localized and are ego-syntonic without impairment of self-assertion, pleasure and affectivity. The predominant defensive and reparative operations are repression and displacement to goals that are ego-syntonic and are socially favored. Regression may occur as a temporary reaction to stress. It is expressed as dependence upon another object that is self-limited and ends spontaneously after a period of psychic recuperation. Identification as a defense is more likely to be with a giving object and with a model of self-reliance and strength than with the aggressor or despised object.

## Range of Defensive Aggression and Defensive Ego Inflation

Scale: $(+1) \longrightarrow (+4)$

+1. Defenses are periodically aggressively over-reactive. The over-reaction is displayed in emotional behavior that is excessively aggressive and is not entirely appropriate to the stimulus. Displacements involve one or more areas of behavior or a particular object. They include reaction-formation of the counterphobic variety, over-assertion in sex and combativeness. Periods of self-control of aggression intervene and make the over-reaction intermittent. Pleasure is temporarily reduced during the over-reaction.

+2. Over-reactive defenses take on a fairly general distribution in most areas of behavior and become chronic. They may appear as aggressive defenses against anxiety and passive inclinations in some but not all areas of behavior. Counterphobic reactions become prominent. Pleasure is diminished generally. Affective ties are periodically invaded by hostile and coercive demands upon the object. Regression is prominent in determining the goals of object attachments.

+3. Identification with the aggressor is a prominent defense against passivity. Projection becomes more apparent. Sadistic pain-infliction on objects occurs periodically. Regression is present in the form of coercive dependency. Fixation on infantile oral aggressive and sexual aims is common in fantasy and may be acted out periodically. Pleasure and affectivity are definitely impaired.

+4. Impulsivity in acting out infantile sexual and aggressive impulses is frequent. Projection and paranoid reactions tend

## Range of Defensive Inhibition and Defensive Ego-Constriction

Scale: $(-1) \longrightarrow (-4)$

−1. Defenses are inhibitory and tend toward passivity that is not entirely appropriate to the stimulus. Displacements involve one or more areas of behavior of a particular object. They include reaction-formation against anger, isolation of affect and minor phobic avoidances. Periods of self-control of fear intervene and make the inhibition intermittent. Pleasure is temporarily reduced during the phases of inhibition.

−2. Inhibitive defenses take on a fairly general distribution in most areas of behavior and become chronic. Passivity and inhibition of assertion invade some but not all areas of behavior. Reaction-formation against sexual and aggressive wishes result in constriction of goals. Pleasure is diminished generally. Affective ties are limited in number and are periodically invaded by pain-dependent (masochistic) trends. Regression is prominent in determining the attachments.

−3. Identification with the weak or despised object is a prominent defense against fear of retaliation for aggression. Pain dependence, especially as moral masochism, is a fundamental defensive reaction. Regression in the form of helpless dependency may be intense. Fixation on receptive oral object attachments and on infantile passivity is common, and may be acted out periodically. Pleasure and affectivity are definitely impaired.

−4. Massive denial of aggressive and sexual wishes is a common defense. Masochistic-pain-dependence and extreme

repeatedly to affect most object relations. Infantile omnipotent demands are actively pursued in all or most areas of behavior. Pleasure is seriously impaired. Paranoid disintegrative reactions may occur.

passivity in object relationships are the rule in all or most areas of behavior. Introjective defenses are prominent. Infantile omnipotent expectations are actively indulged in fantasy, which replaces action. Fantasy tends to the bizarre. Pleasure is seriously impaired. Depressive disintegrative reactions may occur.

*Note:* The nature of conditions which tend to elicit the anxiety and guilt that evoke defenses in a given case must be stated in the list of substantiating data.

## Chart VI. Emergency Emotion Balance

The emergency emotions are the emotions of fear and rage that arise in response to threat and danger.

Mastery of the reactive emergency emotions is maintained at the signal level without impairment of self-assertion or the enjoyment of pleasure. Anxiety or fear and rage, when they occur, are specifically reactive to appropriate stimuli and are also self-limited in duration. They are not automatically repetitive with every new frustration or conflict, nor do the emotions, when experienced in one situation, become generalized to other areas of experience. Emergency emotions are primarily aroused by realistic threats to the security and welfare of the individual. They serve as signals for adaptive behavior which does not impair the efficiency of adjustment reactions to the ordinary experiences of stress or the effectiveness of performance in the areas of work and interpersonal relations.

### Range of Hostility and Rage which Accompany Aggression

Scale: $(+1) \rightarrow (+4)$

+1. Rage is greater in intensity and/or experienced more frequently than is appropriate in situations commonly recognized as threatening, provocative or frustrating and which would ordinarily arouse some anger and/or aggressive act. Rage may be experienced as angry feelings or thoughts and expressed as short-lived irritability, sullenness or sulkiness. Rage is limited in duration and can be consciously controlled by *suppression*. The impairment of functioning is of mild intensity.*

### Range of Fear and Anxiety which Accompany Inhibition

Scale: $(-1) \rightarrow (-4)$

−1. Anxiety is of greater intensity and/or experienced more frequently than is appropriate in situations commonly recognized as capable of arousing a low degree of anxiety (e.g., examination anxiety, stage fright). Anxiety may be experienced as uncomfortable tension, apprehensive thoughts or restlessness.

Anxiety is limited in duration and can be controlled by suppression of the feeling without withdrawal from the provoking situation. In addition, there may be temporary exaggeration of other activity (e.g., increased emphasis on adjunctive actions that provide pleasure and/or movement toward people for support and reassurance).

The impairment of functioning is of mild intensity.*

+2. Rage is not commensurate with the seriousness of the stimulus and/or may be inappropriately prolonged. Rage is experienced intermittently as intense feelings of anger which may be expressed verbally, by an aggressively threatening posture, and/or by hostile defiance of authority. Rage is tempered by judgment but cannot be fully controlled by suppression. It tends to be *displaced* to situations where it may be expressed in ways that are relatively safe from social or physical retaliation (e.g., it may be deflected against a child, spouse or underling known to be sympathetic, tolerant or submissive; it may also be expressed in disguised hostile modes such as sardonic humor and teasing.) The impairment of functioning is usually of moderate intensity.*

+3. Rage is elicited by slight provocation, minor slights and by mild frustration. It may be obviously inappropriate. It tends to intense and prolonged expression and may be displayed with obvious somatic signs ("red" rages), as a paralysis with rage ("white" rages), as threatening assaultiveness, chronic bellicosity and/or tantrum-like behavior. Control of the rage by suppression and displacement is intermittently defective. The degree of impairment of functioning is usually of moderate to severe intensity.*

+4. Rage is commonly elicited by the ordinary demands of life and is a characteristic response to stress. Aggressive, paranoid ideas frequently interfere with interpersonal relations. General hostility toward the environment is a dominant feature of thought and behavior. Suppression and displacement are seldom able to help

−2. The anxiety is not commensurate with the seriousness of the threatening stimulus or may be inappropriately prolonged. The anxious tension may be constantly present in mild form; more severe anxiety may occur in specific situations or recurrent conditions (e.g., driving a car, making a date, week ends, vacations, holidays, etc.) or may be expressed through phobic displacement to specific areas of functioning. The anxiety may be experienced as fear, moderate body tension or apprehensive thoughts. Control of anxiety is mainly through *displacement* of attention and interest to neutral goals, withdrawal from threatening areas, urgent moves toward other persons, efforts to obtain reassurance—all of which constrict the available avenues of effective functioning. The impairment of functioning is usually of moderate intensity.*

−3. Anxiety is elicited without overt external cause or by minor threats or may be obviously inappropriate. Moderate tension is fairly constant and more severe anxiety attacks may occur intermittently. Organized phobias may be present. Anxiety may be experienced as paralyzing crises of fear, as panic-laden thoughts, and/or in the form of extensive phobias. Ominous fantasies may recur of danger, injury and death to one's self or to objects of special significance to the person. Control of the anxiety by suppression and displacement is intermittently defective. Failure of controls leads to immobilizing avoidance and withdrawal and marked regressive phenomena such as clinging dependency. The degree of impairment of functioning is usually of moderate to severe intensity.*

−4. Anxiety is commonly elicited by the ordinary demands of life and is a characteristic response to stress. General anxiety and broad inhibition of function predominate in most areas of behavior. Acute attacks of intense panic may occur. Dyscontrol is a constant threat. Suppression and displacement seldom help control the anxiety control the rage which may lead to physical assaultiveness for real and fancied grievances. The degree of impairment of functioning is usually of severe intensity.*

which frequently is accompanied by massive regression. The degree of impairment of functioning is usually of severe intensity.*

*Scale of the intensity of disorganization accompanying anxiety, rage and guilt.

*Mild:* Pleasure is maintained with brief periods of diminution; anxiety, rage or guilt have no disorganizing impact upon the basic needs for food, sleep and sex. Function in the various areas of behavior is not affected or is temporarily impaired in one or two areas.

*Moderate:* Pleasure is reduced with periodic recovery of the capacity for gratification; anxiety, rage or guilt intermittently impair appetite, disturb sleep and reduce the sexual drive; function in some areas of behavior is definitely impaired but with periods of remission.

*Severe:* Pleasure is markedly reduced without remission; basic needs for food, sleep and sex are chronically disturbed; there is inability to be distracted from the anxiety, rage or guilt; function in most or all areas of behavior remains markedly impaired.

## Chart VII.  Guilt Balance

### Ideal Balance Range (Scale − 0)

Internalized self-restraints that are imposed by the super-ego (conscience and ego-ideal) operate without impairment of self-assertion and without impairment of pleasure. Expectations and demands of the ego-ideal are consistent with the resources and circumstances of the individual and do not impose unattainable standards of behavior, achievement and morality against which the self is evaluated. Self-control is ego-syntonic and arouses neither rage nor anxiety when self-frustration is required. Guilt, when it arises, is short-lived, appropriate, and is usually prophylactic and consistent with self-interest and effective functioning. If a transgression occurs, guilt evokes appropriate efforts at restitution and recollection is available for guidance in avoiding similar transgressions in the future.

### Range of Defensive Aggression Aroused by Guilt

Scale: (+1) → (+4)

+1. The intensity of guilt is usually mild.* Feelings of self-dissatisfaction may occasionally arise because of failure to measure up to somewhat excessive requirements of the ego-ideal. Such mild guilt tends to be rationalized and blame is placed on others as an excuse for apparent failures. Most of the time successful performance and pleasure are not significantly impaired by guilty resentments. Guilt at this level may be inferred from periodically exaggerated assertiveness and mildly hostile and defensive aggressivity toward authority which are aroused by threats of failure. Such reactions do not invade all areas of behavior, tend to

### Range of Defensive Inhibition Aroused by Guilt

Scale: (−1) → (−4)

−1. The intensity of guilt is usually mild.* Feelings of self-dissatisfaction may occasionally arise because of failure to measure up to somewhat excessive requirements of the ego-ideal. Most of the time successful performance and pleasure are not significantly impaired by feelings of guilt. Guilt at this level may be inferred from episodic inhibition of self-assertion or from evidence of expiatory behavior in some areas. When present, inhibition or expiation does not result in social or physical acts of significant self-damage. Guilty feelings and behavior or this type are usually followed by awareness that the reactions

be intermittent, and are usually followed by awareness that the reactions were inappropriate. Any accompanying impairment of pleasure is temporary.

+2. The intensity of the guilt is usually moderate.* Feelings of self-dissatisfaction tend to dominate but are often denied and rationalized by self-justification. Personal failures and experienced inadequacy tend be blamed on others who are often openly criticized and depreciated. Defiant disregard of internalized or of external authority is acted out intermittently in comparatively minor transgressions which invite punitive consequences. There is an exaggerated sensitivity to criticism with expressed resentment and a readiness to blame others. These attributes do not necessarily prevent significant object relationships which continue to be intermittent sources of pleasure. Overall, some impairment of pleasure prevails.

+3. The intensity of guilt which underlies aggressive behavior varies from moderate to intermittently severe.* Feelings of guilt are generally denied and replaced by arrogant claims of self-righteousness which tend to be reaffirmed compulsively. This need always to appear right and virtuous tends to become a fixed part of the person's character and frequently leads to outbursts of projected rage. Criticism and correction must usually be refuted and easily lead to aggressive attack on anyone who questions the person's motivation and behavior. Aggressive provocation of retaliation from the environment may result in serious social or even physical damage. Although self-justification is often translated into blame and accusation of others which inspire counter-hostility, some capacity for constructive cooperation is retained and, under favorable circumstances, effective functioning remains possible. Over-all pleasure is

were inappropriate. Any accompanying impairment of pleasure is temporary.

−2. The intensity of the guilt is usually moderate.* Feelings of self-dissatisfaction tend to dominate the picture although feelings of well-being occur intermittently. Repressed guilt may be inferred from an exaggerated need for external approval, from recurrent self-defeating behavior, or from a tendency to provoke or invite punishment from others in the form of physical and/or social abuse or defeat. There is exaggerated sensitivity to criticism but resentment is seldom expressed overtly. Most areas of behavior are affected by recurrent inhibition of self-assertion. These inhibitions are accompanied by constriction of the sources of pleasure and some impairment of the quality of the pleasure itself. Nevertheless pleasure and success can be experienced without arousing conscious or unconscious guilt or disabling self-punishment.

−3. The intensity of guilt varies from moderate to intermittently severe.* Feelings of self-dissatisfaction are not only chronic but periodically reach the severity of depressive episodes which impair function although they are not usually incapacitating. In addition to such conscious expressions of unworthiness, repressed feelings of guilt can be inferred from the self-devaluation and deprecation of achievements, as well as from repetitive self-defeating and self-punitive behavior. These patterns pervade most areas of behavior and may be accompanied by extensive inhibition of assertion. Object attachments tend to be characterized by painful submissiveness. Pleasurable pursuits are markedly inhibited. Anticipation of pleasure or of success generally evoke so much unconscious guilt and anxiety that pleasure is grossly impaired. Success is often sabotaged but effective functioning is possible in some areas. Other derivatives markedly impaired as a rule. Hypochon-driacal preoccupations, free-floating anxi-ety and phobias may occur but are neither totally incapacitating nor as prominent in the general picture as in the aggressive behavior.

+4. The intensity of guilt is severe.* Pro-jection is a favored defense against guilt and is often accompanied by striking severe reaction-formations. Paranoid attitudes fre-quently overlaid with grandiosity, become a fixed part of the character. Pleasure is gros-sly impaired. The counter-hostility and re-jection by the environment may result in periodic incapacitation. Embedded in the predominant aggression there may be hypochonriacal fears, massive anxiety at-tacks and severe phobias which may add to the tendency to be incapacitated.

of repressed guilt which may appear are hypochondriacal preoccupations, free-floating anxiety and phobic avoidance, al-though such reactions are not totally incapacitating.

−4. The intensity of guilt is severe.* Self-depreciation and self-recrimination are marked and depression may be severe and incapacitating. Repressed guilt may be in-ferred from the frequency of apparently unintended social or physical self-injury. During depressions self-damage may be consciously deliberate. Other derivatives of repressed guilt may be prominent, including hypochonriacal fears, severe chronic anxi-ety and massive phobic avoidance. These may be periodically incapacitating. Plea-sure is grossly impaired.

*See Intensity chart under Emergency Emotion Balance.

## Chart VIII.  Pathology Balance

### Ideal Balance Range (Scale −0)

The ideal range obviously is the absence of pathology. The personality is not dominated by obsessive-compulsive, hysterical, masochistic or paranoid patterns of behavior. Obses-sional or hysterical reactions may appear occasionally but impair pleasure and affectivity mildly and briefly. If they occur at all, such reactions are self-limited and temporary responses to stress or frustration. There may occasionally be specific but mild, obsessive-compulsive symptoms such as excessive orderliness, cleanliness, procrastination, doubt, or hysterical sexual symptoms such as mild and transitory potency disorders or frigidity. As with broader reactions, such symptoms are of brief duration and are spontaneously resolved.

### Range of Predominantly Aggressive (Over-Reactive) Pathology

Scale: $(+1) \longrightarrow (+4)$

+1. Impairment, whether by specific morbid symptoms or by maladaptive char-acter traits, affects ego function in one or some areas of behavior. Where over-reactive pathology occurs in an area of behavior, pleasure and functional efficiency are reduced. The impairment fluctuates in degree but never totally destroys function.

### Range of Predominantly Inhibitive Pathology

Scale: $(-1) \longrightarrow (-4)$

−1. Impairment, whether by specific morbid symptoms or by maladaptive char-acter traits, affects ego functions in one or some areas of behavior. Where inhibitive pathology occurs in an area of behavior, pleasure and functional efficiency are re-duced. The impairment fluctuates in degree but never totally destroys function.

Healthy function periodically returns, and is of longer duration than is the pathology.

*Over-reactive symptoms* which may occur are transitory:

a) *minor ritualizing behavior* that tends to be rationalized, as, for example, excessive hand washing, cleaning, setting things in order in the guise of necessary cleanliness and efficiency.

b) *episodic over-indulgence in sex*

c) *free-floating hostility* with occasional and inappropriate temper outbursts. Pleasure may be temporarily impaired; efficiency less so.

*Over-reactive character traits* which may occur:

a) noticeable but not extreme personal *disorderliness*, sloppiness, and chronic lateness.

b) *socially provocative behavior* that is more amusing than destructive although it often has an aggressive quality.

c) *argumentativeness*, especially on intellectual issues.

d) exhibitionism in social situations; the need to be the center of attention is generally sufficiently restrained as to be tolerated without hostility by others.

+2. Over-reactive compensatory behavior and reaction-formations fluctuate in degree as efforts to deny and control hostility and aggression. They may subside for periods of time but recur often in some areas of behavior. At such times, pleasure and efficiency are impaired.

*Over-reactive symptoms* which may occur intermittently:

function periodically returns, and is of longer duration than is the pathology.

*Inhibitory symptoms* which may occur are transitory:

a) *mild procrastination or doubt* that are followed after a delay by appropriate acts or decisions.

b) *episodic sexual potency loss* (including temporary loss of desire) or other minor conversion symptoms.

c) *free-floating mild anxiety or mild depression*. (Localized phobias of heights, airplanes, tunnels, etc. may occur. They are of such a nature as fairly easily to be avoided. However, if necessary, they can be tolerated despite the fear which is evoked.)

*Inhibitive character traits* which may occur:

a) noticeable but not extreme personal *neatness*, cleanliness and punctuality.

b) *shyness* in social situations which, however, are not avoided despite recurrent mild anxiety.

c) *submissiveness* to authority; periodically anger and rebelliousness may appear but are not sustained.

d) *passivity* in competitive situations with periodic brief displays of competitive aggression.

−2. Inhibition leads to avoidance of specific functions or situations requiring assertion as a means of controlling anticipatory anxiety. The inhibition fluctuates in degree and in extent, subsiding for periods of time but recurring often in some areas of behavior. At such times pleasure and efficiency are impaired.

*Inhibitive symptoms* which may occur intermittently:

a) *counter-phobic actions* which at times may even be physically dangerous or socially inappropriate.

a) *phobic reactions* involving places and moving vehicles especially. The frightening situations can be avoided without major disturbance of work and object attachments. They can be tolerated with mild to moderate fear, particularly if a companion is present in the frightening situation.

b) *ritualistic acts* which usually precede an action but may at times become part of the action and thus interfere with its successful accomplishment.

b) *procrastination and doubt* that are usually resolved by forming a dependent tie to an authority whose intervention is sought before an action or decision is made.

c) *brooding* with a projective quality.

d) *compulsive sexuality* may occur periodically with reduced pleasure and potency.

c) *brooding* with a depressive quality

d) *periodic potency disorders* such as premature ejaculation or vaginal frigidity.

e) recurrent minor conversion symptoms and compulsive acts such as headaches, backaches, localized tics, and nail biting related primarily to unconscious efforts to control rage and aggression.

e) recurrent minor conversion symptoms such as aches and pains, paresthesias, hyperventilation symptoms, weakness and dizziness; mild and fluctuating hypochondriasis. All these symptoms are related primarily to efforts to control anxiety about assertion and forbidden gratification of pleasure needs.

f) periodic temper outburts which temporarily impair object relationships in marital, work and social areas of behavior.

f) attacks of moderate anxiety and/or depression that impair pleasure but do not seriously affect participation in work and social relationships except briefly.

*Over-reactive character traits* which may occur:

a) compulsive carelessness in dress and lack of personal cleanliness.

*Inhibitive character traits* which may occur:

a) compulsive concern with appearing neat, clean, and orderly although disorderliness may be prominent in areas of living hidden from public view.

b) defiance of custom and tradition but without becoming anti-social.

b) social shyness especially in contacts with the opposite sex.

c) proneness to be pugnacious and argumentative in social relationships; persistent efforts to control and dominate others.

c) passivity and submissiveness which may periodically be self-defeating and even masochistic.

d) dramatic self-presentation that periodically becomes flamboyant exhibitionism. It is often inappropriate but not anti-social.

d) repetitive fantasies, without overt action, of aggressive and pleasurable wish fulfillment. They are particularly concerned with demonstration of power.

+3. Pleasure and efficiency in most areas of behavior are markedly impaired. There is a strong trend toward emotional alienation and isolation from objects that often evokes the defense of overt, aggressive, as-if behavior.

*Over-reactive symptoms* which may occur:

a) chronic impulsivity.

b) frequent attacks of uncontrolled anger. Impulses to irrational violence against others are usually controlled but not always.

c) compulsive rituals may be prominent features and tend to invade actions as well as to follow actions in efforts at undoing.

d) compulsive sexuality, often with difficulty in ejaculation (praecox or retardation). Pleasure in orgasm is markedly reduced.

e) chronic tics and conversion symptoms may be present, particularly those affecting motor function.

f) sexual perversions which have an aggressive as well as sexual purpose may occur.

*Over-reactive character traits* which may occur:

−3. Pleasure and efficiency in most areas of behavior are markedly impaired. There is a strong trend toward emotional alienation and isolation from objects so that inhibition of object relatedness is pronounced. Aggressive as-if behavior may occur in fantasy but seldom overtly.

*Inhibitive symptoms* which may occur:

a) chronic phobias involving places, vehicles, and objects that threaten contamination with disease or other physical damage. The phobic situation can be avoided only at the price of moderate impairment of work and socio-cultural functioning. Mobility in phobic areas is possible if accompanied by a companion.

b) moderate to severe anxiety and depression invade object relations, social behavior and work for periods of time; recurrent hypochondriasis occurs. There may be occasional outbursts of rage which tend to increase the anxiety and depression.

c) procrastination and doubt periodically end in paralysis of action or decision. When acts do ensue they are either the decisions of others upon whom insistent demands have been made to take over responsibility, or they are impulsive acts to end the painful tension. Ritualistic acts of undoing may be present in one or more areas.

d) chronic inhibition of sexual desire and performance; masochistic pain dependence may become a necessary part of sexual arousal.

c) major sensory and motor conversion reactions which markedly inhibit functions may occur intermittently.

f) passive homosexual fantasies or acts.

*Inhibitive character traits* which may occur:

a) exaggerated need for contact with objects but without lasting attachments or strong affection.
b) constant coercive efforts to control and dominate dependency objects as well as others.

c) periodic trends of suspiciousness and distrust which may be defensive reactions to self-referential activity.

d) envy and indiscriminate competitiveness.
e) somewhat grandoise ambitions with exaggerated notions of talent and ability.
f) periodic anti-social acting out of destructiveness toward other persons and toward social institutions.
g) addiction to alcohol or drugs as means of releasing aggression may be present.

+4. Organized paranoid delusional symptoms are evidence of progressive disintegration. Chronic anti-social aggression and destructiveness may be acted out.

a) marked shyness and withdrawal from objects although inner needs for close relations may be felt.
b) chronic obsessive character traits signifying predominance of fear and inhibition impair functions in most areas. Dependency cravings for care and service are pronounced.
c) passive dependence upon objects is based upon the investment of these objects with the magical power to fulfill their infantile ominpotent expectations.
d) avoidance of overt competition with impounded assertion in all areas.
e) magical fantasies of pleasure and power are frequent.

f) fearful submission to authority is often strongly masochistic.

g) addiction to alcohol or drugs as a means of reducing anxiety may be present.

−4. Pan-anxiety and total inhibition of function, depression with psycho-motor retardation, seclusiveness and active hypochondriacal delusions of illness signify progressive disintegration.

## Chart IX.  Social Integration Balance

### Ideal Balance Range (Scale − 0)

This represents a balance between altruistic identification with the group and egocentric striving for omnipotence without regard for other members of the society of which the person is a part.

Cooperation and competition are not, however, mutually exclusive. Social roles are appropriate to the standards of the society and are a consistent source of gratification and self-esteem. The ego-ideal thus provides and facilitates achievement of social adaptive goals without arousing internal conflict.

Strivings that serve self-interest can be postponed or renounced in favor of altruistic goals when the former threaten the stability of the group with which the person identifies. Antisocial behavior is never pursued; neither depression for failure to meet social standards nor projected blame for frustration are significant.

Range of Predominant Aggressivity in the Socialization Process

Scale: $(+1) \rightarrow (+4)$

+1. Competitive striving is pursued in cooperative activity. The preferred role is that of social dominance. Recognition of the limits to one's importance is not easily made. Hostility for failure to receive acknowledgment is present but is usually well controlled.

+2. Social identifications and positions on social issues and interests of the group of which the person is a part are chosen which provide opportunities for dominance and prestige, in the guise of cooperation. Intra-group hositility is often diverted by displacement of outsiders in the form of disguised prejudice or discrimination. Friendships occur within the circle of like-minded persons.

+3. Compulsive group activity appears to take precedence over family ties and responsibilities. Preferred social identifications are those which enhance prestige through aggressive dominance and permit aggressive self-display. Intra-group ties are many but superficial. These persons are sensitive to rebuff which arouses persecutory anxiety to which they respond with overt anger. Prejudice is usually acted out. Active efforts are often made to recruit companions for campaigns of prejudice or discrimination.

+4. Social fanticism or frankly anti-social behavior with a paranoid or sociopathic coloring may be openly pursued. Anti-social behavior is engaged in through affiliation with groups dedicated to destruction of the rights of others. Affective ties within the group are absent or are of a superficial nature.

Range of Predominant Inhibition in the Socialization Process

Scale: $(-1) \rightarrow (-4)$

−1. The preferred role is that of a follower in cooperative activity. Competitive strivings are given up in the interest of social harmony so promptly as to suggest avoidance of reasonable competition. Unpopular positions arouse anxiety and are usually avoided: they may be tolerated on matters of principle.

−2. Social identifications and positions on social issues and interests of the group of which the person is a part are chosen which provide opportunities for passivity and submissive dependence upon an authority in the guise of cooperation. Oppositional impulses arouse anxiety which may be defended against by impounding assertion within the preferred group. Overt hostility at outsiders can occur. Friendships occur within the circle of like-minded persons.

−3. Social anxiety readily leads to withdrawal from group participation. There is a tendency to feel disliked or rejected by the group that leads to suppressed hostility and periods of depression. Group involvement occurs intermittently through identification with victims. Intra-group ties are few in number and are passively pursued. Prejudice is often an outlet for aggression if it can be carried out with the support and protection of a strong authority.

−4. Social participation and engagement in common activities with others is avoided. Seclusiveness is preferred with compensatory phantasies of superiority over others. The fantasies may be of grandiose gestures of righting wrongs. There is often a self-referential fear of aggression by others. This leads to more seclusiveness, suppressed rage punctuated possibly by explosive paranoid outbursts.

# The Application of Ego Strength Scales to Psychoanalytic Clinic Records

by John J. Weber, M.D., Jack Elinson, Ph.D.,
and Leonard M. Moss, M.D.*

In March, 1965, Weber, Elinson, and Moss presented the first report of a project which was begun in 1959,[7] and which involved the participation of nine psychoanalysts** from the Columbia University's Psychoanalytic Clinic for Training and Research. This team of coders extracted information from the Psychoanalytic Clinic records of 1,348 adult patients and prepared this data for electronic machine processing.

The Columbia Psychoanalytic Records Project was designed to study change in the patients' adaptation from the beginning to the end of psychoanalysis and psychoanalytically oriented psychotherapy. Measurements of change were then to be correlated with other information such as the patients' background; predictive factors mentioned in the Clinic record at the beginning of treatment; ratings of the therapists; and information concerning the outcome of treatment subsequent to that recorded in the Clinic record.

This project hopes to distil and organize information from almost twenty years of experience with analysis at an analytic training center and to establish techniques for the objective measurement of change in adaptation. The project is not a controlled study of the effectiveness of

*The work was supported by the Health Research Council of the City of New York (U-1286), by Columbia University's Psychoanalytic Clinic for Training and Research, and by its Department of Psychiatry.
**Andre Ballard, M.D., Paul Bradlow, M.D., Max Cohen, M.D., Seymour Jacobson, M.D., Peter Laderman, M.D., Alvin Shapiro, M.D., Josef Weissberg, M.D., and Drs. Weber and Moss. The authors wish to express their appreciation to Elizabeth Van Velzer and Martin Breitman for their assistance in the study and in the preparation of the manuscript.

psychoanalysis or psychotherapy, nor is it a study of the processes by which psychoanalysis or psychotherapy affect change in the patients' adaptation. However, the organization of information from these charts, the establishment of techniques to appreciate and evaluate change, and the determination of those factors which are highly correlated with change are necessary preliminaries to a study of the more complex issues of analysis, i.e. the process of analysis, the effectiveness of analysis as a therapeutic technique, and the verification and elaboration of psychodynamic concepts.

The records studied were those of adult patients who had ended their treatment as ambulatory patients at the Psychoanalytic Clinic or in private offices of their therapists between 1945 and 1962. These therapeutic services are offered in conjunction with the Clinic's program of psychoanalytic training for physicians and the patient's ability to pay is not a factor. The records studied included those of 588 patients who were accepted for psychoanalysis, 434 who began psychotherapy on the Reparative Service, and 326 patients who were in psychotherapy on the Psychosomatic Service.

Schedules were devised to record sociologic and psychiatric data from the written record for two points in time, at the beginning and at the end of Clinic treatment. Another schedule was developed to code predictions of outcome which were made at the time of admission. Information concerning the therapists themselves and faculty ratings of the candidates as therapists were included in the study. In addition, questionnaires were sent to each therapist who had graduated from the Clinic's training program inquiring about the 1,134 patients who had been treated by this group in the course of their training. The graduates were asked if the patient had continued treatment privately after Clinic treatment ended, and if so what additional changes had occurred and how private treatment ended. In answer to this questionnaire, information was received on 831 patients from 73.3% of the therapists who were solicited.

In 1962 Karush, Easser, Cooper, and Swerdloff[6] reported on their development of ego strength scales or adaptive balances. With some modifications of nomenclature and recording, the work was published two years later.[4] Cooper et al.[1] presented the latest report of the group in October, 1965, bringing up to date the experience of this team in using ego strength scales after clinical interviews of patients. The areas which the scales were designed to record have the greatest importance in psychoanalytic theory and clinical practice and involve concepts which are as hard to render objectively as they are difficult to structure theoretically. Even if one should object, as Wallerstein suggested in his discussion of their work,[6] "that the concept of ego strength has been broadened to encompass the complex interplay of all the organism's functions," the ego strength scales would represent a logical addition to a study of change during analysis and psychotherapy.

The ego strength scales were included in the psychoanalytic records study because it was felt that they would supplement very well other measures of change which were developed for the records study. It was further thought that the application of these scales to large numbers of psychoanalytic records would complement their original development and use in evaluating smaller numbers of patients on the basis of clinical interviews. The scales were incorporated into the records study with minor modifications only. All of the scales or balances are reproduced in this volume.*

Coding took place over a period of approximately two years. Each of the nine collaborating psychoanalysts was responsible for coding a random one-tenth sample of case records. The final random tenth sample was used to measure individual reliability and each record in this group was coded by at least two of the collaborating analysts. The outcome of the reliability study will be presented in the next section, preparatory to describing the results obtained when adaptive balances were correlated with other clinical data.

---

*In the present work severity was recorded 0, 1, 2, 3 or 4 and polarity was modified as follows in order to deal with the problems posed by written records and electronic machines:

(+)     Active (aggressive)
(±)     Indicating adaptation *at the time history was taken* (or at the end of the Columbia Psychoanalytic Clinic record) was predominantly aggressive, but there were variable or alternating periods of passivity.
(∓)     Indicating adaptation *at the time history was taken* (or at the end of Columbia Psychoanalytic Clinic record) was predominantly passive, but there were variable or alternating periods of aggressivity.
(−)     Passive (inhibited)

Whole digit designations only were used to indicate severity since the ego strength group was not yet using the half-point scale. (They were using upward or downward directed arrows instead to indicate small differences, a technique which was not carried over for machine use.)

## RELIABILITY OF THE EGO STRENGTH SCALES
## WHEN APPLIED TO CLINIC RECORDS

The reliability with which the ego strength scales were applied to Clinic records was assessed by two independent methods. Group reliability was determined by measuring the variation which occurs when different random samples of cases are coded by different coders. Individual reliability was determined by comparing how the same case was coded independently by two or more coders.

### GROUP RELIABILITY

The 1,348 records were assigned at random for coding to the nine clinical coders. Theoretically, under the assumption of complete coder consistency or perfect reliability, the distribution of all coded variables obtained by each coder would be expected to show only small variations from one random subsample to another. Differences larger than expected by chance alone might reasonably be attributed to differences in the coding practices of the several coders.

Table 1 shows the variation in coding severity on the Dependency Balance at the beginning of treatment. It is a prototype of the data developed for each of the scales, both at the beginning and at the end

**TABLE 1**

Severity Coding at the Beginning of CPC Treatment

Clinical Coders

| S E V E R I T Y | | All | 1 | 2 | 3 | 4 | 5 | 6 | 7 | 8 | 9 |
|---|---|---|---|---|---|---|---|---|---|---|---|
| | 0 | 0.0 | 0.0 | 0.0 | 0.0 | 0.0 | 0.0 | 0.0 | 0.0 | 0.0 | 0.0 |
| | 1 | 1.9 | 3.3 | 0.0 | 0.0 | 0.0 | 1.9 | 3.4 | 0.7 | 6.2 | 2.3 |
| | 2 | 38.6 | 71.2 | 6.8 | 16.7 | 34.7 | 30.2 | 44.8 | 46.4 | 67.1 | 33.1 |
| | 3 | 53.7 | 24.8 | 91.9 | 77.6 | 60.5 | 60.4 | 43.4 | 50.3 | 20.5 | 48.5 |
| | 4 | 4.7 | 0.0 | 0.6 | 4.5 | 4.8 | 6.9 | 7.6 | 2.6 | 1.4 | 16.2 |
| Not Coded | | 1.0 | 0.7 | 0.6 | 1.3 | 0.0 | 0.6 | 0.7 | 0.0 | 4.8 | 0.0 |
| Total % | | 99.9 | 100.0 | 99.9 | 100.1 | 100.0 | 100.0 | 99.9 | 100.0 | 100.0 | 100.1 |
| No. Cases | | (1348) | (153) | (161) | (156) | (147) | (159) | (145) | (151) | (146) | (130) |

Variation among coders rating severity on the Dependency Balance (I) at the beginning of Clinic treatment. CPC figures are in percent of sample coded by each clinical coder.

of treatment, and shows the distribution of scale values obtained by each coder for his random subsample of cases. From this table it may be noticed that a small proportion of the cases (only one %, overall) were not coded, primarily because, in the judgment of the coder, there was insufficient information in the case record. None of the coders used category 0 (ideal balance) for this scale at the beginning of treatment. The relatively extreme scale categories, 1 and 4, were used infrequently. Most of the code designations were in scale categories 2 and 3. In general, this pattern of coding (i.e., a small percentage of cases not coded at all, rare use of category 0, infrequent use of categories 1 and 4, and a concentration of codes in categories 2 and 3) was characteristic for all scales at the beginning of Clinic treatment.

**TABLE 2**

Dichotomized Severity Coding at the Beginning of CPC Treatment

Clinical Coder

|   | All | 1 | 2 | 3 | 4 | 5 | 6 | 7 | 8 | 9 |
|---|-----|-----|-----|-----|-----|-----|-----|-----|-----|-----|
| S Less severe |  |  |  |  |  |  |  |  |  |  |
| E (0,1,2) | 40.9 | 75.0 | 6.9 | 16.9 | 34.7 | 32.3 | 48.6 | 47.1 | 77.0 | 35.4 |
| V |  |  |  |  |  |  |  |  |  |  |
| E More severe |  |  |  |  |  |  |  |  |  |  |
| R (3,4) | 59.0 | 25.0 | 93.1 | 83.1 | 65.3 | 67.7 | 51.4 | 53.0 | 23.0 | 64.6 |
| I |  |  |  |  |  |  |  |  |  |  |
| T Total % | 99.9 | 100.0 | 100.0 | 100.0 | 100.0 | 100.0 | 100.0 | 100.1 | 100.0 | 100.0 |
| Y No. Cases | (1335) | (152) | (160) | (154) | (147) | (158) | (144) | (151) | (139) | (130) |

Variation among clinical coders rating severity on the Dependency Balance (I) at the *beginning* of Clinic treatment. CPC severity codes have been dichotomized into "less" and "more" severe dysfunction. Cases not coded have been eliminated. Figures are in percent of sample coded by each clinical coder.

To make the comparison of coders easier, a table was derived from the previous table by eliminating the few cases which were not coded at all and by dichotomizing the scale. The latter was done by combining the "less severe" categories 0, 1, and 2, and the "more severe" categories of dysfunction, 3 and 4. Table 2 shows this information, re-grouped according to the procedure just outlined. This table shows significant* variation among the nine clinical coders in the coding of Dependency Balance (1) even when treated as a two-point scale. Note for example the extreme range in coding cases as "less severe" from 6.9% for coder 2 to 77.0% for coder 8. Coders 1 and 8 coded significantly less severely than the average of all coders, while coders 2 and 3 coded significantly more severely.

*Throughout the remainder of this work, "significant" variations will refer to differences which are large enough to be classified as greater than expected chance variation by at least 1:20. These figures were derived by applying the data to the tables found in Lazerwitz, B., "A Comparison of Major United States Religious Groups," *Journal of the American Statistical Association,* September, 1961, p. 577.

The inference from this table must be that coding practices varied in the coding of this variable more than is to be expected from sampling. This conclusion might be similarly drawn from an inspection of the distributions of dichotomized scale categories obtained for each of the other eight ego strength scales at the beginning of treatment.

The coding of severity was more reliable at the end of Clinic treatment than at the beginning as can be seen from inspection of Table 3. The range of proportions coding scale 1 as "less severe" was from 36.6% to 88.9% at the end of treatment compared to a wider range of 6.9% to

**TABLE 3**

Dichotomized Severity Coding at the End of CPC Treatment

Clinical Coder

|  | All | 1 | 2 | 3 | 4 | 5 | 6 | 7 | 8 | 9 |
|---|---|---|---|---|---|---|---|---|---|---|
| S Less severe E V (0,1,2) | 59.1 | 68.6 | 49.4 | 36.6 | 54.6 | 62.9 | 59.0 | 67.3 | 88.9 | 52.3 |
| E More severe R (3,4) | 40.9 | 31.4 | 50.6 | 63.4 | 45.5 | 37.1 | 41.0 | 32.7 | 11.1 | 47.7 |
| I T Total % | 100.0 | 100.0 | 100.0 | 100.0 | 100.1 | 100.0 | 100.0 | 100.0 | 100.0 | 100.0 |
| Y No. Cases | (1298) | (153) | (158) | (153) | (143) | (159) | (144) | (150) | (108) | (130) |

Variation among coders in coding severity on the Dependency Balance (I) at the *end* of Clinic treatment. Severity codes have been dichotomized into "less" and "more" severe dysfunction. Cases not coded have been eliminated. Figures are in percent of sample coded by each clinical coder.

77% at the beginning of treatment. Table 3 indicates that only coder 8 coded significantly less severely than the average of all coders combined. The remaining eight coders showed only a chance variation from the average. Again, as was the case in the coding at the beginning of treatment, the pattern of coding for ego strength scale 1 was similar to the pattern that was obtained for the remaining eight ego strength scales.

To facilitate the reliability analysis of polarity coding, these ratings were regrouped into a two point scale by combining active (+) and variable, but active dominant (+ −) into one category designated as *predominantly active;* and combining passive (−) and variable but passive dominant (− +) into another category designated as *predominantly passive.*

The findings derived from the group reliability study may be summarized as follows:

1. Severity was coded within a wide range of variation (low reliability) at the beginning of treatment. At the end of treatment coding of severity was significantly more reliable, i.e. there was significantly less variation among coders. Polarity was recorded with more reliability than severity when both dimensions were considered as a dichotomized two-point scale. The reliability of polarity coding decreased at the end of treatment.

2. Coders whose recordings varied significantly from the average of all other coders ("extreme coders") were equally divided among those who coded significantly less severely or more severely for severity, and predominantly active or predominantly passive for polarity. If an individual coder demonstrated a tendency to code in an extreme direction on either dimension of polarity or severity, he tended to show this same variation with remarkable consistency on all balances coded at the beginning as well as at the end of Clinic treatment.

## INDIVIDUAL RELIABILITY

Reliability may also be examined from another point of view. How well do different coders agree when coding Adaptive Balances independently from the same case record?

Table 4 shows how coder 1 compared with all other coders in the recording of severity on the dependency scale at the beginning of treatment. In 46.4% of the cases coder 1 agreed with all other coders by recording the same severity (sum of all underlined figures along the diagonal on Table 4). About half the time (51.1%) coder 1 coded less

**TABLE 4**

Individual Reliability of Severity Coding—
Beginning of CPC Treatment

|  | Severity | All Other Clinical Coders | | | | | |
|---|---|---|---|---|---|---|---|
|  |  | 0 | 1 | 2 | 3 | 4 | Not Coded |
|  | 0 | 0.0 | 0.0 | 0.0 | 0.0 | 0.0 | 0.0 |
|  | 1 | 0.0 | 0.0 | 0.0 | 0.0 | 0.0 | 0.0 |
| Coder | 2 | 0.0 | 0.0 | 24.4 | 46.3 | 2.4 | 2.4 |
| # 1 | 3 | 0.0 | 0.0 | 0.0 | 22.0 | 2.4 | 0.0 |
|  | 4 | 0.0 | 0.0 | 0.0 | 0.0 | 0.0 | 0.0 |
|  | Not Coded | 0.0 | 0.0 | 0.0 | 0.0 | 0.0 | 0.0 |

Number of cases coded = 41

Comparison of Coder # 1 with all other clinical coders recording severity independently on the Dependency Balance (I) at the beginning of Clinic treatment from identical case records. Figures are expressed in percent of sample coded.

severely. In no instance was coder 1 more severe than others in the coding of this variable. Thus, coder 1 was found to be an "extreme coder" by the individual as well as the group reliability methods. He codes significantly less severely than all other coders regardless of whether he was coding the same case record or a different random sample of records.

The results of the individual reliability study confirm the findings obtained by the group reliability method. Each coder reflects his own "style" in interpreting the scales. That is, when compared to other coders by either method, if he codes more or less severely on one scale he tends to code more or less severely on all scales.

## RELIABILITY OF CODING CHANGE

A primary aim of the Columbia Psychoanalytic Records Project is the study of change in the patients' adaptation and the development of appropriate techniques to measure this change.

The authors anticipated that there would be more agreement among coders on the coding of change than on the coding of the variable itself. A coder who codes significantly less severely might rate a particular record severity 2 at both the beginning and end of treatment. Another coder who records more severely might rate the same record severity 3 at both the beginning and end of treatment. Although these two coders do not agree on the rating of severity in this case, they do agree that no change has taken place.

Table 5 shows the agreement among coders as to severity change on the Dependency Balance (1). The designation, "+2" indicates change of two severity categories in the direction of greater health, "+1" a change of one category in the same direction, "−2" indicates a change of two severity categories in the less healthy direction, etc. This technique of comparison is used to facilitate the treatment of the data, but it does introduce some distortion, methodologically and clinically. For example, a change from severity 4 to severity 3 is quite different clinically from a change from severity 2 to severity 1. Nevertheless, they are both designated +1 by this technique. Table 5 indicates that 49.5% of the pairs of coders agreed there was no change. 11.3% of the pairs agreed there was some improvement, but none of the pairs of coders agreed that any cases had gotten worse. Thus 58.0% of the pairs were in exact agreement as to change or lack of change. It is important to note that in only 2.1% did one coder see improvement and another see change

**TABLE 5**

Individual Reliability Coding Severity Change

Coder "B"

| Severity Change | +2 | +1 | 0 | −1 | −2 | Not Coded |
|---|---|---|---|---|---|---|
| +2 | 0.0 | 1.1 | 1.1 | 0.0 | 1.1 | 0.0 |
| +1 | 2.2 | 8.0 | 11.7 | 0.5 | 0.0 | 0.0 |
| Coder "A"  0 | 1.6 | 13.8 | 49.5 | 2.7 | 0.0 | 1.1 |
| −1 | 0.0 | 0.5 | 3.7 | 0.0 | 0.0 | 0.0 |
| −2 | 0.0 | 0.0 | 0.0 | 0.0 | 0.0 | 0.0 |
| Not Coded | 0.0 | 0.0 | 1.1 | 0.5 | 0.0 | 0.5 |

Number of cases coded = 188

Amount of severity change compared between 188 pairs of coders recording identical case records. The Depedency Balance (I) is illustrated here. "+" indicates change in the direction of greater health; "−" indicates change in the direction of greater dysfunction. Figures are expressed in percent of the total number of cases coded.

for the worse in the same case. Finally, disregarding the amount of improvement seen, a total of 61.3% of the pairs agreed as to the presence or absence of improvement.

As was anticipated, the greatest agreement among coders is found when comparing assessment of change. This is only slightly greater, however, than the percentage of agreement on the coding of severity either at the beginning or at the end of treatment. Most of the disagreement arises when one coder sees change and the other coder does not. Disagreement about the *direction* of change is extremely rare.

## FACTORS RELATED TO RELIABILITY OF CODING

Before the coding procedures were undertaken a pilot study was conducted to determine what information might consistently be found in Clinic records. This study indicated that the earliest Clinic records were clearly less thorough and less systematically organized than later ones. The authors assumed that a more reliable rating could be made from a more complete case record. To test this hypothesis, all cases were divided into two approximately equal groups, those which had applied to the Clinic in the earlier years (1945–1952) and those which had applied in the more recent years (1953–1962). The reliability with which each group was coded was then compared. From this evidence it cannot be said that the more recent cases were recorded in such a way as to increase the reliability with which ego strength scales were coded from Clinic records.

A rating which enabled the coders to express the confidence they felt in recording ego strength on each case was not included in the original code schedules. At an early meeting, however, several of the participating psychoanalysts expressed the concern that they were not confident of their ratings of ego strength from certain records. This was generally attributed to a lack of pertinent information which made them feel uneasy in forming the judgments necessary for an evaluation of various ego strength variables. In such instances, the coders considered their ratings to be estimations rather than sound assessments of the variable to be coded.

A simple scale was devised to enable the coder to express the degree of confidence with which he evaluated ego strength for each written record. Based on this scale, when coders are more confident of their judgment coding is significantly more reliable than when they are less confident. There is no significant difference in reliability between over-all ratings and those in which the coder expressed confidence. When coders are more confident of their judgment in recording ego strength, the influence of coder style is still evident and "extreme coders" may be identified.

## SUMMARY OF RELIABILITY STUDY

The greatest variation among coders was found on the rating of severity of dysfunction at the beginning of treatment. Change in severity from the beginning to the end of Clinic treatment was recorded with somewhat greater reliability. Each coder demonstrated a characteristic and consistent style in the assessment of ego strength. It is therefore possible to determine the degree of distortion, if any, in the rating of a particular ego strength variable which can be attributed to an individual coder.

## EGO STRENGTH SCALES APPLIED TO THE ENTIRE CLINIC POPULATION

Many observations indicate the striking similarity with which various balances were coded. These similarities may be observed when looking at the distribution of severity codings for the entire patient population.

Figure 1 is a bar graph indicating the distribution of severity codings on each of the nine adaptive balances. At the beginning of Clinic treatment

## BEGINNING OF CPC TREATMENT

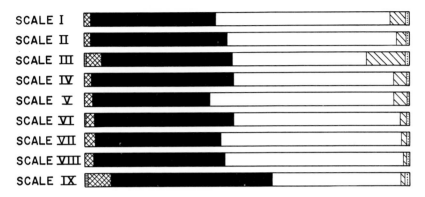

## END OF CPC TREATMENT

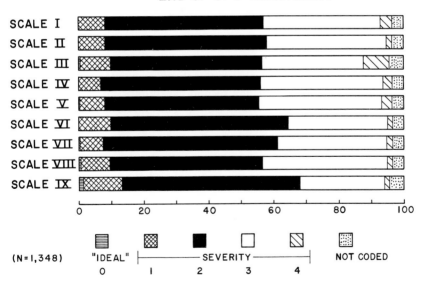

*Figure 1.* Percentage distribution of severity ratings for each of the nine adaptive balance scales at the beginning and end of CPC treatment for the total patient population.

there is a regular pattern in the distribution of severity coding, a pattern which repeats from one balance to another. Each balance is essentially a two point scale with severity "2" or severity "3" coded in the vast majority of cases. Almost no cases are coded "0," not a surprising finding at the beginning of treatment since this balance is defined as an "ideal" reference point from which the patient is expected to more or less diverge. However, the scarcity of "1" and "4" designations reduces the original scale of 5 points to a two-point scale as far as most patient records are concerned. The proportion of cases coded "less severe" falls into a narrow range of 39.0% to 46.0% on all balances.

There are two exceptions to this general pattern of the two-point scale at the beginning of Clinic treatment and the uniformity of the more/less severe codings. The first difference is to be found in the Sexual Balance (III). This balance has more cases coded severity "4" than any other balance. The reason for this is not difficult to discover. By far the greater number are coded polarity minus (inhibited), a choice which is dictated by the way the scale is constructed in defining the interval between "3 minus" and "4 minus." The scale includes elements of pleasure and performance, and by its construction forces a severe choice among passive patients. By contrast, category "4 plus" in the same balance indicates a much more severe type of sexual pathology than "4 minus" and is rarely used.

The Social Balance (IX) is characteristically scored less severely than other balances and represents the second exception. This may reflect some characteristics of the scale itself. During our regular meetings the nine collaborating psychoanalysts remarked about the many different, and often divergent, components of adaptation which went into the description of the Social Balance. They also remarked on the relative paucity of information in the histories at the beginning of treatment in the area of social relationships, friendships, group activities, etc. Presumably the histories often do not emphasize sufficiently the severity of disturbance in the social area.

Figure 1 also indicates the distribution of severity codes at the end of Clinic treatment. Once again, the same striking similarity can be seen from one balance to another. Because of the increase in frequency of severity "1" coding at the end of treatment, the scales have been expanded to three point scales. The net change in severity coding from beginning to end of treatment is comparable from one balance to another.

## TABLE 6

Polarity Coding at the Beginning of Clinic Treatment

| Adaptive Balance | Predominantly Active (+) | (±) | Predominantly Passive (∓) | (−) | Ideal Balance (0) | Not Coded |
|---|---|---|---|---|---|---|
| I | 12.5 | 15.5 | 26.6 | 44.7 | 0.0 | 1.0 |
| II | 14.1 | 15.5 | 23.3 | 46.1 | 0.1 | 1.0 |
| III | 11.3 | 10.5 | 19.0 | 57.1 | 0.4 | 1.5 |
| IV | 11.7 | 14.7 | 23.0 | 49.2 | 0.0 | 1.0 |
| V | 12.6 | 14.3 | 24.1 | 47.9 | 0.0 | 0.9 |
| VI | 13.0 | 13.3 | 30.2 | 42.5 | 0.1 | 0.9 |
| VII | 12.6 | 12.6 | 25.9 | 47.9 | 0.0 | 1.0 |
| VIII | 9.9 | 13.0 | 28.2 | 47.9 | 0.1 | 0.9 |
| IX | 14.4 | 10.9 | 20.3 | 52.1 | 0.8 | 1.4 |

Distribution of polarity is shown at the *beginning* of CPC treatment. "Predominantly Active" refers to the combination of + and ± categories. "Predominantly Passive" refers to the combination of ∓ and − categories. Figures given represent percent of the total patient population (1,348).

The distribution of polarity codes for the entire patient population at the beginning of treatment (Table 6) once again shows this similarity among balances. When polarity codes are dichotomized into predominantly active and predominantly passive, each balance is coded predominantly passive within a narrow range (69.4%–76.1%). Polarity codes (+) and (+−) are more or less equally distributed but (−) is coded more

## TABLE 7

Polarity Coding at the End of Clinic Treatment

| Adaptive Balance | Predominantly Active (+) | (±) | Predominantly Passive (∓) | (−) | Ideal Balance | Not Coded |
|---|---|---|---|---|---|---|
| I | 18.9 | 19.3 | 25.2 | 33.1 | 0.0 | 3.7 |
| II | 17.4 | 18.7 | 22.2 | 37.9 | 0.1 | 3.7 |
| III | 13.0 | 11.4 | 19.4 | 51.5 | 0.6 | 4.5 |
| IV | 14.0 | 16.1 | 22.6 | 43.3 | 0.2 | 3.8 |
| V | 14.9 | 17.6 | 25.8 | 37.9 | 0.1 | 3.6 |
| VI | 16.2 | 18.9 | 26.9 | 34.3 | 0.0 | 3.6 |
| VII | 14.8 | 15.5 | 26.5 | 39.2 | 0.1 | 3.8 |
| VIII | 12.4 | 15.9 | 26.9 | 40.8 | 0.3 | 3.6 |
| IX | 16.0 | 12.0 | 20.3 | 46.5 | 0.9 | 4.5 |

Distribution of polarity codes is shown at the *end* of CPC treatment. "Predominantly Active" refers to the combination of (+) and (±) categories. "Predominantly Passive" refers to the combination of (∓) and (−) categories. Figures given represent percent of the total patient population (N = 1,348).

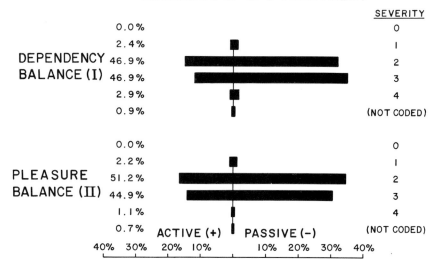

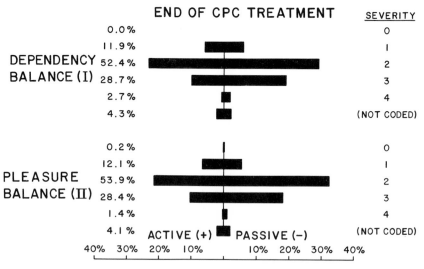

*Figure 2.* Shifts in polarity and severity ratings from the beginning to the end of CPC treatment are shown for two adaptive balances: Dependency (I) and Pleasure (II). Only psychoanalytic patients are represented.

than twice as often as $(-+)$. Table 7 shows the percentage distribution of polarity codes at the *end* of Clinic treatment. Once again all balances show a net shift of similar magnitude. There are fewer polarity $(-)$ codes, about the same percentage of $(-+)$ codes but a small net shift into the two active polarities. Only on the Sex Balance (III) is there little net shift in the direction of greater activity.

The similarities that have been mentioned persist even when the two variables of severity and polarity are chartered together. Figure 2 compares the net shift in polarity and severity from the beginning to the end of Clinic treatment for two balances, Dependency (I) and Pleasure (II). Severity is indicated by the numbers 0–4 at the side of the figure. Polarity in a "predominantly passive" (minus) direction is indicated by the length of the bar to the right of the midline. Polarity in a "predominantly active" direction is indicated by the length of the bar to the left of the midline. It should be noted that only psychoanalytic patients are shown.

This complex figure compares the net shift of two variables (polarity and severity) taken together. On both balances shifts are very similar in their magnitude and direction. There is a net shift toward less severe categories and toward more active polarities at the end of treatment. The balances demonstrated are representative of the other seven scales as well.

**TABLE 8**

Interrelation of Severity Coding Between Two Balances

Dependency Balance (I)
N = 1348

|  | Severity | 0 | 1 | 2 | 3 | 4 | Not coded |
|---|---|---|---|---|---|---|---|
|  | 0 | 0.0 | 0.0 | 0.0 | 0.0 | 0.0 | 0.0 |
|  | 1 | 0.0 | 0.9 | 0.1 | 1.6 | 0.0 | 0.0 |
| Defense | 2 | 0.0 | 1.0 | 27.4 | 7.5 | 0.1 | 0.1 |
| Balance (V) | 3 | 0.0 | 0.0 | 9.6 | 43.8 | 3.1 | 0.0 |
|  | 4 | 0.0 | 0.0 | 0.1 | 2.4 | 1.6 | 0.0 |
|  | Not Coded | 0.0 | 0.0 | 0.0 | 0.0 | 0.0 | 0.9 |

Coded in the same category    74.6%
Coded within one scale point    23.7%
                                                98.3%

Interrelation (Gamma = .904) between the coding of severity on the Defense Balance (V) and the Dependency Balance (I) at the beginning of Clinic treatment. Figures are expressed in percent of sample coded.

Each of the nine adaptive balances is regarded as a measure of a different facet of "ego strength." Each is conceptualized differently and the descriptions of categories of adaptive dysfunction are quite distinct from one scale to another. Yet, when applied to a large number of written records the distribution of severity ratings was fairly similar for each adaptive balance. All scales tend to change together and in the same direction. Moreover, the pattern of each coder's ratings was remarkably consistent from scale to scale (suggesting a possible halo effect) even though coders varied significantly in their style of assessing ego strength. Thus, the scales all appear to measure a common factor ("ego strength" or general clinical adaptation) and each balance appears to represent a different perspective of the same factor. To further clarify this issue the interrelation among the nine ego strength scales was examined.

A uniformly high degree of association between pairs of scales was found. This is illustrated in Table 8 where the high degree of association (gamma = .904)* between the Dependency Balance (I) and the Defense Balance (V) is clearly shown. At the beginning of treatment 3/4 of the cases were recorded in the same severity category on both scales. 98.3% of all records were coded in the same category or within one category on the scale. One of the lowest degrees of association (gamma = .464) was found between the Dependency (I) and the Sex (III) Balance. Even between this pair of scales 50.8% were coded alike and 93.8% were coded in the same category or within one category point on the scale.

This data indicates a greater agreement among scales than among coders. The uniformly high degree of association between pairs of scales suggests that each scale is primarily measuring a factor common to all scales. Residual factors which are specific to each balance have a secondary influence upon the overall distribution of ratings.

It has already been established that the adaptive balances, when applied to Clinic records, fall essentially into a two-point scale. Severity "2" or severity "3" is coded in the vast majority of cases. Severity "1" was used often enough at the end of Clinic treatment to turn the balances into three-point scales. Much information on change can be extracted from such figures, as will be shown later, but it is our clinical impression

*Gamma is a statistical measure of association between two variables. For a fuller discussion, see Goodman, Leo A. and Kruskal, William H., "Measures of Association for Cross-classification," *Journal of American Statistical Association,* Vol. 49 (1954), pp. 732–2764, and Vol. 54 (1959), pp. 123–163.

that better differentiation of categories is desirable in the ranges which are used most often, i.e., severity 2 and 3. Perhaps the half-point designations currently employed by the ego strength group permits this, but such designations were not in use at the time this study was organized. Designations of polarity add an element of flexibility to the coding, but they also fall into fairly fixed patterns, as will be mentioned, and so contribute less to specificity than might be anticipated.

One practical disappointment which results from this limitation of the coding "vocabulary" is that the records study has not turned up any diagnostic or otherwise characteristic adaptive balance profiles at the beginning of treatment. The possibility of developing such profiles was an original objective of the ego strength research, and it remains an important consideration in the work of that group. Individual differences similar to those reproduced by Karush et al.,[4] can be observed among the profiles derived from our coding of charts at the beginning of treatment. Most profiles fall into a narrow range of patterns, however, because of the limitations imposed by the two-point severity scale at the beginning of treatment, and the tendency of some coders to employ a uniform designation of polarity or severity from one balance to another. The practical implication of this fact is that one cannot take the ego strength codings of any single Clinic case record and draw important diagnostic or prognostic conclusions from this datum alone.

When applied to a large and heterogeneous population, ego strength scales are impressive for their similarities. As soon as one goes beyond the application of adaptive balances to the gross population and compares groups of case records which have been selected according to various discrete clinical or diagnostic criteria, ego strength scales begin to show interesting and provocative differences. Some of these findings will be systematically presented below, but it should be stated that the more precisely one can define the clinical groups of patients, the greater the chance of uncovering differences in the ego strength scales among these groups. Thus the ego strength scales alone do not bring out the most pertinent information. When they are cross-tabulated with other information, they prove to be of great value in describing differences in severity of adaptive failure and the degree of change in various areas of adaptation.

In the sections which follow, patients will be grouped according to:

A)   Type of treatment (Reconstructive and "Other")

B) Length of time in Columbia Psychoanalytic Clinic treatment
C) Diagnostic groups (Psychoneurotic, Neurotic Personality, and Psychotic or Psychotic Personality)
D) Specific diagnostic categories (Anxiety Neurotic, Obsessional Neurotic, Compulsive Personality)
E) Conditions under which Columbia Psychoanalytic treatment ended

Sub-groups in each category will be compared according to the profile of severity on each of the nine balances at the beginning of treatment as well as change in the scales from beginning to end of Columbia Psychoanalytic Clinic treatment.

## EGO STRENGTH SCALES AND TYPE OF TREATMENT

The charts studied came from three services which offered two distinct kinds of treatment. Psychoanalysis was the modality employed on the Reconstructive Service, and analytically oriented psychotherapy was offered on both the Reparative and Medical Services. On these latter services the difference lay in the choice of patients. Those with primary complaints of a psychosomatic nature were usually assigned to the Medical Service, while the Reparative Service did not specialize in its selection of patients for psychotherapy. Frequency of interviews among patients in psychotherapy was most often two per week, while analytic patients were characteristically seen four times a week.

Information is available separately on the records of patients treated in each of the three services, but in this report patients treated in psychoanalysis will be compared to the combined group of reparative and psychosomatic patients, here referred to as "Other" Services or "Other" treatment.

The first general finding in comparing the two groups at the beginning of treatment is that the patients who received "Other" treatment were rated higher (less healthy) on the severity scales than the patients who were treated in psychoanalysis. Figure 3 represents the distribution of severity ratings at the beginning and end of Columbia Psychoanalytic Clinic treatment for both Reconstructive and "Other" Services. Only three of the nine balances are shown. The Dependency Balance (I) is representative of the majority of the balances (which include Pleasure (II), Affect (IV), Defense (V), Pathology (VIII), and Social (IX)) and illustrates the finding that Reconstructive patients are coded significantly less severely ("healthier") at the beginning of treatment than are patients on the "Other" Services. In fact, one might make the generalization that the analytic

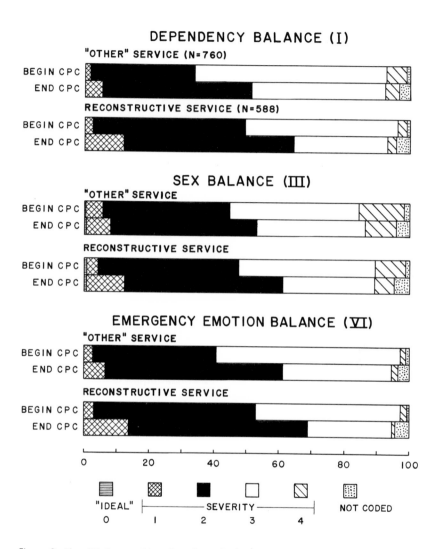

*Figure 3.* The shift in severity ratings from the beginning to the end of CPC treatment is shown for patients in psychoanalysis and psychotherapy. Three adaptive balances are represented: Dependency (I), Sex (III), and Emergency Emotions (VI).

patient begins treatment at a level of severity approximately the same as the level at which the "Other" patients end their Clinic treatment.

Figure 3 also illustrates the Emergency Emotion Balance (VI), which is similar to the Guilt Balance (VII). Again the patients in analysis are coded significantly less severely at the beginning of treatment. However, in the case of the manifest pathological emotions of fear, rage, and guilt as measured by these balances (VI and VII), the "Other" patients are coded significantly less severely at the end of their Clinic treatment than are the analytic patients at the beginning of analysis.

A noteworthy exception to the above generalizations is the Sex Balance (III). In Figure 3, analytic and non-analytic patients show no significant differences in the dichotomized (more/less severe) severity coding at the beginning of Columbia Psychoanalytic Clinic treatment. There are, however, significantly more "4 minus" codes among the patients on the "Other" Services. The fact that the Sex Balance (III) behaves in this exceptional manner may relate to the way in which patients are selected for analysis. This is not the place to review the criteria for selecting patients on the various services, but one of the most frequent considerations in assigning patients to the Reparative (included in "Other") Service arises when the analysts on the Admissions Service think there is some doubt about the patient's suitability for analysis. Our data indicated that 22.8% of the Clinic population for whom such information is available was assigned to the Reparative Service because of doubts about the patient's suitability for analysis. From the data concerning the Sex Balance (III) already referred to in this section, it is clear that the degree of severity of disturbance in the area of sexual performance is *not* of primary importance in determining the patients' suitability for analysis.

A comparison of polarity codings for Reconstructive and "Other" patients at the beginning of treatment indicates that analytic patients were significantly more aggressive on the Pleasure (II), Sex (III), Affect (IV), and Social (IX) Balances. Note that these include measurements of welfare emotions and interpersonal relations. On balances which measure emergency emotions, pathology and defenses, the two patient populations did not differ significantly on the active-passive (aggressive-inhibited) axis. At the end of treatment, both populations changed in the direction of becoming more active. Only in the Sex (III) and Social (IX) Balances did the "Other" patients remain significantly more passive than analytic patients.

There is a significant change toward lesser severity on both services in all balances from the beginning to the end of Columbia Psychoanalytic Clinic treatment, as indicated in Table 9. Reconstructive patients show somewhat greater net improvement on all balances when compared with the "Other" service. The magnitude of this difference between analytic and "Other" patients varies depending upon the particular balance studied. For example, reconstructive patients show improvement on the Dependency Balance (I) in 30.8% of all cases and get worse (are coded more severely at the end of the treatment) in 5.0%. This represents a net improvement of 25.8%. The same figures for "Other" patients are 27.2% improvement, 4.9% worse, and a net improvement of 22.3%. There is thus no significant difference in the net improvement between the Reconstructive and "Other" patients as measured by the Dependency Balance (I).

**TABLE 9**

Change in Severity from Beginning to End of Clinic Treatment

| Adaptive Balance | Reconstructive Service N = 564 | | | | "Other" Service N = 732 | | | |
|---|---|---|---|---|---|---|---|---|
| | Improved | No Change | Worse | Net Change | Improved | No Change | Worse | Net Change |
| Dependency (I) | 30.8 | 64.2 | 5.0 | +25.8 | 27.2 | 67.8 | 4.9 | +22.3 |
| Pleasure (II) | 30.2 | 63.8 | 6.0 | +24.2 | 25.4 | 70.6 | 4.0 | +21.4 |
| Sex (III) | 30.2 | 63.9 | 5.9 | +24.3 | 18.8 | 76.6 | 4.6 | +14.2 |
| Affect (IV) | 24.1 | 70.1 | 5.8 | +18.3 | 22.5 | 71.6 | 5.9 | +16.6 |
| Defense (V) | 33.2 | 61.5 | 5.3 | +27.9 | 26.0 | 69.5 | 4.6 | +21.4 |
| Emergency Emotions (VI) | 32.7 | 62.8 | 4.5 | +28.2 | 30.4 | 64.4 | 5.0 | +25.4 |
| Guilt (VII) | 30.2 | 64.9 | 4.9 | +25.3 | 27.2 | 68.3 | 4.5 | +22.7 |
| Pathology (VIII) | 30.2 | 65.7 | 4.1 | +26.1 | 22.1 | 72.3 | 5.6 | +16.5 |
| Social (IX) | 25.9 | 68.8 | 5.3 | +20.6 | 21.3 | 73.8 | 4.8 | +16.5 |

Change in severity on each balance from beginning to end of CPC treatment has been calculated for patients on Reconstructive (psychoanalytic) and "Other" (psychotherapeutic) Services. Net change is the difference between percent rated improved and percent rated worse. All figures are in percent.

This picture is quite different, however, when the Pathology Balance (VIII) is considered. Reconstructive patients show a net improvement of 30.2% while "Other" patients rated a net improvement of only 22.1%, a difference that is statistically significant in a patient population of this size. The Defense Balance (V) behaves similarly in this regard.

These differences will be elaborated in greater detail in subsequent sections. One consideration, however, must be explored at this time. Can this difference in net improvement between Reconstructive and "Other" patients be explained on the basis of the analytic patient's greater time in treatment?

## TIME IN CLINIC TREATMENT AND ADAPTIVE BALANCES

Treatment on the "Other" Services is conducted for an average of approximately 9 months, although a sizable number of patients have been treated for two years or even longer. The entire span of the patients' treatment usually takes place in the Columbia Psychoanalytic Clinic. Less than 20.0% of the patients were seen privately by the same therapist after Columbia Psychoanalytic Clinic treatment ended, and of these a large number were seen in consultation only. It may be assumed, then, that the changes which took place over the total span of the patient's treatment experience are described in the Clinic record and so coded on the ego strength scales.

The situation is quite different for the Reconstructive patients. Relatively few complete their analyses while at the Clinic and about 50% continued treatment privately with the same therapist after the therapist completed his academic requirements and graduated from the Clinic. Only that treatment which takes place while the therapist is a candidate at the Columbia Psychoanalytic Clinic is included in the Clinic record. The average time *in* the Clinic for analytic patients is $1\frac{1}{2}$ years while the *average* length of an analysis is $2\frac{1}{2}$ years, as determined from our follow-up questionnaires.* Thus, the changes noted on the ego strength scales for patients on the Reconstructive Services as recorded in the Clinic records refer to $1\frac{1}{2}$ years of a treatment which spans an average of $2\frac{1}{2}$ years.

The patient population for each service has been grouped according to the length of time in Columbia Psychoanalytic Clinic treatment. For each group, the percentage of those who improved, those who got worse,

*These average figures, it must be remembered, include those patients who leave treatment early or are dropped from analysis. They do not represent the average length of time for an analysis which is continued to completion.

and the net change has been calculated. Figure 4 shows the data on change in severity for the Pathology Balance (VIII), illustrated here because it is representative of the pattern of change measured in the other balances. The figure does *not* represent a serial view of change within the same patients at different points in time. The graph is a representation of different groups of patients, each group having had a particular distribution of time in Clinic treatment. Any group may contain patients whose treatment was completed to a maximum benefit or terminated for a variety of reasons, including being dropped from treatment by their therapist, feeling satisfied or dissatisfied with the treatment received, and leaving against the therapist's advice. (See section on conditions at end of treatment.)

PATHOLOGY BALANCE (VIII)—ALL PATIENTS

CHANGE IN SEVERITY

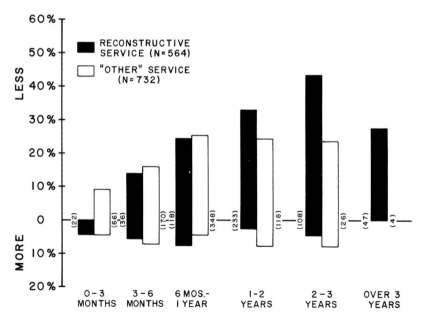

TIME IN CPC TREATMENT

Figure 4. Change in severity rating on the Pathology Balance (VIII) from the beginning to the end of CPC treatment is shown for groups with varying times in treatment. Patients in psychoanalysis and psychotherapy are compared.

The length of time patients are in treatment bears a direct relationship, within certain limits, to the improvement which occurs from the beginning of treatment to the end. This is true on both the Reconstructive and "Other" Services, although there are differences in the time pattern as will be seen below. Patients whose adaptation worsens during treatment constitute a small and fairly constant segment of the population in each time period and in both types of treatment.

There is a steeply rising rate of improvement with time in both types of treatment. The percentage of improved patients in "Other" treatment reaches a maximum in the 6 months to 1 year category, and then levels out at a plateau or falls off. Patients treated in analysis, however, continue to show a larger segment improving until the 2–3 years of treatment category, at least. The group of patients in analysis at the Clinic 3 years or longer shows a variable response, depending on the particular balance observed.

As has been indicated above, the analytic patients show a significantly greater percentage of improvement than "Other" patients as measured by the Pathology Balance (net change is +26.1% and +16.5% respectively). Is the greater improvement among Reconstructive patients accounted for by their longer time in treatment? The data showing change on the Pathology Balance (VIII) is restated below by time in treatment:

|  | Reconstructive | | | |
|  | Improvement | No Change | Worse | Net Change |
|---|---|---|---|---|
| Under 1 year (N = 176) | 18.7% | 74.5% | 6.8% | +11.9% |
| 1–2 years (N = 233) | 33.0% | 64.4% | 2.6% | +30.4% |
| Over 2 years (N = 155) | 38.7% | 58.0% | 3.2% | +35.5% |
| Total = 564 | 30.2% | 65.7% | 4.1% | +26.1% |

|  | "Other" | | | |
|  | Improvement | No Change | Worse | Net Change |
|---|---|---|---|---|
| Under 1 year (N = 585) | 21.2% | 73.7% | 5.1% | +16.1% |
| 1–2 years (N = 118) | 24.5% | 67.7% | 7.7% | +16.8% |
| Over 2 years (N = 30) | 30.0% | 63.3% | 6.7% | +23.3% |
| Total = 733 | 22.1% | 72.3% | 5.6% | +16.5% |

When analytic patients who were in treatment up to one year are compared with "Other" patients who were in treatment the same length of time, "Other" patients show a larger net improvement. These findings are reversed in the next two time periods (1–2 years, over 2 years) where analytic patients show much more net improvement. This data indicates that factors other than time must be involved.

Similar data is presented below describing change on the Dependency Balance (I) by time in treatment:

Reconstructive

|  | Improvement | No Change | Worse | Net Change |
|---|---|---|---|---|
| Under 1 year (N = 176) | 15.3% | 76.8% | 7.9% | + 7.4% |
| 1–2 years (N = 232) | 35.7% | 62.0% | 2.2% | +33.5% |
| Over 2 years (N = 154) | 40.9% | 53.2% | 5.8% | +35.1% |
| (Total = 562) | 30.8% | 64.2% | 5.0% | +25.8% |

"Other"

|  | Improvement | No Change | Worse | Net Change |
|---|---|---|---|---|
| Under 1 year (N = 584) | 25.2% | 70.3% | 4.5% | +20.7% |
| 1–2 years (N = 118) | 36.4% | 58.4% | 5.1% | +31.3% |
| Over 2 years (N = 30) | 30.0% | 56.7% | 13.3% | +16.7% |
| (Total = 732) | 27.2% | 67.8% | 4.9% | +22.3% |

The general finding which deserves to be emphasized is that "Other" patients in treatment under 1 year show greater net improvement on all balances compared to patients in analysis the same length of time. For those in treatment over 2 years patients in analysis show significantly greater net improvement on all scales. Results for the 1–2 year period vary depending on the balance considered. On most balances (e.g., the Dependency Balance demonstrated here) both groups show comparable change. Analytic patients show significantly greater net improvement on the Sex (III), Defense (V) and Pathology (VIII) balances for the intermediate 1–2 year period.

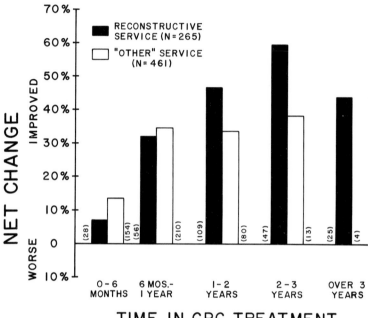

## PATHOLOGY BALANCE (VIII) - SEVERITY 3

TIME IN CPC TREATMENT

Figure 5. Net change in severity rating for patients coded severity 3 on the Pathology Balance (VIII) at the beginning of treatment is shown for groups with varying times in treatment. Patients in psychoanalysis and psychotherapy are compared. Net change represents the difference between the patients rated improved and those rated worse from the beginning to the end of CPC treatment.

A much more accurate and detailed view of change with time in treatment can be obtained by comparing patients whose adaptive dysfunction was identical at the beginning of treatment. Figure 5 shows a comparison of net change by time in Columbia Psychoanalytic Clinic treatment of patients on the Reconstructive and "Other" Services who were coded severity 3 on the Pathology Balance (VIII) at the beginning of treatment. Figure 6 shows the same data for patients coded severity 2 at the beginning of treatment. It is readily apparent that both groups (severity 3 and 2) respond differently to treatment.

Figure 5 indicates that for analytic patients who were coded severity 3 at the beginning of treatment there is a steady, gradually rising rate

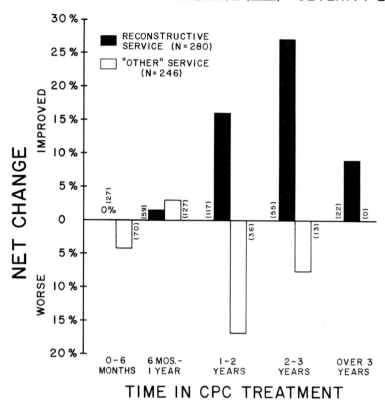

Figure 6. Net change in severity rating for patients coded severity 2 on the Pathology Balance (VIII) at the beginning of treatment is shown for groups with varying times in treatment. Patients in psychoanalysis and psychotherapy are compared. Net change represents the difference between the patients rated improved and those rated worse from the beginning to the end of CPC treatment.

of improvement (net change in the direction of less severe) with time through the 2–3 years period of treatment. This is true of all balances studied. This rate of improvement drops off slightly on this balance beyond 3 years, but on other balances such as Defense (V) and Dependency (I) improvement continues among the patients in treatment more than 3 years.

The situation with "Other" patients is generally quite different. Up to one year in treatment, "Other" patients show more improvement than analytic patients but beyond one year the rate of improvement does not seem to increase further with longer time in treatment. In other words, up to one year of treatment, psychoanalytically oriented psychotherapy seems to effect more rapid and greater change, but beyond one year the percentage of patients responding favorably does not increase. The effects of psychoanalysis are slower for the patients chosen. However, response to analysis is reflected by the increasing proportion of patients who show improvement with greater time in treatment.

Figure 6 shows the net change with time of those patients who were coded severity 2 (healthier than the patients just presented) at the beginning of treatment on the analytic and "Other" Services. There is very little net change through the first year of treatment on either service. Starting with the 1-2 year period analytic patients show steadily increasing improvement up to the 2-3 year period. This drops off again beyond three years. For the "Other" Service, however, the net change is in the direction of getting worse. This clearly indicates that for the healthier patient (coded severity 2) at the beginning of treatment, analysis is accompanied by significant improvement after a period of time. Analytically oriented psychotherapy not only fails to improve these patients, but, in a significant number, with time they show a net change in the direction of more severe pathology. The Pathology Balance (VIII) is used here to illustrate this point. The same picture with some minor variations is found on all balances. In fact, on the Defense Balance (V), "Other" patients show a net change in the negative direction for all time periods.

Thus, the difference between analytic and non-analytic patients' improvement in pathology is not accounted for only on the basis of time in treatment, but is a consequence of the nature of the therapeutic experience itself, or the type of patient selected. Some speculations on this point are stimulated by similar data derived from the Dependency Balance (I). The change over time for patients coded severity 3 on the Dependency Balance (I) at the beginning of treatment is presented in Figure 7. "Other" patients improve more rapidly up to a year and then the percentage of improvement reaches a plateau. Further time in treatment does not yield a greater increment of improved patients. On the analytic service there is a gradually increasing percentage of improvement, with the largest increment in the 1-2 year period. It is particularly important to note the

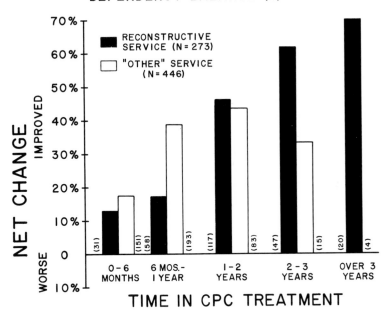

Figure 7. Net change in severity rating for patients coded severity 3 on the Dependency Balance (I) at the beginning of treatment is shown for groups with varying times in treatment. Patients in psychoanalysis and psychotherapy are compared. Net change represents the difference between the patients rated improved and those rated worse from the beginning to the end of CPC treatment.

statistically significant difference between services in the group treated from 6 months to one year. In this group, "Other" patients improved more often than did patients in psychoanalysis.

The graph of patients coded severity 2 on the Dependency Balance (I) at the beginning of treatment is shown in Figure 8. Surprisingly enough, here too "Other" patients improve significantly more at the 6 months–1 year time period than do patients in analysis. Once again, with more time in treatment the picture for severity 2 patients changes. After 1 year analytic patients show a much greater increment of improvement while "Other" patients show a net change for the worse. Why are "Other" patients improved over the short term, and why do they remain the same

## DEPENDENCY BALANCE (I) - SEVERITY 2

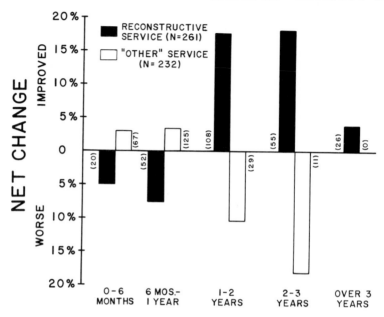

TIME IN CPC TREATMENT

*Figure 8.* Net change in severity rating for patients coded severity 2 on the Dependency Balance (I) at the beginning of treatment is shown for groups with varying times in treatment. Patients in psychoanalysis and psychotherapy are compared. Net change represents the difference between the patients rated improved and those rated worse from the beginning to the end of CPC treatment

(severity 3) or get worse (severity 2) with further treatment? This is in contrast to analytic patients who, after a time period of almost a year, begin to show steadily increasing improvement with further treatment time.

The explanations which come to mind have to do with the process of treatment, an issue which the Columbia Psychoanalytic Records Project was originally not designed to study, and they involve the nature of the patient–therapist relationship in analysis and in psychotherapy. Treatment on the Reparative and Psychosomatic Services (psychotherapy) is most likely directed to relief of symptoms and distress, and establishing a more harmonious adaptive balance as soon as possible. Such treatment relies heavily on various reassuring measures taken by the therapist, on partial insights, on the unresolved transference, and on strengthening defenses. These goals can be achieved more quickly than those sought in analysis, but they represent a different order of phenomena so far as the therapeutic process is concerned. The effectiveness of this type of patient–therapist relationship in bringing about greater independence in the patient (as measured on the Dependency Balance (I)) would appear to be limited. Beyond a year, no substantial increment of greater independence results from longer exposure to this supportive atmosphere.

Analysis is a very different kind of treatment from that which is applied on the "Other" Services. In analysis the emphasis falls on the process of analyzing symptoms, drives and defenses, and on the transference. The achievement of understanding and insight assume major roles in the conduct of therapy. In analysis the therapist assumes a much less supportive role and he may set about blocking the neurotic dependency demands of the analytic patient. This process produces much valuable material, the analysis of which may be a vital part of the psychoanalytic process, leading to fundamental insights on the part of the patient. However, it is frustrating to the patient, demanding and taxing of him. Over the short term in analysis (under a year) it may lead to a low rate of improvement for the sicker patients (severity 3), or an actual change toward greater dysfunction for some healthier patients (severity 2). However, with continued time in treatment, the effectiveness of this procedure manifests itself in steadily increasing improvement over time to a level which is much greater than that achieved by analytically oriented psychotherapy.

Patients in treatment for comparable periods of time were found to respond differently to psychoanalysis and psychoanalytically oriented psychotherapy as measured by change on the ego strength scales. This differential response was explored in detail for the Pathology (VIII) and Dependency (I) Balances and attributed to the effects of the two therapeutic techniques employed. The possibility remains, however, that the differences observed are related to the types of patients treated on the two services rather than the type of treatment used. To explore this further the next change will describe changes in adaptation from the beginning to the end of Clinic treatment for various diagnostic groups on each service.

## DIAGNOSIS AND EGO STRENGTH SCALES

Table 10 presents the diagnosis recorded in both types of treatment combined into four major groups. In a later section these groups will be broken down into more specific diagnostic categories. All diagnoses given are those which were coded at the end of treatment. This is considered to be more representative of the therapist's impression (or the coder's when he supplied the diagnosis) than the initial diagnosis, since it is based on more information and greater experience with the patient. This final diagnosis does not necessarily reflect the original thinking about the patient, however, nor the reasons he was assigned to a particular service.

**TABLE 10**

Principal Diagnosis as Recorded at the End of Clinic Treatment

| | Reconstructive Service | | "Other" Service | |
|---|---|---|---|---|
| Diagnostic Group | N | % | N | % |
| A. Psychoneurosis | 266 | 45.2% | 239 | 31.4% |
| B. Neurotic Personality Disorders | 206 | 35.0% | 221 | 29.1% |
| C. Psychosis and Psychotic Personality (borderline) | 83 | 14.1% | 236 | 31.1% |
| D. Other, including psychosomatic | 33 | 5.7% | 64 | 8.4% |
| Total | 588 | 100.0% | 760 | 100.0% |

All diagnoses are represented in both types of treatment. Psychoneurosis and neurotic personality disorders are significantly more frequent in analysis. The "Other" Services have a much larger percentage of patients diagnosed psychosis or psychotic personality (including borderline conditions). These three diagnostic groups are represented on each service in sufficient numbers to permit comparisons between them. The fourth group ("Other, including psychosomatic"), which is small in number and consists of many unrelated diagnostic categories, will not be considered in this section.

## DIAGNOSTIC GROUPS AND SEVERITY OF DYSFUNCTION AT THE BEGINNING OF TREATMENT

Table 11 shows the distribution of less severe (0, 1, 2) and more severe (3, 4) ratings at the beginning of treatment for each diagnostic group on each service. Patients diagnosed neurotic personality in analysis are

**TABLE 11**

Distribution of Severity Coding at the Beginning of CPC Treatment by Diagnostic Group and Service

| Adaptive Balance | Reconstructive Service | | | | | | "Other" Service | | | | | |
|---|---|---|---|---|---|---|---|---|---|---|---|---|
| | Psychoneurosis N = 264 | | Neurotic Personality N = 203 | | Psychosis & Psychotic Personality N = 81 | | Psychoneurosis N = 234 | | Neurotic Personality N = 218 | | Psychotic & Psychotic Personality N = 227 | |
| | Less Severe | More Severe | Less Severe | More Severe | Less Severe | More Severe | Less Severe | More Severe | Less Severe | More Severe | Less Severe | More Severe |
| Dependency (I) | 53.1 | 46.9 | 52.7 | 47.3 | 24.1 | 75.9 | 47.1 | 53.0 | 35.0 | 65.0 | 19.3 | 80.8 |
| Pleasure (II) | 56.6 | 43.4 | 60.4 | 39.5 | 24.1 | 75.8 | 45.4 | 54.6 | 42.3 | 57.8 | 20.2 | 79.8 |
| Sex (III) | 49.3 | 50.7 | 53.7 | 46.3 | 26.5 | 73.3 | 56.4 | 43.6 | 48.2 | 51.8 | 31.1 | 68.9 |
| Affective (IV) | 58.1 | 41.9 | 58.5 | 40.5 | 21.7 | 78.2 | 50.0 | 50.0 | 47.5 | 52.5 | 21.1 | 78.9 |
| Defense (V) | 47.2 | 52.8 | 51.4 | 48.5 | 19.2 | 80.8 | 40.8 | 59.2 | 39.5 | 60.5 | 19.3 | 80.7 |
| Emergency Emotions (VI) | 51.3 | 48.3 | 62.5 | 37.5 | 38.6 | 61.4 | 44.1 | 55.9 | 48.6 | 51.4 | 27.0 | 73.0 |
| Guilt (VII) | 50.2 | 49.8 | 49.7 | 50.3 | 32.5 | 67.4 | 42.8 | 57.2 | 44.9 | 55.1 | 21.5 | 78.4 |
| Pathology (VIII) | 55.5 | 44.5 | 62.4 | 37.6 | 26.5 | 73.4 | 42.8 | 57.1 | 45.3 | 54.7 | 19.3 | 80.7 |
| Social (IX) | 69.5 | 30.5 | 74.0 | 25.8 | 36.1 | 63.8 | 58.5 | 41.5 | 61.4 | 38.6 | 32.6 | 67.4 |

Severity codes on each balance at the beginning of Clinic treatment have been arranged according to type of treatment and have been dichotomized into "Less Severe" (category 0, 1, 2) and "More Severe" (category 3, 4). Three major diagnostic groups are shown; psychoneurosis, neurotic personality, and psychosis including psychotic personalities or borderline patients. Cases not coded have been eliminated. Figures are in percent.

significantly healthier than those in "Other" treatment in all balances except Sex (III) and Guilt (VII), where the differences are in the same direction but less pronounced. Patients in analysis diagnosed psycho-neurotic are healthier than patients in "Other" treatment in all balances except Sex (III). The differences are large and reach the level of statistical significance for the Pleasure (II), Pathology (VIII), and Social (IX) Balances.

This pattern is somewhat different for the psychotic and borderline group. Here, although Reconstructive patients are healthier than "Other" patients in all balances except Sex (III), the differences are generally small. The reconstructive psychotic patients coded significantly less severely than psychotics of the "Other" Services at the beginning of treatment only on the Emergency Emotion (VI) and Guilt (VII) Balances. This would tend to suggest that when there was a doubt about the patient's psychotic diagnosis or integrative capacity, the patient was more likely to be assigned to analytic treatment if he did not manifest severe disturbance in the pathological affects of fear, rage, and guilt. This finding is important from a prognostic standpoint in view of the experience which this psychotic borderline group had in analysis compared with "Other" treatment, as will be described later.

It has previously been observed that analytic and non-analytic patients cannot be distinguished on the basis of severity of dysfunction of the Sex (III) Balance at the beginning of treatment. From the data just presented it is clear that this is true regardless of diagnosis.

So far, diagnostic groups have been compared from one service to the other. The three groups will now be compared within each service. As could be expected, the Psychotic and Psychotic Personality group on each service is significantly sicker on each scale than other diagnostic groups on the same service.

Important distinctions appear when the psychoneurotic and neurotic personality groups are compared. In analysis, the psychoneurotic group is coded significantly more severely on the Emergency Emotion (VI) Balance. This difference is also reflected in the Pathology Balance (VIII), but not to the same level of significance. On all other balances there is a very close similarity of initial severity ratings between the two groups.

In "Other" treatment the neurotic personality shows greater dysfunction than the psychoneurotic on the Dependency Balance (I). These two groups are generally similar on all other balances

The explanation of these differences is not readily apparent. The significant differences just described are in the expected directions. It is to be expected, because of the diagnostic definitions used *(American Psychiatric Association Diagnostic and Statistic Manual of Mental Diseases, 1952)*, that psychoneurotic patients would show more manifest symptomatology, such as emergency emotions and structured pathology, but this distinction diminishes in importance on the "Other" Services. It might also be expected that the neurotic personality would demonstrate greater severity of disturbance in character traits. A dependent adaptation, as reflected in the Dependency Balance (I), might be considered such an index. However, the neurotic personality is coded more severely than psychoneurotic patients on the Dependency Balance (I) in "Other" treatment, but not in analytic treatment. This data suggests that the manifestation of more severe disturbance in dependent character traits raised doubts about the diagnosis and about the analyzability of the neurotic personality. In such cases the patient would more likely be assigned to "Other" Services for therapy. Once again this distinction should be borne in mind when change in the neurotic personality in analysis is compared with change in non-analytic therapy.

## DIAGNOSTIC GROUPS AND CHANGE IN THERAPY— RECONSTRUCTIVE AND "OTHER" SERVICES COMPARED

Perhaps the most striking finding derived from this material relates to the well-known clinical dictum that psychoanalysis is not considered the treatment of choice for patients who are diagnosed psychotic or have borderline psychotic personalities. The findings of this study strongly support such a clinical impression.

In analysis (Table 12) patients diagnosed psychotic and those diagnosed psychotic personality may show change during treatment toward healthier adaptation (average of 19.6% for all balances combined), but they show more change in the direction of greater severity (16.9%) than do psychoneurotics and neurotic personalities in the same type of treatment. The result is a net change which is close to zero for the psychotics or borderline patients who are in analysis. This same diagnostic group shows a net improvement of 17.1% in "Other" treatment.

An even clearer demonstration of the fact that psychoses and analysis constitute a mismatch appears when only severity 2 (the less severe) psychotics and borderline diagnoses are compared for their response

**TABLE 12**

Change in the Severity Ratings Among Three Diagnostic Groups of Patients on the Reconstructive Service

| Adaptive Balance | Psychoneurosis N = 264 | | | | Neurotic Personality N = 203 | | | | Psychosis and Psychotic personalities N = 81 | | | |
|---|---|---|---|---|---|---|---|---|---|---|---|---|
| | Improved | No Change | Worse | Net Change | Improved | No Change | Worse | Net Change | Improved | No Change | Worse | Net Change |
| Dependency (I) | 31.2 | 65.8 | 3.0 | +28.2 | 33.5 | 64.0 | 2.5 | +31.0 | 22.5 | 60.0 | 17.5 | +5.0 |
| Pleasure (II) | 31.4 | 62.2 | 6.4 | +25.0 | 32.5 | 65.0 | 2.5 | +30.0 | 17.3 | 67.9 | 14.8 | +2.5 |
| Sex (III) | 30.9 | 64.5 | 4.6 | +26.3 | 30.4 | 67.1 | 2.5 | +27.9 | 27.2 | 54.3 | 18.5 | +8.7 |
| Affects (IV) | 25.0 | 70.1 | 4.9 | +20.1 | 27.6 | 69.9 | 2.5 | +25.1 | 13.6 | 69.1 | 17.3 | −3.7 |
| Defense (V) | 32.9 | 63.0 | 4.1 | +28.8 | 37.8 | 59.7 | 2.5 | +35.3 | 21.0 | 61.7 | 17.3 | +3.7 |
| Emergency Emotions (VI) | 37.1 | 60.3 | 2.6 | +34.5 | 30.0 | 68.5 | 1.5 | +28.5 | 22.2 | 58.1 | 19.7 | +2.5 |
| Guilt (VII) | 31.4 | 64.8 | 3.8 | +27.6 | 34.2 | 64.3 | 1.5 | +32.7 | 19.8 | 61.7 | 18.5 | +1.3 |
| Pathology (VIII) | 33.0 | 63.6 | 3.4 | +29.6 | 33.0 | 65.5 | 1.5 | +31.5 | 12.3 | 74.1 | 13.6 | −1.3 |
| Social (IX) | 25.5 | 71.1 | 3.4 | +22.1 | 28.4 | 67.6 | 4.0 | +24.4 | 21.0 | 64.2 | 14.8 | +6.2 |
| Overall % | 31.0 | 65.0 | 4.0 | +27.0 | 31.9 | 65.8 | 2.3 | +29.6 | 19.6 | 63.5 | 16.9 | +2.7 |

Change in severity on each balance from beginning to end of Clinic treatment has been calculated for patients in three diagnostic groups. Only patients in psychoanalysis (Reconstructive Service) are shown. Net change is the difference between percent rated improved and percent rated worse. Over-all % represents average of all balances combined. Figures are in percent.

during treatment. The percentage of patients showing change toward improved or worse adaptation was computed for each of the nine balances, and an average calculated for all balances combined. Of those patients coded severity 2 at the onset of treatment, 2.0% improved, and 44.4% became worse.

Comparable figures for the psychotic and psychotic personality group in "Other" treatment are stated here for the sake of comparison.

Psychosis and Psychotic Personality

|  | Improved | Worse | Net Change |
|---|---|---|---|
| All | | | |
| Analysis (N = 81) | 19.6% | 16.9% | + 2.7% |
| "Other" treatment (N = 227) | 23.8% | 6.7% | +17.1% |
| Severity 2 at Onset of Treatment | | | |
| Analysis | 2.0% | 44.4% | −42.4% |
| "Other" treatment | 10.6% | 18.6% | − 8.0% |
| Severity 3 at Onset of Treatment* | | | |
| Analysis | 24.0% | 8.3% | +15.7% |
| "Other" treatment | 25.7% | 3.5% | +22.2% |

These figures confirm the clinical impression that the patient with a potential for psychotic breakdown (borderline or psychotic personality) or with manifest integrative weakness is best treated in non-analytic therapy. This applies particularly if the patient demonstrates a relatively healthy adaptation (severity 2) at the onset of treatment.

How do the neurotic patients treated in analysis compare with similar patients in "Other" treatment? On the basis of over-all change, the psychoneurotics do almost as well on either service. When this is broken down into more or less severe at the beginning of treatment, the healthier (severity 2) patients do better in analysis. Among the sicker patients (severity 3), there is no difference between the services, except in the area of sexual pathology. As measured on the Sex Balance (III), psychoneurotics in analysis do significantly better than psychoneurotics in "Other" treatment. This data may be summarized as follows:

---

*In all diagnostic categories and in both types of service it is observed that a higher proportion of patients rated severity 3 show improvement than patients rated severity 2. From the point of view of statistical probability, of course, there is more room for improvement for those rated "3" than for those rated "2." It should be kept in mind also that the possibility of "no change" may be considered a positive effect of treatment for patients who might otherwise have become worse.

Psychoneurosis

| | Improved | Worse | Net Change |
|---|---|---|---|
| **All** | | | |
| Analysis (N = 264) | 31.0% | 4.0% | +27.0% |
| "Other" treatment (N = 234) | 29.5% | 3.8% | +25.7% |
| **Severity 2 at Onset of Treatment** | | | |
| Analysis | 15.1% | 6.3% | + 8.8% |
| "Other" treatment | 9.2% | 6.9% | + 2.3% |
| **Severity 3 at Onset of Treatment** | | | |
| Analysis (N = 115) | 49.4% | 0.3% | +49.1% |
| "Other" treatment (N = 81) | 46.3% | 0.2% | +46.1% |
| **Sex Balance (III); Severity 3 at Onset of Treatment** | | | |
| Analysis | 44.3% | 0.8% | +43.5% |
| "Other" treatment | 32.1% | 1.2% | +30.9% |

In contrast, neurotic personalities show significantly more improvement in analysis compared with "Other" treatment. This was true on all balances and for all categories of severity at the beginning of treatment, and is summarized as follows:

Neurotic Personality

| | Improved | Worse | Net Change |
|---|---|---|---|
| **All Patients** | | | |
| Analysis (N = 203) | 31.9% | 2.3% | +29.6% |
| "Other" treatment (N = 218) | 20.9% | 3.8% | +17.1% |
| **Severity 2 at Onset of Treatment** | | | |
| Analysis | 19.5% | 3.1% | +16.4% |
| "Other" treatment | 4.4% | 5.9% | − 1.5% |
| **Severity 3 at Onset of Treatment** | | | |
| Analysis | 51.1% | 0.3% | +50.8% |
| "Other" treatment | 34.1% | 0.4% | +33.7% |

Using the gross measure of over-all change, there is little difference in the response of psychoneurotics regardless of the type of treatment. Neurotic personalities, however, show much greater change when treated in analysis.

## DIAGNOSTIC GROUPS ON THE RECONSTRUCTIVE SERVICE

Table 12 indicates the change on all the adaptive balances for the diagnostic groups in reconstructive treatment. The two neurotic groups show the same magnitude of change in analysis. Although patients diagnosed neurotic personality show a greater net improvement on all balances excpet Emergency Emotions (VI), when compared with those diagnosed psychoneurotic, the differences between these two groups

**TABLE 13**

Change in Severity Ratings Among Three Diagnostic Groups of Patients Coded Severity 2 at the Beginning of CPC Treatment

Reconstructive Service

| Adaptive Balance | Psychoneurosis | | | | | Neurotic Personality | | | | | Psychotic and Psychotic Personality | | | | |
|---|---|---|---|---|---|---|---|---|---|---|---|---|---|---|---|
| | N | Improved | No Change | Worse | Net Change | N | Improved | No Change | Worse | Net Change | N | Improved | No Change | Worse | Net Change |
| Dependency (I) | 133 | 12.8 | 82.0 | 5.2 | +7.6 | 101 | 23.8 | 71.3 | 4.9 | +18.9 | 18 | 5.6 | 61.1 | 33.3 | −27.7 |
| Pleasure (II) | 144 | 16.0 | 73.6 | 10.4 | +5.6 | 116 | 19.8 | 75.8 | 4.3 | +15.5 | 18 | 0.0 | 61.1 | 38.9 | −38.9 |
| Sex (III) | 120 | 15.8 | 76.7 | 7.5 | +8.3 | 99 | 18.1 | 78.8 | 3.1 | +15.0 | 21 | 4.8 | 57.2 | 38.0 | −33.2 |
| Affects (IV) | 146 | 12.3 | 80.2 | 7.5 | +4.8 | 112 | 14.3 | 82.1 | 3.6 | +10.7 | 16 | 0.0 | 43.8 | 56.2 | −56.2 |
| Defense (V) | 116 | 13.8 | 78.4 | 7.8 | +6.0 | 97 | 22.6 | 72.3 | 5.2 | +17.4 | 14 | 0.0 | 42.8 | 57.2 | −57.2 |
| Emergency Emotions (VI) | 129 | 18.6 | 77.5 | 3.9 | +14.7 | 118 | 19.5 | 79.6 | 0.8 | +18.7 | 29 | 3.4 | 48.3 | 48.3 | −44.9 |
| Guilt (VII) | 128 | 11.7 | 83.0 | 5.4 | +6.3 | 97 | 12.4 | 84.5 | 3.1 | +9.3 | 24 | 0.0 | 45.9 | 54.1 | −54.1 |
| Pathology (VIII) | 140 | 17.9 | 76.4 | 5.7 | +12.2 | 116 | 25.8 | 72.5 | 1.7 | +24.1 | 20 | 0.0 | 55.0 | 45.0 | −45.0 |
| Social (IX) | 154 | 16.9 | 79.9 | 3.2 | +13.7 | 124 | 19.4 | 79.0 | 1.6 | +17.8 | 26 | 3.8 | 69.3 | 26.9 | −23.1 |
| Overall % | 1210 | 15.1 | 78.6 | 6.3 | +8.8 | 980 | 19.5 | 77.3 | 3.1 | +16.4 | 186 | 2.0 | 53.8 | 44.4 | −42.4 |

Change in Severity on each balance has been calculated for patients in psychoanalysis (Reconstructive Service) who were coded Severity 2 at the beginning of CPC treatment. Patients in three diagnostic groups are compared. Net change is the difference between percent rated improved and percent rated worse. Overall percent represents average of all balances combined. Figures are in percent.

are generally quite small. Even in the Defense Balance (V), where there is the largest differential of net change, this does not approach the level of statistical significance.

Striking differences appear, however, when these two groups are compared according to the severity of dysfunction at the beginning of treatment. Table 13 indicates that, for patients coded severity 2 at the beginning of treatment, the neurotic personality group shows much greater net improvement than the psychoneurotic group. This reaches the level of statistical significance on several balances: (Dependency (I), Pleasure (II), Defense (V), and Pathology (VIII). Thus, among the healthier patients at the beginning of analysis, those diagnosed neurotic personality (or without well-structured neurotic symptoms) show more improvement in analysis, even on the Pathology Balance (VIII).

## DIAGNOSTIC GROUPS ON THE "OTHER" SERVICES

On the "Other" Services the psychoneurotic group demonstrated significantly greater over-all net improvement (+25.7%) than the two other groups (Table 14). The neurotic personality and the psychotic and psychotic personality group showed the identical over-all change of 17.1%. These figures are derived by averaging all balances together and represent a gross approximation of over-all change. Actually, when compared with the neurotic personality group, a greater proportion of psychotic patients improved and a greater proportion became worse with the result that the change over all balances for these two groups was identical. It is interesting to note that the patients on the "Other" Services diagnosed neurotic personality improved significantly less on the Pleasure (II) and Social (IX) Balances than all other patients, including psychotics and borderlines.

## SPECIFIC DIAGNOSTIC CATEGORIES AND CHANGE IN TREATMENT

The specific diagnostic categories (Table 15) which constitute the larger psychoneurotic group are quite dissimilar in the way they respond to treatment. The obsessive neurosis and the anxiety neurosis are described in this text because there is a sufficient number of patients in each group to permit statistical comparisons. The psychoneurotic "Other types" category was not included, however, even though there are sufficient cases in the category, because of the non-specific clinical criteria by which "Other

## TABLE 14

Change in Severity Ratings Among Three Diagnostic Groups of Patients on the "Other" Services

| Adaptive Balance | Psychoneurosis N = 234 | | | | Neurotic Personalities N = 218 | | | | Psychotic and Psychotic Personalities N = 228 | | | |
|---|---|---|---|---|---|---|---|---|---|---|---|---|
| | Improved | No Change | Worse | Net Change | Improved | No Change | Worse | Net Change | Improved | No Change | Worse | Net Change |
| Dependency (I) | 31.2 | 65.8 | 3.0 | +28.2 | 24.8 | 71.5 | 3.7 | +21.1 | 25.0 | 66.7 | 8.3 | +16.7 |
| Pleasure (II) | 29.5 | 66.7 | 3.8 | +25.7 | 18.4 | 78.4 | 3.2 | +15.2 | 29.6 | 66.0 | 4.4 | +25.2 |
| Sex (III) | 20.0 | 77.0 | 3.0 | +17.0 | 16.6 | 79.2 | 4.2 | +12.4 | 18.6 | 75.6 | 5.8 | +12.8 |
| Affects (IV) | 28.3 | 66.1 | 5.6 | +22.7 | 17.9 | 78.9 | 3.2 | +14.7 | 21.6 | 70.9 | 7.5 | +14.1 |
| Defense (V) | 31.2 | 65.4 | 3.4 | +27.8 | 25.2 | 70.7 | 4.1 | +21.1 | 22.3 | 70.7 | 7.0 | +15.3 |
| Emergency Emotions (VI) | 37.6 | 58.6 | 3.8 | +33.8 | 24.3 | 72.7 | 3.0 | +21.3 | 29.8 | 61.9 | 8.3 | +21.5 |
| Guilt (VII) | 32.5 | 64.5 | 3.0 | +29.5 | 28.0 | 67.9 | 4.1 | +23.9 | 24.2 | 70.5 | 5.3 | +18.9 |
| Pathology (VIII) | 29.9 | 67.1 | 3.0 | +26.9 | 16.9 | 77.6 | 5.5 | +11.4 | 19.2 | 71.6 | 9.2 | +10.0 |
| Social (IX) | 24.8 | 69.5 | 5.7 | +19.1 | 15.7 | 81.1 | 3.2 | +12.5 | 24.4 | 70.7 | 4.9 | +19.5 |
| Overall % | 29.5 | 66.7 | 3.8 | +25.7 | 20.9 | 75.3 | 3.8 | +17.1 | 23.8 | 69.5 | 6.7 | +17.1 |

Change in severity on each balance from beginning to end of Clinic treatment has been calculated for patients in three diagnostic groups. Only patients in psychotherapy ("Other" Services) are shown. Net change is the difference between percent rated improved and percent rated worse. "Overall %" represents an average of all balances combined. Figures are in percent.

**TABLE 15**

Principal Diagnoses as Recorded at the End of Clinic Treatment

| Diagnosis | Reconstructive | | "Other" | |
|---|---|---|---|---|
| | N | % | N | % |
| A. Psychoneurosis | | | | |
| Anxiety reaction | 77 | 28.9 | 76 | 31.8 |
| Obsessive-compulsive reaction | 72 | 27.1 | 53 | 22.2 |
| Depressive reaction | 17 | 6.4 | 34 | 14.2 |
| Phobic reaction | 28 | 10.5 | 16 | 6.7 |
| Other psychoneurotic reactions | 72 | 27.1 | 60 | 25.1 |
| Total | 266 | 100.0 | 239 | 100.0 |
| B. Neurotic Personality Disorders | | | | |
| Compulsive personality | 146 | 70.8 | 146 | 66.1 |
| Passive-dependent personality | 21 | 10.2 | 33 | 14.9 |
| Passive-aggressive personality | 29 | 14.1 | 31 | 14.0 |
| Other personality disorders | 10 | 4.9 | 11 | 5.0 |
| Total | 206 | 100.0 | 221 | 100.0 |
| C. Psychosis | | | | |
| Schizophrenia | 56 | 88.9 | 180 | 95.2 |
| Other | 7 | 11.1 | 9 | 4.8 |
| Total | 63 | 100.0 | 189 | 100.0 |
| Psychotic Personality (borderline) | | | | |
| Schizoid | 13 | 65.0 | 36 | 76.6 |
| Other | 7 | 35.0 | 11 | 23.4 |
| Total | 20 | 100.0 | 47 | 100.0 |
| D. Other | | | | |
| Psychosomatic | 5 | 15.2 | 40 | 62.5 |
| Other* | 28 | 84.8 | 24 | 37.5 |
| Total | 33 | 100.0 | 64 | 100.0 |

*This group includes such unrelated diagnostic categories as psychopaths, sociopaths, drug addiction, homosexuality, and alcoholism. These pathological manifestations are usually included as a secondary diagnosis.

types" was defined. This group tended to be used as a catch-all diagnosis when no other neurotic classification could be found to fit the clinical data.

Two-thirds of those diagnosed neurotic personality on both services were specifically diagnosed compulsive personality. 21.6% of all patients treated at the Clinic are included in this category. The following sections will deal with three specific diagnostic categories (anxiety neurosis, obsessional neurosis, and compulsive personality) and changes in these categories as measured on the ego strength scales from the beginning to the end of Columbia Psychoanalytic Clinic treatment.

## DIAGNOSTIC CATEGORIES—RECONSTRUCTIVE AND "OTHER" SERVICES COMPARED

Both the anxiety neurotic and the obsessional neurotic on the "Other" Services showed substantial improvement in severity codings during treatment on all scales, regardless of the initial severity. Patients with the same diagnosis showed even greater improvement on the Reconstructive Service, although the difference did not approach the level of statistical significance. This data is summarized in Table 16 which shows the average change for all balances combined. The compulsive personality in "Other" treatment, on the other hand, showed significantly less improvement when compared with patients of the same diagnosis in analysis. This difference was particularly marked when patients coded severity 2 are considered. The compulsive personality coded severity 2 at the beginning of treatment showed a net change for the worse in "Other" treatment.

## DIAGNOSTIC CATEGORIES ON THE RECONSTRUCTIVE SERVICE

Table 17 shows the change in these three diagnostic categories for each adaptive balance. The anxiety neurotic changes in the less severe direction most often, the obsessional neurotic next most often, and the compulsive personality least often. These over-all differences, however, are small and only two comparisons derived from this table reach the level of statistical significance. The obsessional neurotic improves less and gets worse much more often on the Affect Balance (IV) than the anxiety neurotic. Also, the anxiety neurotic improves significantly more often on the Emergency Emotion Balance (VI) than the compulsive personality.

Table 17, which includes all patients in each diagnosis, demonstrates that on the Dependency Balance (I) the anxiety neurotic shows more improvement than other diagnostic categories. The difference is not large enough to be statistically significant for the numbers of patients involved.

Significant differences among these diagnostic categories do emerge, however, when those patients who were rated either severity 2 or severity 3 at the beginning of treatment are compared separately. When severity 2 patients (healthier) are considered alone (Table 18), those diagnosed compulsive personality show the greatest proportion of improvement on

## TABLE 16

Comparison of Change in Severity Ratings Among Three Diagnostic Categories of Patients
On the Reconstructive and "Other" Services

| Diagnostic Group | All Patients | | | |
|---|---|---|---|---|
| | Improved | No Change | Worse | Net Change |
| Anxiety Neurosis | | | | |
| Recon. N = 77 | 39.4 | 58.7 | 1.9 | +37.5 |
| "Other" N = 76 | 30.5 | 67.3 | 2.2 | +28.3 |
| Obsessive Neurosis | | | | |
| Recon. N = 72 | 35.1 | 61.1 | 3.8 | +31.3 |
| "Other" N = 50 | 31.0 | 66.0 | 2.9 | +28.1 |
| Compulsive Personality | | | | |
| Recon. N = 144 | 32.4 | 65.3 | 2.3 | +30.1 |
| "Other" N = 144 | 21.7 | 73.6 | 4.7 | +17.0 |
| | Severity 2 | | | |
| | Improved | No Change | Worse | Net Change |
| Anxiety Neurosis | | | | |
| Recon. | 21.6 | 75.6 | 2.8 | +18.8 |
| "Other" | 11.1 | 84.6 | 4.3 | + 6.8 |
| Obsessive Neurosis | | | | |
| Recon. | 21.8 | 71.3 | 6.9 | +14.8 |
| "Other" | 12.7 | 80.9 | 6.4 | + 6.3 |
| Compulsive Personality | | | | |
| Recon. | 20.3 | 76.8 | 2.9 | +17.4 |
| "Other" | 4.1 | 88.5 | 7.4 | − 3.3 |
| | Severity 3 | | | |
| | Improved | No Change | Worse | Net Change |
| Anxiety Neurosis | | | | |
| Recon. | 61.8 | 38.2 | 0.0 | +61.8 |
| "Other" | 46.3 | 53.4 | 0.3 | +46.0 |
| Obsessive Neurosis | | | | |
| Recon. | 47.9 | 51.4 | 0.6 | +47.3 |
| "Other" | 45.2 | 54.8 | 0.1 | +45.1 |
| Compulsive Personality | | | | |
| Recon. | 53.8 | 45.7 | 0.4 | +53.4 |
| "Other" | 37.5 | 62.3 | 0.2 | +37.3 |

Change in severity on each balance from beginning to end of Clinic treatment was
calculated for patients in three diagnostic categories. The figures presented here represent
an average for all balances combined. Net change is the difference between percent rated
improved and percent rated worse. Figures are in percent.

**TABLE 17**

Change in Severity Ratings Among Three Diagnostic Categories of Patients on the Reconstructive Service

| Adaptive Balance | Anxiety Neurosis N = 77 | | | | Obsessional Neurosis N = 72 | | | | Compulsive Personality N = 144 | | | |
|---|---|---|---|---|---|---|---|---|---|---|---|---|
| | Improved | No Change | Worse | Net Change | Improved | No Change | Worse | Net Change | Improved | No Change | Worse | Net Change |
| Dependency (I) | 42.8 | 54.6 | 2.6 | +40.2 | 33.3 | 63.9 | 2.8 | +30.5 | 30.6 | 66.6 | 2.8 | +27.8 |
| Pleasure (II) | 41.5 | 55.9 | 2.6 | +38.9 | 34.7 | 55.5 | 9.7 | +25.0 | 34.7 | 62.5 | 2.8 | +31.9 |
| Sex (III) | 33.8 | 63.5 | 2.7 | +31.1 | 32.0 | 65.2 | 2.8 | +29.2 | 32.2 | 64.3 | 3.5 | +28.7 |
| Affects (IV) | 37.7 | 62.3 | 0.0 | +37.7 | 23.6 | 68.0 | 8.3 | +15.3 | 27.8 | 70.1 | 2.1 | +25.7 |
| Defense (V) | 37.7 | 61.0 | 1.3 | +36.4 | 43.0 | 54.2 | 2.8 | +40.2 | 39.6 | 59.0 | 1.4 | +38.2 |
| Emergency Emotions (VI) | 49.3 | 49.3 | 1.3 | +48.0 | 36.1 | 63.9 | 0.0 | +36.1 | 28.4 | 70.9 | 0.7 | +27.7 |
| Guilt (VII) | 39.5 | 59.2 | 1.3 | +38.2 | 37.5 | 59.7 | 2.8 | +34.7 | 35.6 | 63.0 | 1.4 | +34.2 |
| Pathology (VIII) | 42.8 | 55.9 | 1.3 | +41.5 | 37.5 | 58.3 | 4.2 | +33.3 | 33.1 | 64.8 | 2.1 | +31.0 |
| Social (IX) | 28.6 | 67.5 | 3.9 | +24.7 | 38.0 | 60.6 | 1.4 | +36.6 | 29.3 | 66.5 | 4.2 | +25.1 |
| Overall % | 39.4 | 58.7 | 1.9 | +37.5 | 35.1 | 61.1 | 3.8 | +31.3 | 32.4 | 65.3 | 2.3 | +30.1 |

Change in severity on each balance from beginning to end of Clinic treatment has been calculated for patients in three diagnostic groups. Only patients in psychotherapy ("Other" Services) are shown. Net change is the difference between percent rated improved and percent rated worse. Over-all % represents the average of all nine balances combined. Figures are in percent.

**TABLE 18**

Change in Severity Ratings Among Three Diagnostic Categories of Patients Coded Severity 2 at the Beginning of Treatment

| Adaptive Balance | Anxiety Neurosis | | | | | Obsessional Neurosis | | | | | Compulsive Personality | | | | |
|---|---|---|---|---|---|---|---|---|---|---|---|---|---|---|---|
| | N | Improved | No Change | Worse | Net Change | N | Improved | No Change | Worse | Net Change | N | Improved | No Change | Worse | Net Change |
| (I) Dependency | (35) | 17.1 | 77.1 | 5.7 | +11.4 | (34) | 8.8 | 85.3 | 5.9 | + 2.9 | (76) | 25.0 | 69.8 | 5.3 | +19.7 |
| (II) Pleasure | (45) | 22.2 | 73.4 | 4.4 | +17.8 | (37) | 24.3 | 56.8 | 18.9 | + 5.4 | (84) | 21.5 | 73.7 | 4.8 | +16.7 |
| (III) Sex | (31) | 19.3 | 77.5 | 3.2 | +16.1 | (30) | 20.0 | 73.3 | 6.7 | +13.3 | (67) | 19.4 | 76.2 | 4.5 | +14.9 |
| (IV) Affects | (43) | 23.2 | 76.8 | 0.0 | +23.2 | (37) | 13.5 | 75.7 | 10.8 | + 2.7 | (84) | 15.5 | 82.0 | 2.5 | +13.0 |
| (V) Defense | (34) | 17.6 | 79.5 | 2.9 | +14.7 | (28) | 32.1 | 64.4 | 3.6 | +28.5 | (75) | 21.3 | 76.0 | 2.7 | +18.6 |
| (VI) Emergency Emotions | (39) | 30.8 | 66.6 | 2.6 | +28.2 | (32) | 25.0 | 75.0 | 0.0 | +25.0 | (90) | 20.0 | 78.9 | 1.1 | +18.9 |
| (VII) Guilt | (36) | 16.7 | 80.5 | 2.8 | +13.9 | (31) | 19.3 | 77.5 | 3.2 | +16.1 | (67) | 11.9 | 85.1 | 3.0 | + 8.9 |
| (VIII) Pathology | (41) | 21.9 | 75.7 | 2.4 | +19.5 | (36) | 27.8 | 63.9 | 8.3 | +19.5 | (90) | 24.4 | 73.3 | 2.2 | +22.2 |
| (IX) Social | (52) | 23.1 | 75.0 | 1.9 | +21.2 | (38) | 26.3 | 71.1 | 2.6 | +23.7 | (88) | 21.6 | 77.3 | 1.1 | +20.5 |
| Overall % | | 21.6 | 75.6 | 2.8 | +18.8 | | 21.8 | 71.3 | 6.9 | +14.9 | | 20.3 | 76.8 | 2.9 | +17.4 |

Change in severity on each balance from beginning to end of Clinic treatment has been calculated for patients in three discrete diagnostic categories who were rated severity 2 at the beginning of Clinic treatment. Only patients in psychoanalysis (Reconstructive Service) are shown. Net change is the difference between percent rated improved and percent rated worse. Over-all % is an average of all balances combined. Figures are in percent.

the Dependency Balance (I). In fact, the compulsive personality shows significantly greater net change than the obsessional neurotic even for the relatively small number of cases involved.

When the severity 3 patients are considered, however, the anxiety neurotic (+66.7%) and the obsessional neurotic (+57.2%) show significantly greater improvement than the compulsive personality (+40.7%) on the same Balance (I). In fact, the compulsive personality does no better on this balance in analysis (+40.7%) than in other treatment (+36.5%) when coded severity 3 at the onset of treatment.

Among the severity 2 (healthier) patients at the beginning of treatment the obsessional neurotic improved much less on the Pleasure Frustration Balance (II) and the Affect Balance (IV) than the other two categories, but the improvement on the Social Balance (IX) was the same for all. Actually, the obsessional neurotic became worse on the Affect Balance (IV) and the Pleasure Balance (II) in a significant number of cases but, again, did not tend to get worse on the Social Balance (IX). Thus, the obsessional can improve in the area of social performance in spite of little or no improvement in the affective or pleasure capacity. This same tendency may be observed for those patients coded severity 3 at the beginning of analysis.

Considering patients who were rated severity 2 at the onset of analysis, the anxiety neurotic showed greatest improvement on the Emergency Emotion (VI) Balance; the obsessional neurotic had greatest net improvement on the Defense Balance (V); while the compulsive personality stood out on the Dependency Balance (I). Each diagnostic category showed greatest movement toward health on those balances which clinically and psychodynamically might be anticipated to be key areas for that diagnosis. All three categories showed similar change as measured on the Sex (III) and Pathology (VIII) Balances. Thus, it can be seen that all balances do not move together or in the same direction when patients are divided into finer diagnostic and treatment groups, and identified for severity at the beginning of treatment.

## DIAGNOSTIC CATEGORIES ON THE "OTHER" SERVICES

Table 19 shows the change on each balance for patients on the "Other" Services. The anxiety and obsessive neurotics show about the same net improvement while compulsive personality patients improve much less. A

**TABLE 19**

Change in Severity Ratings Among Three Diagnostic Categories of Patients on the "Other" Services

| Adaptive Balance | Anxiety Neurosis N = 76 | | | | Obsessional Neurosis N = 50 | | | | Compulsive Personality N = 144 | | | |
|---|---|---|---|---|---|---|---|---|---|---|---|---|
| | Improved | No Change | Worse | Net Change | Improved | No Change | Worse | Net Change | Improved | No Change | Worse | Net Change |
| Dependency (I) | 35.5 | 61.9 | 2.6 | +32.9 | 34.0 | 62.0 | 4.0 | +30.0 | 25.0 | 70.9 | 4.1 | +20.9 |
| Pleasure (II) | 26.3 | 73.7 | 0.0 | +26.3 | 36.0 | 64.0 | 0.0 | +36.0 | 20.1 | 75.0 | 4.9 | +15.2 |
| Sex (III) | 19.8 | 77.6 | 2.6 | +17.2 | 20.0 | 78.0 | 2.0 | +18.0 | 16.3 | 78.1 | 5.6 | +10.7 |
| Affects (IV) | 27.6 | 69.8 | 2.6 | +25.0 | 32.6 | 63.3 | 4.1 | +28.5 | 19.4 | 77.8 | 2.8 | +16.6 |
| Defense (V) | 36.9 | 60.5 | 2.6 | +34.3 | 28.0 | 70.0 | 2.0 | +26.0 | 30.6 | 63.8 | 5.6 | +25.0 |
| Emergency Emotions (VI) | 42.1 | 56.6 | 1.3 | +40.8 | 36.0 | 58.0 | 6.0 | +30.0 | 22.2 | 74.3 | 3.5 | +18.7 |
| Guilt (VII) | 27.6 | 69.8 | 2.6 | +25.0 | 36.0 | 62.0 | 2.0 | +34.0 | 28.4 | 66.0 | 5.6 | +22.8 |
| Pathology (VIII) | 35.5 | 63.2 | 1.3 | +34.2 | 28.0 | 70.0 | 2.0 | +26.0 | 17.4 | 75.7 | 6.9 | +10.5 |
| Social (IX) | 22.7 | 73.7 | 4.0 | +18.7 | 28.5 | 67.4 | 4.1 | +24.1 | 15.4 | 81.1 | 3.5 | +11.9 |
| Overall % | 30.5 | 67.3 | 2.2 | +28.3 | 31.0 | 66.0 | 2.9 | +28.1 | 21.7 | 73.6 | 4.7 | +17.0 |

Change in severity on each balance from beginning to end of Clinic treatment has been calculated for patients in three discrete diagnostic categories. Only patients in psychotherapy ("Other" Services) are shown. Net change is the difference between percent rated improved and percent rated worse. Over-all % represents the average of all balances combined. Figures are in percent.

major finding is the significantly smaller improvement of the compulsive personality as measured by the Pathology Balance (VIII) when compared with either of the other two groups. Statistically significant differences are a greater improvement by the obsessional neurotics on the Pleasure-Frustration Balance (II) when compared with the compulsive personality; and greater improvement in Emergency Emotions (VI) for anxiety neurotics compared with compulsive personalities.

Table 16, presented above, shows changes for patients coded severity 2 at the beginning of "Other" treatment. Among these healthier patients the anxiety and obsessional neurotics both showed small net change in the direction of improvement, whereas the compulsive personalities showed an over-all change in the direction of getting worse. This contrasts with the situation in analysis where the compulsive personalities coded severity 2 at the beginning of treatment achieved substantial improvement.

Thus far only severity has been considered as a factor in relating ego strength scales and diagnosis. Polarity also deserves attention in this context, and some examples of its significance will be given below.

## DIAGNOSTIC CATEGORIES AND CHANGE IN POLARITY

Polarity ratings at the beginning of treatment for various diagnostic categories are listed in Table 20 in order of greatest activity. Two categories, passive-aggressive personality and passive-dependent personality, are included here because polarity is an important consideration in the definition of the diagnosis. The psychotic and borderline group is included for comparison with the neurotic diagnostic categories. The distribution of polarity ratings was so uniform from one balance to another for each diagnosis that the ratings in this section can be presented as an average of all balances combined without distorting the data.

On the analytic service the passive-aggressive personalities compared with the passive-dependent personalities show a striking difference in polarity designation which confirms the diagnostic nomenclature used. The obsessive neurotic group coded almost as inhibited as the passive-dependent personalities, and significantly less active than all other diagnostic categories. Polarity ratings are almost identical among the anxiety neurotics, the compulsive personalities, and the psychotic and borderline patients at the beginning of treatment. This is unlike the findings

**TABLE 20**

Dichotomized Polarity Ratings for Six Diagnostic Categories of Patients at the
Beginning of CPC Treatment

| Diagnosis | Reconstructive Service | |
|---|---|---|
| | Predominantly Active (+) | Predominantly Passive (−) |
| Passive-Aggressive Personality N = 29 | 43.4% | 56.6% |
| Anxiety Neurosis N = 77 | 29.3% | 70.7% |
| Psychotic or Psychotic Personality N = 83 | 29.2% | 70.8% |
| Compulsive Personality N = 146 | 28.5% | 71.5% |
| Obsessive Neurosis N = 72 | 14.2% | 85.8% |
| Passive-Dependent Personality N = 21 | 10.1% | 89.9% |

| Diagnosis | "Other" Service | |
|---|---|---|
| | Predominantly Active (+) | Predominantly Passive (−) |
| Psychotic or Psychotic Personality N = 236 | 31.8% | 68.2% |
| Passive-Aggressive Personality N = 31 | 26.3% | 73.7% |
| Compulsive Personality N = 146 | 22.5% | 77.5% |
| Obsessive Neurosis N = 53 | 19.2% | 80.8% |
| Anxiety Neurosis N = 76 | 10.6% | 89.4% |
| Passive-Dependent Personality N = 33 | 1.3% | 98.7% |

Polarity ratings at the beginning of treatment have been dichotomized into predominantly active (+) and predominantly passive (−) categories. On each service the diagnoses are listed in order of greatest activity. Figures represent an average of all balances combined.

on severity ratings where significant differences were observed among the same diagnostic categories at the beginning of treatment.

On the "Other" Services the psychotic group was coded most active, even more active than the passive-aggressive personality, but this difference was not at the level of statistical significance. Patients diagnosed anxiety neurosis were coded significantly more active on the analytic service than those with the same diagnosis in non-analytic treatment.

Change in polarity from the beginning to the end of Clinic treatment was found to be more or less uniform for all scales within each diagnostic category, and the data will once again be expressed as an average of all balances combined. Using the three point scale (Active, Mixed, Passive) the proportion of patients on the Reconstructive Service who were coded "more active" (range of 15.6%–19.7%) or showed "no change" (range 69.5%–78.2%) at the end of Clinic treatment was remarkably similar from one diagnosis to the other. Patients on the "Other" Services showed less shift in polarity at the end of treatment than patients with the same diagnosis in analysis. There is no apparent difference in the information obtained when change in polarity from the beginning to the end of Clinic treatment is measured using two, three or four points to group polarity variables.

At the beginning of treatment the passive-dependent and passive-aggressive patients are respectively scaled more passive and more active than patients in other diagnostic categories. Those patients in both groups who show change toward lesser severity (greater health) do not reflect a simultaneous change in polarity. Polarity ratings remain relatively fixed and tend to retain their original polar distributions, particularly on the Dependency (I) and the Emergency Emotion (VI) Balances. It is evident that general patterns of polarity designation can be correlated with some personality diagnoses. Furthermore, severity and polarity can be shown to operate as independent variables among some groups of patients.

## EGO STRENGTH SCALES RELATED TO CONDITIONS UNDER WHICH COLUMBIA PSYCHOANALYTIC CLINIC TREATMENT TERMINATED

In the section which follows, change in the ego strength scales will be compared with another indicator of clinical change, namely the conditions under which Clinic treatment terminated. The data presented in this section applies only to patients treated on the Reconstructive Service.

Conditions coded at the end of Clinic treatment included:

A. Patient and therapist both agreed to end treatment and therapist felt patient had essentially achieved "maximum benefit" from treatment.

B. Patient and Therapist both agreed to end treatment but therapist felt "maximum benefit" had not been achieved.

C. Therapist ended treatment; felt patient was untreatable or type of treatment was inappropriate.

D. Therapist ended treatment; felt patient did not need treatment, not enough pathology.
E. Patient ended treatment against advice of therapist; felt unimproved or treatment not worthwhile.
F. Patient felt improved and ended treatment against advice of therapist.
G. Treatment ended for reasons "external" to therapy—i.e., patient moved out of town, spouse moved, serious illness or death in family required patient's attendance for a long period of time, pregnancy and childbirth, etc. (specified).
H. Other reasons (specified).
R. No information or does not apply.

The code also included a notation on whether the therapist ended his assignment to the Psychosomatic or Reparative Service, whether he was graduated from his psychoanalytic training program, and whether the patient planned to continue treatment with the same therapist or elsewhere. Patients who continued treatment privately because the therapist completed his psychoanalytic training are included in group R (no information or does not apply).

The concept of maximum benefit was used to indicate that both therapist and patient were prepared to end treatment, that progress had been made in the opinion of both, and that even though some further change might be anticipated with much expenditure of time and effort, it was a satisfactory practical end-point for treatment. Not maximum benefit implied a less satisfactory ending in the therapist's view, and might even be applied when no progress had been made, provided that the decision to stop treatment was mutually satisfactory to therapist and patient.

When these conditions are tabulated against ego strength ratings recorded at the beginning of Clinic treatment, the following observations may be made:

For the categories

(A) *Agreed to end, maximum benefit* and
(B) *Agreed to end, but not maximum benefit;*

The over-all adaptive balances of these two groups at the beginning of treatment are similar to one another. Surprisingly, they are not grossly healthier in profile than other categories to be described below. In fact, they code as severely on the Defense Balance (V) as those patients whom the therapist terminated as untreatable, and more severely than all other groups.

The only difference in severity profile between the maximum benefit and not maximum benefit group at the beginning of treatment is found on the Guilt Balance (VII) where the maximum benefit group has a significantly higher proportion of severe codes. The maximum benefit group is the guiltiest of all groups at the onset of analysis.

The patients whose treatment was terminated by the therapist are seen to have been generally more disturbed at the beginning of treatment than other patients. Those patients whose treatment ended for a variety of other reasons (patient ended, "external" circumstances, continued in private treatment) were not clearly delineated from the maximum benefit group.

There are clear connections between change in severity and the conditions under which Clinic treatment was terminated. This is illustrated in Table 21 which shows change on the Defense Balance (V) for patients treated in analysis. The maximum benefit group is striking in that 79.5%

## TABLE 21

Change in Severity Ratings on the Defense Balance (V) Compared with Conditions
Under which CPC Treatment Terminated

| Conditions under which CPC Treatment Terminated | Improved 2 Severity Categories | Improved 1 Severity Category | Total Improvement | No Change | Worse (1 Severity Category) |
|---|---|---|---|---|---|
| Maximum Benefit (N = 39) | 30.8 | 48.7 | 79.5 | 20.5 | 0.0 |
| Not Maximum Benefit (N = 29) | 6.9 | 27.6 | 34.5 | 65.5 | 0.0 |
| Therapist Ends Treatment (N = 62) | 0.0 | 1.6 | 1.6 | 80.6 | 17.8 |
| Patient Ends Treatment (N = 45) | 2.2 | 15.5 | 17.7 | 75.6 | 6.7 |
| Reasons "External" to Treatment (N = 36) | 2.7 | 21.6 | 24.3 | 70.3 | 5.4 |
| Other Reasons Specified (N = 22) | 0.0 | 31.8 | 31.8 | 63.7 | 4.5 |
| No Information or Continued Privately (N = 329) | 1.2 | 35.5 | 36.7 | 59.4 | 3.9 |

The amount of change in severity ratings on the Defense Balance (V) from the beginning to the end of CPC treatment is presented for patients on the Reconstructive Service who are grouped according to the conditions under which their CPC treatment was terminated. Most patients in the "No Information or Continued Privately" group continued in analysis with the same therapist after CPC treatment ended.

of the patients improved one or two severity categories, and none of the patients was recorded as worse. By contrast, in the not maximum benefit group only 34.5% improved. Those patients whose analyst ended treatment were clearly the group showing the most change for the *worse*, 17.8% being so recorded and 80.6% unchanged. Among those patients who ended treatment against advice, small numbers were recorded at both ends of the scale, but 75.6% of them changed not at all. Those patients who interrupted treatment for "external" reasons, other reasons, and on whom there was no information (the latter usually went on with treatment privately) form a pattern comparable to the *not* maximum benefit group. The other ego strength scales show similar patterns, with minor differences only.

The change recorded in this maximum benefit group is worthy of additional comment. Not only was the percentage of patients improved more than twice that of any other group but the percentage of patients in the maximum benefit group improving two severity points is about the same as the total improvement in each of the other groups, indicating the magnitude of change that can be expected from successfully completed analysis.

Only 234 or 41.5% of all patients started in the Reconstructive Service are coded in the Clinic record as having completed treatment. Of those who are so coded 39 or 16.7% (6.9% of all Reconstructive patients) completed their analysis to maximum benefit in the Clinic. This is the only group of patients who successfully completed their analysis for whom we have complete information about the total span of improvement. From information contained in the follow-up questionnaire it is known that 77* (38.7%) of the 199 patients who continued privately with the same therapist went on to maximum benefit. Those patients who completed private treatment to maximum benefit showed only slightly more improvement at the time the Clinic record ended than did the average of all patients who continued privately.

The figures for improvement on the Defense Balance (V) for the two maximum benefit groups are presented for comparison:

*Eight cases appear on each of the two maximum benefit groups since eight patients coded as having been treated to maximum benefit at the Clinic were subsequently treated privately and coded by the therapist as having completed private treatment to maximum benefit.

|  | Improved 2 Severities | Improved 1 Severity | Total Improvement | No Change | Worse |
|---|---|---|---|---|---|
| Maximum Benefit-Analysis completed in Clinic (N = 39) | 30.8% | 48.7% | 79.5% | 20.5% | 0 |
| Maximum Benefit-Analysis completed privately (N = 77) | 5.2% | 41.6% | 46.8% | 50.6% | 2.6% |

Those who went on to complete analysis privately to maximum benefit had an average of two additional years of treatment. Assuming that both groups treated to maximum benefit reach the same end point as measured by change on the ego strength scales, the above figures indicate the substantial improvement that may be estimated to take place in the last years of analysis.

## CONCLUSIONS

This study has analyzed the use of ego strength scales to measure change in the patients' adaptation from the beginning to the end of Clinic treatment on the basis of written clinical records. Nine collaborating psychoanalysts rated ego strength for 1,348 patients with limited reliability as determined by the group reliability and individual reliability methods. The greatest variation among coders was found on the rating of severity of dysfunction at the beginning of treatment. Change in severity from the beginning to the end of Clinic treatment was recorded with somewhat greater reliability. Each coder demonstrated a characteristic and consistent style in the assessment of ego strength. It is therefore possible to determine the degree of distortion, if any, in the rating of a particular ego strength variable which can be attributed to an individual coder.

When applied to the entire patient population all balances were coded similarly at the beginning of treatment and showed comparable change at the end of treatment. Significant differences appeared when the ego strength ratings of patients in psychoanalysis and psychoanalytically oriented therapy were compared. The data presented on time in treatment and diagnosis indicate that as the patient population is more precisely defined the adaptive balances become more selective and more useful. Polarity appears to function as a variable independent of severity in the case of some patients who change over the course of Clinic treatment.

A high degree of correlation among scales was described. The question was raised as to whether the scales all measure one common factor ("ego strength" or general clinical adaptation) and each rating represents a different perspective of the same factor. The impression of this study regarding scale specificity is that all scales respond to a common factor, and that each scale also responds to a specific element, or a cluster of such elements. This can be formulated as $M_1$ (measure) = C (common factor) + $S_1$ (special factor) + e (error) in the case of a single special factor or, $M_2$ (measure) = C (common factor) + $S_{2,3,4}$ (special factors 2, 3, and 4) if special factors are clustered in an individual scale.[3]

The common factor (C) might be related to a quantitative measure of the degree of healthy or adaptive personality functioning which is *eclipsed* by the pathological manifestation upon which the balance comments. In such a balance the various categories of dysfunction in order of increasing severity represent quantitative gradations such as; "the pathological factors are occasionally, often, or always present or are present in a psychotic form." The Pathology Balance is an example of a scale which is predominantly a quantitative measure of dysfunction.

According to the theoretical model presented above, Measure$_1$ would be particularly valuable in measuring change if the specific factor $S_1$ could be represented as steps on a scale based on qualitative psychodynamic differences. The Dependency Balance could be an example of such a scale.

When a scale is based upon a cluster of specific factors (Measure$_2$), the scale loses some of its value to measure change selectively in clinically discrete patient populations, particularly when the specific factors are related to diverse components of adaptation. The Social Balance appears to be a scale of this type.

The practical value of a scale designed to measure one particular aspect of "ego strength" or adaptation lies in its usefulness in measuring clinical change. Other measures of adaptation and clinical change were used in the Records Project. No attempt was made to cross-tabulate changes in the same area of personality functioning as measured by the ego strength scales and other scales developed specifically for the Records Project. For example, the presence or absence of manifest pathological emotions of fear, rage, depression, and guilt might be cross-tabulated with the Emergency Emotions and Guilt Balances. Interpersonal relationships (work, family, or social) as a major area of disturbance could be correlated with the Dependency and Affect Balances. Sex as a problem area and other specific clinical manifestations of disturbance in the area of sexual performance could be cross-tabulated with the Sex Balance.

Such correlations might elaborate some of the specific factors measured by the ego strength scales. These cross-tabulations are beyond the scope of this presentation and will be reported at a future date.

The concept of the ego is a theoretical one only, grouping together various functions, processes, or activities which are involved in growth, development, attempts to adapt to life and to survive. Psychoanalysts differ considerably in their understanding and use of the concept "ego" or the concept "ego strength," so it should not come as a surprise if scales which attempt to measure the ego and its strength produce discussion and debate. Wallerstein stated in his discussion of the ego strength scales, ". . . not only have a variety of defensive, integrative, and conflict-free executive functions of the ego been drawn into this comprehensive assessment, but so also have been judgments concerning the pressures of the drives, the nature of the instinctual fixations, the nature and psycho-dynamic meaning of the symptoms, the quality of the object-investments, the nature and intensity of the superego demands, and the degree of the environmental stresses, together with the appropriateness of the organism's response to these external pressures."[6]

For the present authors, the resolutions of such questions is secondary in importance to the challenge of developing techniques to record descriptions and measure clinical change from written records, whether that change be characterized as a measure of ego strength, clinical adaptation, or in some other similar descriptive term. Whatever they may be termed, the scales focus attention on certain areas of human function in life, and they require the person who uses them to think more sharply about the "ego" and about human adaptation. Some clinicians object to scales as too confining, forcing incorrect or unsubtle judgments. Our experience has been the opposite, that scales sharpen the user's evalua-tions and broaden his horizons, even when—or because!—they are shown to be deficient in certain respects. It may be that the same things could be studied more economically, or with a less complex instrument (subse-quent work will investigate this point), but there is no doubt that, in the hands of a coding team, the ego strength scales are successful in organiz-ing certain aspects of the patient's record at the beginning of treatment and then reporting complex changes as they may be recorded at the end of treatment.

The use of scales in psychological research is certainly not new, and electronic machines have been used before, although rarely in analytic work. The combination of clinically oriented scales applied with electronic machines to large numbers of psychoanalytically treated cases is a new procedure which is capable of advancing knowledge another step. Freud had an early interest in systematic data collection,[5] but when in answer to his critics he complained that psychoanalysis could not offer statistics based on comparisons of a small number of heterogeneous cases he was, of course, giving the only answer which was then scientifically possible.[2] It is our suggestion that other techniques are possible now, and that data gathering and data processing in psychoanalysis is entering a new and exciting period. Psychoanalysis has traditionally dealt with observations and conclusions derived from the treatment of one individual, or a few at most, as reported by the analyst who conducted the treatment. Such reports have obviously been productive and stimulating in the past. Many new observations have been reported in such fashion and many theoretical issues have been introduced. There is no reason why such work should stop in psychoanalysis, now or ever, but there is every reason to make use of large collections of information about psychoanalysis and psycho-analytic patients.

Multiple variables can now be correlated simultaneously by electronic machine techniques. The significant patterns which emerge present a broad view of the experience of many psychoanalysts working with large numbers of psychoanalytic patients. Observations and conclusions derived in this manner cannot be duplicated by the observations of individuals or small groups of analysts working with a more limited number of patients no matter how astute, experienced, and intuitive these analysts may be. Knowledge gained from the application of electronic machine techniques complements that derived from the intensive study of the individual patient.

Ego psychology itself is not the only subject which could be approached with these new methods of data processing. Similar techniques can be applied to studies which would attempt to classify behavior or diagnosis in psychoanalysis, and to indexing and analyzing the material of inter-views as recorded in any of a variety of ways. Studies of prediction, a lively area of psychoanalytic research interest, might utilize such tech-niques. Work on the therapeutic process and on follow-up studies could also employ such an approach. Relationships of social class to the modes of treatment sought, recommended, and utilized would appear to lend themselves naturally to such an investigative tool.

There is no need to review all of the possible applications of large scale studies, or to cite a number of workers who have approached some of these areas from other directions. The authors are of the opinion, however, that many such applications could be made with profit to the field of psychoanalysis. Further studies of this kind are indicated if psychoanalysts and psychotherapists are to be able to enlarge their own clinical experience, observe the therapeutic process from a distance, validate or invalidate their concepts and resolve differences with the aid of new information.

## Bibliography

1. Cooper, A., Karush, A., Easser, B. R., Swerdloff, B. The Adaptive Balance Profile and Prediction of Early Treatment Behavior. Presented at the Twentieth Anniversary Celebration of the Psychoanalytic Clinic for Training and Research, October 30, 1965. (This volume, pages 183–214.)
2. Freud, S. New introductory lectures on psychoanalysis. *Standard Edition*, Vol. XXII. London: The Hogarth Press, 1964, pp. 151–157.
3. Harman, H. *Modern Factor Analysis*. Chicago: University of Chicago Press, 1960.
4. Karush, A., Easser, B. R., Cooper, A., Swerdloff, B. The Evaluation of ego strength. I: a profile of adaptive balance. *J. Nerv. Ment. Dis.* 130: 332–349, 1964.
5. Nunberg, H., and Federn, E., eds., *Minutes of the Vienna Psychoanalytic Society*, *Vol. 1: 1906–1908*. New York: International Press, Inc., 1962, p. 372 et. seg.
6. Wallerstein, R. Presented at the Meeting of the American Psychoanalytic Association, Toronto, 1962.
7. Weber, J. J., Elinson, J., Moss, L. M. On the fate of the psychoanalytic clinic patient. Presented at the Association for Psychoanalytic Medicine at the New York Academy of Medicine, March, 1965. Ed's. abstract: *Bull. Ass. Psychoanal. Med.*, 5: 7–10, 1965.

# Discussion: The Adaptive Balance Profile and Prediction of Early Treatment Behavior (Cooper, et al.) The Application of Ego Strength Scales to Psychoanalytic Clinic Records (Weber, et al.)

by Peter H. Knapp, M.D.

Although I am no longer personally involved in the growing field of psychotherapy research, I have played a role as go-between in the uneasy romance between psychoanalysis and present-day research methods. I am familiar with the issues facing Drs. Cooper, Karush, Easser and Swerdloff, and Drs. Weber, Elinson and Moss. I applaud their attack upon the problems they confront.

I would like to discuss their papers together. Both communications have areas of overlap. They have common *conceptual strategies;* similar *methods,* in that they use some of the primary data, though they approach it with different questions and specific tools and emerge with different *results;* finally they share an important *socio-cultural milieu.* I wish to focus seriatim on these factors.

(1) *Conceptual strategies.* When man attempts to study man, that is, a system as complex as himself and a subject which cannot fail to arouse feelings in himself, he faces difficulties and has a bewildering array of possible solutions. In the field of psychotherapy research a variety of strategies can be discerned. It may be helpful to see them as ranged along four polar dimensions—arbitrarily selected, neither definitive nor mutually exclusive. They are:

   a. The dimension of *theoretical model,* going from simplified to highly complex.

b. The dimension of *intensity of observation,* going from gross to microscopic.

c. The dimension of *manipulation of variables,* going from naturalistic to experimental.

d. The dimension of *rigor* and *control,* going from the exploratory, hypothesis-generating approach to controlled hypothesis testing.

On these four continua the present investigators place themselves for the most part in a middle-of-the-road position, like a well-known recent ex-president of Columbia University. My attempt at humor is not meant as an attempt to disparage. If one is seriously interested in extending the boundaries of knowledge in this complex area, I believe that one should be temperate and flexible. Understanding is not advanced exclusively by intense focus on one part of the unknown beast under study, nor is the task of making our complicated psychoanalytic instrument of knowledge into a research tool automatically accomplished by methodological extremism.

Let me be more specific. The *theoretical model* of both groups of investigators is anchored around the concept of *adaptive balance.* I prefer stressing this term and the specific personality areas derived from it, rather than using the words "ego strength" which have such different meanings to different persons and which carry such a weight of controversial theory behind them. In focusing on the nine variables inherent in this schema, one inevitably *simplifies.* One must in research. The trick is to be aware of how one has simplified. This particular simplified focus upon some intrapersonal factors leaves out of the immediate field of systematic inquiry other elements—for example, other intrapersonal factors, e.g., motivation; also biologic factors; also a number of external variables, both as they may play a role in the patient (e.g., early trauma) or in assessment of outcome (e.g., social criteria of change); and finally specific factors in the other member of the therapeutic dyad, e.g., countertransference, commitment and empathy. The present authors are aware of such a variety of factors. To have attempted to account for all of them might have meant to design a behemeth. The question is how *useful* their simplification is—and how *flexible.* When, guided by the particular course of events, they see the need, can they shift models, like the master in Detroit, or must they plow along the road in the same old frame, be it Volkswagen or Rolls Royce?

As to *intensity of observation,* both groups have elected to study their material at the macroscopic level, using the rich resources of clinical interviews and especially of clinic records. This involves pros and cons to which I will return, but the important strategic decision was to make use of what was available in abundance, rather than to seek out new sources of data.

With respect to *manipulation of variables* both groups of authors elected to take the natural situation of psychoanalytic therapy and study it *in situ.* They left experimental manipulations for the future—although it is worth noting that certain "experiments of nature" presented themselves, as they do in such an extended study. For example, the opportunity arose in the material of Weber, et al., to compare psychotherapy with classical psychoanalysis in a number of patients who started at the same level of severity in several important respects. This opportunity gives a hint as to how in the future, using a carefully selected population, one might attempt deliberate planned variations in treatment modality. Another experiment of nature might be found even in their own material, I suggest, by examining the course of patients who moved from one form of therapy to another.

As to *control,* the decision was also to say: Not yet. With that decision I agree. Why set up elaborate, sometimes paralyzing systems to distinguish fact from artifact before you are yet sure of finding any fact? This is not to deny that, as these studies progress, a need for controls will not develop— a need for both intrinsic controls, such as having the final judgments of outcome done by judges who have not rated earlier phases, at least of their particular sample under scrutiny (the strategy of the Menninger Clinic research); a need also for extrinsic controls, using criteria for change which come from beyond productions of either patient or therapist, possibly even getting involved with the complexities of untreated comparison groups, such as siblings. If Dr. Weber and his cohorts can study 800 cases in 1/7 of the Clinic's present lifetime, there is no limit to what he can do in the next twenty years!

We have arrived at further questions of method. How does one get the *crude data,* and, of course, exactly what is their nature? In an earlier discussion of this work Dr. Goldman spoke of the gold mine inherent in clinic records. Certainly they tell much—sometimes too much. I gather that the change has been in the clinic as a whole toward having weekly summaries, rather than verbatim notes. Obvious advantages accrue in following the broad sweep of a case. Disadvantages should also be noted. Records inevitably distort and omit. In particular evidence about change may be distorted, and evidence about just what the doctor did may be omitted. In our own work we have gone so far as to say that if one really wants to know about the latter, the minimum is a careful typescript of interviews. (And proponents of studying filmed interviews thunder that even such material is a travesty, omitting over 50% of the crucial interchange.) Obviously we are faced with the Scylla of distortion and the Charybdis of overcomplexity. A possible answer is to seize both horns of the dilemma—though gingerly. By this I mean to summarize sweeps of time but also to do considerable verbatim recording (with or without tape recorder), and then to sample systematically.

Gold is worth little until it has been extracted from ore. What further methods have been applied to reduce these data? The basic tool of both studies, whether working with clinical interviews or records, has been to apply scales, based on the model of adaptive balance. It is an accepted method—relying on definitions and applications of them by practiced judges—based upon our conventional scientific "morality," that science begins with quantification. It is worth noting that it had been criticized from two sides. Psychoanalytic clinicians protest that such ratings do violence to subtle clinical concepts and the complexity of clinical phenomena, when these are forced into procrustean scales. The detailed naturalistic investigator (such as Scheflen and Birdwhistell) protest from a different direction that such scales represent pseudoquantities based on clinical concepts such as transference which have not been verified as true entities. Again I like the middle of the road. (Perhaps I should say I like Ike!) I agree with Dr. Weber that our clinical concepts are sharpened by defining them and applying our definitions. The task need not perpetuate conceptual rigidity; if we are constantly confronting concepts with actual raw phenomena. Again this leads to a plea in long-range design that detailed material about transactions in the therapeutic situation be included.

The use of scaling methods presents problems. One is that of reliability between judges. In dealing with this one can iron out differences in prolonged committee session, or decide, which in part Dr. Weber and his co-authors did, to live with the differences. The latter choice, which may also yield interesting information about differences between rating patterns and the underlying viewpoints that they reflect, has one disadvantage, namely that it prohibits using judges interchangeably, for example to vary them in "before and after" judgments.

A related and more serious problem for these studies was that of *sensitivity of the scale*. Does it measure the many nuances we encounter, or as in the famous barb of Dorothy Parker directed at an actress, does it "run the gamut of emotion from A to B"? The "A to B" difficulty was encountered by these studies and particularly acknowledged by Dr. Weber. His group could handle it at times by simply treating their data as dichotomous. However, when they came to making judgments of degrees of change, which might be small but crucial, the grossness of the measure probably stood in their way.

Fortified by the wisdom of hindsight one might suggest for the future a longer period of pilot rating, and expansion of the scale, the step actually carried out by Cooper and his group, so that it covers more of the range we encounter.

Two other problems in application of rating scales are: first, shared bias and second, independence of the variables. To what extent do common assumptions about the nature of the phenomena (in this case, for example, therapeutic effect) lead to "reliable" judgments which are nevertheless irrelevant (not necessarily "valid")? To what extent *was* a judgment of "ego strength" made in some implicit way by clinicians and then parcelled out to the nine component variables? The answer to both questions can come only from further detailed study of more material. The authors are aware of these problems. Weber and his group found both uniformities in the level at which the adaptive variables were assessed in their overall population, and differences when specific subgroups were examined. Exploration of these interlocking similarities and differences will be important in distinguishing more from less global factors, in the task of counting heads among the halos.

As to techniques of mathematical treatment of the data, the studies present a contrast. Cooper and his group used a highly sophisticated technique of correlation. Essentially, if I understand them, they compared a predicted pattern of adaptive balance with a given rating of outcome variables. Their results appear to be significant, but unclear. I am not positive from their necessarily abbreviated and preliminary presentation just *which* patterns and which specific outcomes correlated with each other. One must also recall a *caveat* issued by some statisticians though questioned now by others, against using techniques devised for normally distributed populations or quantities, on data which are quantitatively enumerated but not necessarily so distributed, i.e., the debate between parametric and nonparametric approaches.

Weber and his group used methods that were simpler. In their full manuscript they are able to display a vast number of enumerated data, giving a clear picture of many of the relationships which they found. It is gratifying to see it set out *in extenso,* rather than having it picked over until a small number of nuggets could be found which reached the magical 5% level of confidence.

Finally a word about results. Let us not in enthusiasm for methods overlook these, for results did emerge.

Cooper and his group have shown that one can select at the start of treatment, on the basis of sound clinical criteria, those patients who will do well as guaged by outcome criteria. They appear to have passed a point which a group of ours reached in a similar study some years ago. They are still left with some of the same problems which confronted us. One must be sure that the outcome measures are not just a restatement of some of the initial assessments. And given a patient who has "done well" over a six-month period one is still faced with fascinating long-range questions. Which patients do well ultimately? Does an initial, possibly compliant, attitude in analysis really lead to eventual change? Assuming that the latter can be assessed, what ingredients actually go into it?

Weber and his group, whose study covered a wider time span, found some further answers. Some are confirmations of the expected: patients selected for psychoanalysis are "healthier"; psychoanalysis is not the treatment of choice for patients with psychotic trends. But even in these "expected" results, the authors showed the advantages of looking at data over and over again, much as one must look at clinical material until the specific truth emerges. They showed that of patients with "psychotic features" the ones that did relatively the very worst in psychoanalysis, judged by their measures, were those who had had a large element of stability in their pre-therapeutic personality. The results reinforce those voices who urge a greater degree of respect for existing defensive structure. At times the results show the capability of revealing novel findings. I was impressed by the fact that neurotic "characters" appeared to do well, judged by their measures, as "classical" neurotics, hitherto regarded as ideal cases. The finding would appear to be another link in the chain of evidence, supported also by the two first papers in this symposium, showing that when an individual has erected a classical neurotic structure for himself he may be "sicker" than his more characterologically involved, but also less rigidly encrusted brother.

In short, there is no dearth of facts to be found out when we learn how to look and take the time to do so.

I wish to say one last word about the *socio-cultural factors* which have made these studies possible. Both groups of investigators had support, in terms of time and money, which permitted genuine interdisciplinary learning. In particular I was impressed by the fine Italian hand of Dr. Elinson, with its public health imprint. Both studies reflect a dedication to searching out facts. In that respect the Psychoanalytic Clinic for Training and Research, in a university medical setting, differs from many, though not all, other psychoanalytic societies and institutes. The Columbia Psychoanalytic Clinic is an integral part of a scientific community, receiving many kinds of tangible and intangible support, which enables them to pursue research aims. They have a commitment to seeking facts, which is different from defending a clinical tradition upon which their very identity, as well as livelihood, depends. Difficulties in psychoanalytic research have been both scientific and cultural. Of the two I feel that the scientific have been the more serious; yet many problems have stemmed from lack of just such a cultural milieu and tradition. The Columbia Clinic is to be congratulated for supplying these ingredients and these investigators for the use they are making of them.

# Applied Psychoanalysis

# Psychoanalysis and Social Research

## by Herbert Hendin, M.D.

The importance of applying psychoanalysis to the study of psychosocial problems, i.e. problems that are both psychological and social in nature, seems to be becoming more and more evident. Since Abram Kardiner, one of the founders of the Columbia University Psychoanalytic Clinic, is probably the outstanding pioneer in this field, and since I believe that no area in psychoanalysis offers more promise for productive research in the forthcoming decades, it seems particularly appropriate for the 20th anniversary of the Columbia University Psychoanalytic Clinic to attempt to chart some of the research areas that should be most rewarding.

A variety of clinical problems ranging from homosexuality to suicide fall somewhat obviously into the domain of "psychosocial." My own recent study[3] of suicide in the three Scandinavian countries raised one point that is worth stressing in the context of this presentation. Each of the three countries has its own characteristic psychodynamic patterns with regard to suicide—patterns that are revealing of both suicide and the culture as a whole.

To summarize briefly: In Sweden one sees what may be called a "performance" type of suicide. Based on rigid performance expectations with strong self-hatred for failure and set in the matrix of a particular Swedish affectivity problem, this performance concern is also traceable to an early mother–child separation with an emphasis on achievement as a way of earning parental affection. Life is often viewed as a "living death" and after-life fantasies envision a perpetuation of this situation.

In Denmark one encounters primarily a "dependency loss" type of suicide. Specific Danish features are a tendency toward passivity, over-sensitivity to abandonment, and an effective use of the technique of arousing guilt in others; once again, these features have their basis in Danish family patterns. Consistent with these factors were characteristic afterlife fantasies of reunion after death with a dependency object.

Norway derives from its rural areas what is best described as a "moral" form of suicide. It stems from aggressive anti-social behavior and strong guilt feelings aroused by such behavior, with the entire consellation cast in a puritanical setting. Characteristic afterlife fantasies of such suicidal subjects are of a punitive hell with torture by flames.

All three suicidal patterns are encountered in the United States; but as ours is a nation of subcultures, the multiplicity and mixture of patterns here make the task of identifying them extremely difficult. Sweden, Denmark and Norway—small in population and related, but distinctive in culture—give us the opportunity to observe their patterns in a pure form and under their original formative conditions.

After a study of suicide in Scandinavia, the "dependency loss," "performance" and "moral" types of suicide, as we see them in the United States, could not only be more clearly defined, but critical factors distinguishing the psychodynamics of each type, such as the differing attitudes toward death and various fantasies about an afterlife, could be identified and made meaningful. By limiting the variables, the study of suicide in the more homogeneous Scandinavian cultures simplifies identification of the same phenomena in the United States. In other words, the Scandinavian countries give us a vast clinical laboratory for studying the psychodynamics of suicide.

Such a "cross-cultural laboratory" would probably prove equally valuable in the study of other clinical entities. After all, the number of ways in which individual and social maladjustment may be expressed is clearly limited: suicide, neurosis, crime, alcoholism, and a few other conditions. It is reasonable to assume that these entities vary qualitatively, i.e., in meaning and significance, as well as quantitatively from culture to culture.

Depression, for example, often a second cousin of suicide, has a different form of clinical expression in Sweden from that found in Denmark. More common in Sweden is an anxiety type of depression in which the individual redoubles his activity with diminishing effectiveness. This symptomatology seems to be the result of a combination of an early mother–child separation and the young child's learning to use his performance as a means of winning parental affection. In Denmark dependency is encouraged to a later age, based on the suppression of aggression rather than on performance. Hence the classical depressive picture with diminished activity and a yearning for maternal care predominates.

That clinical entities will vary in meaning from culture to culture or in different subcultures should not be surprising. As far back as ancient Greece and Rome homosexuality appears to have had its own particular psychodynamic features and there is some evidence that it was integrated without the potency difficulties with women that so usually accompany it today. Currently I have been studying suicide among Negroes at Harlem Hospital and while it is too early for definitive conclusions, the evidence is already suggestive that these are striking psychodynamic features particularly characteristic of Negro suicide.

My own interest in the wider, even more fascinating question of the relation of culture to character was to some extent the natural outgrowth of my work in Scandinavia. One begins asking questions about the motives of Danes, Swedes and Norwegians for suicide and about the differences in the suicide rates of the three countries. Such question, however, lead naturally to a consideration of what makes a Dane a *Dane,* a Swede a *Swede,* or a Norwegian a *Norwegian.* Decisive elements responsible for differences in Norwegian, Swedish and Danish character turned out to include: ways in which dependency is encouraged or discouraged; methods of family discipline; relationship between the sexes; attitudes toward work and success; handling of aggression and emotionality; and attitudes toward death.

A character trait as well as a clinical syndrome may vary in psychodynamic significance from culture to culture. It is, for example, with some justification that the Swede has been called "ambitious" and "industrious" in the usual descriptions of his national character. However, psychoanalytic interviewing reveals the very particular meaning these traits have in Swedish character: that is, their relationship to the early maternal separation and to the emphasis on competitive performance as a way of repairing self-esteem and winning parental love and affection. Industriousness is also attributed to the Germans, Swiss and Japanese, but what evidence we have indicates that the trait in those peoples has a rather different psychodynamic structure from that found in Sweden. Thus, even when a character description is superficially correct, its significance is unclear without insight into its underlying psychology.

Of course, such delineation as was possible among Norwegians, Swedes and Danes was aided by the small size and relative homogeneity of the respective populations. However, having seen first hand the difficulties of psychologists and sociologists in studying these cultures, I would say that of most decisive importance in this work was the use of psychoanalytic interviewing techniques.

The information elicited by the usual interviewing procedures, even when conducted by trained observers, is of limited value and can be misleading. The answers to questions usually reflect what the subject wants to feel, thinks he feels, or thinks he is expected to feel. As psychoanalysis has demonstrated, individuals are not consciously aware of most of the significant attitudes and dynamic patterns shaping their thinking and behavior.

Sophisticated description of social institutions and social behavior based on their characteristic patterns have given us such provocative designations as "the other-directed man" and "the organization man." "Social character" is the popular term in social science for describing such patterns of social behavior. Character, however, refers to what one is—feelings and motives included—and not merely to observable behavior. It is one thing to describe social institutions and social behavior; to understand them fully one must be able to grasp their effect on the individual. This requires a more sensitive instrument than has been available in psycho-social research.

Psychoanalysis would seem to be such an instrument. In his daily work with patients, the psychoanalyst elicits feelings and motives, the unconscious as well as the conscious, the unexpressed as well as the expressed. Yet the very word "patient" suggests another side of the problem. Has the experience with patients any validity with a non-patient population where, presumably, the pain of sickness and the desire for help, which lead a patient to expose himself, do not exist?

In the recently developing attempts to apply psychoanalysis to the study of social problems, the psychoanalyst usually works on the premise that patients are a barometer of the pressures existing on all people in the society, whether or not they need or seek help. The natural outgrowth of the desire to test this premise is the study of the non-patients. Working in

Scandinavia I had the opportunity of utilizing psychoanalytic interviews with both patients and non-patients. The predominant psychological constellations seen in Norwegian patients differed from those of Swedish patients, but the patterns observed in both groups correlated well with those observed in Norwegians and Swedes who were non-patients. The patients in both countries seemed to serve as an exaggerated mirror for viewing the psychosocial problems of their society, suggesting that valuable results might be obtained by utilizing both patients and non-patients in psychosocial research and emphasizing the importance of studying further the possibilities of psychoanalytic interviews with non-patients.

Together with Willard Gaylin and Arthur Carr, I worked on a pilot project designed to formally test and demonstrate the psychoanalytic approach in the psychosocial exploration of non-patient populations. The full details of this study have just been published,[2] but I would like to give a brief outline of the procedure employed since it bears on the present discussion.

Nurses were selected as the test group, purely from the standpoint of availability. Since asking for volunteers would obviously have been self-defeating, the following procedure was followed: A hospital was selected where the investigators were not known. Forty nurses, the entire day roster, exclusive of psychiatric nurses, were approached. In a most general and non-specific way, they were told that only twelve of their group were being asked to participate in the research, but that since a random sampling was needed, it was hoped that all would agree to cooperate. All did agree to participate, if chosen. Twelve nurses were then selected by lot.

They were each seen for five hours on a twice-a-week basis. Thus the interviews were completed within three weeks. Spacing of the sessions was based on the desire to achieve continuity from session to session and to allow enough time for development of the subject's emotional reactions to the interviewing and the interviewer. It is a psychoanalytic cliché that the patient often exposes his significant psychodynamic constellations in the first few hours—that even the core of the neuroses may be represented in the first dream brought by the patient to the analyst. Based on this observation and experience with non-patients in Scandinavia, it was hoped that five sessions would prove adequate. Each nurse was also given a standard battery of psychological tests. The psychologist conducting the actual testing worked completely apart from the interviewers, however, and prepared an independent evaluation of each nurse.

Most striking in the study was the fullness of the psychodynamic picture that emerged with each subject. Associative linkages, transference reactions, and dreams contributed to information that was at least comparable to that derived from actual patients seen over a similar period of time. This picture was often in marked contrast to the self-image first presented by the subject.

While the subjects were non-psychiatric nurses who had never had any prior contact with the interviewers, it is certainly possible that nurses in general may have a willingness to cooperate with doctors that office workers, for example, would not have. As one observed the varying ways in which transference operated with different nurses, however, one was impressed with its intensity and the personal nature of its motivation, supporting the impression that it was not primarily a function of the fact that the subjects were nurses.

One reason for the use of the somewhat awkward term "non-patient" stems from the fact that the subjects in this study turned out to have as much evidence of impairment in function as comparably seen patients in psychiatric practice. There is, however, no reason to believe that nurses are a more disturbed group than any other. They undoubtedly reveal the personality strengths and weaknesses of a large majority of the general population who never come to the attention of any psychopathologist, either psychoanalyst, psychiatrist, or psychologist.

It is apparent that the distinction between patient and non-patient is not the same as that between sick and well. The discrepancy between how these individuals function and any textbook description of "healthy" or "ideal" adjustment was striking. The interesting question then arises as to what integrative forces permit individuals to function, often with purpose and adaptation, constructively and productively in spite of underlying difficulties.

Or, on the other hand, what makes one individual with problems seek help while another does not? It is interesting to note that the nurses with affectivity problems, for example, did not torture themselves over their inability to feel more—they were simply resigned to it in ways that private patients who come for help with these difficulties are not. Obviously a major factor is the nurse's own expectations and aspirations for herself. The very procedure used in this study could profitably be further employed as a research tool in understanding what does or does not motivate people to seek psychiatric help, as well as in helping to understand what molds their expectations and aspirations.

If the procedure used with the nurses proves successful with other groups, then the psychoanalytic interview should provide a tool for the study of the "non-patient" that is better than any other now available. The use of this tool in literally hundreds of psychosocial projects where one wants specific information about groups who are not patients, is an existing possibility. Problems ranging from the study of working-class aspirations and frustrations to changing sexual morés could be studied more sensitively and accurately than ever before.

The non-patient also provides another barometer for studying cultures and sub-cultures. My own preference at present is to use a variety of such barometers—suicidal subjects, homosexual subjects, neurotic subjects, and non-patients—rather than a random sampling of subjects from a particular culture.

Whether studying a society or a social problem, the psychoanalytic frame of reference plays a key role. Psychoanalysts working with classical libidinal theory have perpetually stubbed their toes on the implications and applications of cross-cultural and psychosocial research. Hartmann, for example, has indicated many times his discomfort with psychoanalytic studies that emphasize differences among cultures, on the ground that the essence of the psychoanalytic process is the uncovering of data indicating the underlying similarity of people regardless of their cultural background. However, based on the similarity of unconscious constellations, the same thing could also be said of individual patients sharing the same culture. The analytic process, however, would seem to be more accurately described as the uncovering of the different ways in which patients integrate these constellations into adaptive or maladaptive behavior. Analysis per se cannot be said to reveal the sameness of people. It is merely that an instinctual frame of reference tends to stress unconscious factors that are universal since from an instinctual standpoint the differences between Swede and Dane or Sioux and Comanche are not that significant.

Talcott Parsons,[5] the leading contemporary sociologist attempting to work with analytic theory, undertakes Herculian labors similar to those of Hartmann in trying to make libidinal theory a workable sociological tool. He devotes, for example, a major essay to demonstrating that social forces affect the ego as well as the id of the developing child—a commonplace that from an adaptational point of view seems self-evident.

Erik Erikson[1] provides the best illustrations of the difficulties encountered by those working even with a modified version of libidinal theory in attempting the study of a society. He decided that the ferocity of the Sioux Indians derived from the fact that when the Sioux infant bit the maternal breast he was punished, and when he became enraged he was tightly strapped to a cradle board. This suppressed rage was presumed to be stored up by the child and was later used to make him into a fine warrior. Cross-cultural studies of other tribes as well as clinical experience make it unlikely that crushing a child's rage on a cradle board would lead to creation of an effective fighting man. Certainly one would need psychodynamic evidence with individual subjects, which Erikson did not have, to support so unlikely a conclusion.

Erikson makes no reference to the adaptive problems of the Sioux, nor does he deal with anything that might bear on the creation of fine warriors other than the suppression of biting rage on the cradle board. The contrast between this study and Kardiner's sensitive examination of the adaptive problems and character of the warlike Comanche[4] makes clear the importance of the analytic frame of reference in doing such work.

It is now two generations since psychoanalysis began to tackle problems that had been considered purely the province of anthropology. Now something similar seems to be occurring with psychoanalysis and sociology. Will the lead in psychosocial research be taken by analysts interested in meeting the challenge presented by psychosocial problems? Or will the work be attempted mainly by sociologists trying to absorb what they can of analytic knowledge? My hope is that psychoanalysts will play an increasingly larger role in psychosocial research, for I am convinced that psychoanalysis provides the best instrument for meeting this challenge.

## Bibliography

1.  Erikson, E. *Childhood and Society*. New York: Norton, 1950.
2.  Hendin, H., Gaylin, W., and Carr, A. *Psychoanalysis and Social Research*. New York: Doubleday, 1965.

3.  Hendin, H. *Suicide and Scandinavia.* New York: Doubleday Anchor, 1965.
4.  Kardiner, A. *The Psychological Frontiers of Society.* New York: Columbia University Press, 1945.
5.  Parsons, T. The Superego and the Theory of Social Systems. *Psychiatry,* 15: 1, 1952.

# Discussion: Psychoanalysis and Social Research (Hendin)

by Eugene B. Brody, M.D.

In a general sense psychoanalysis *is* social research. Clinical psycho-analysis is a social process involving the immediate participation of two people. One of these is a societally designated helper. The other has adopted the well-established social role of the seeker-after-help, the patient. A shared primary goal is the modification of some aspect of the patient's thinking, feeling or acting. This usually means the alleviation of his psychic pain.

An important corollary for the analyst is the investigation of his patient's life history. This corollary goal involves no less than the synthesis of a biography containing the sequential impact of society and culture on the person who is now the patient. It is a biography which includes fantasies and dreams and other elusive, partially conscious traces of events and relationships. In a sense, also, it is a description of the ego, following Freud's conclusion that the character of the ego is a precipate of aban-doned object-cathexes and that it contains a record of past object-choices.

But there is another aspect to this biography: it is dependent in part on the stimulus which the patient receives from his analyst's interpretations of the evolving transference neurosis. It is not a static deposit waiting to be mined by the analytic prospector. It is a product of a social relation-ship, in which the transactions between helper and helped provide his-torical clues to the nature of earlier events. Thus, even in final form it may contain areas of conjecture and speculation.

Finally, the way in which this biography is constructed, and its very nature are functions of the complaints which led to the person's having been defined as "sick" and of the circumstances which led, at last, to his becoming a patient. Thus, the data obtained by the analyst from a help-seeker are deeply influenced by society and culture because these determine not only the modal ways of expressing anxiety and communicating in symptom language, but the ways in which such expressions are viewed by the patient himself and by others.

Dr. Hendin's first and major assumption is that a relevant sample of psychoanalytic biography can be obtained from individuals who are not in the status of patient—who have not adopted the social role of he-who-wants-help. His group of research subjects, nurses, were functioning members of society and did not perceive themselves as significantly impaired. To the degree that they were insightful into personal difficulties they were, as he put it, "resigned," (to which we may contrast the view of the emotionally disturbed person as continuing to "struggle" with inner difficulties). On the other hand, when these young women were given the opportunity to lie down on a doctor's couch and talk about themselves each was quickly converted into something akin to a patient. Their state of adapted resignation—or the nature of the intrapsychic and interpersonal equilibria which they had achieved—did not preclude the possibility of self-revelation. The opportunity to relate dependently to a non-involved, sympathetic but morally neutral, professionally trained helper was embraced in most cases readily and with ease, and, on occasion, eagerly.

The material gained from these interviews, in a situation encouraging the expression of usually suppressed thoughts and feelings, appears to have been significant, indeed. Certainly, in comparison with the rigid poverty of rating scale and questionnaire data it presents an abundance of riches. The question at hand, however, does not concern the usefulness of this type of investigative maneuver. Dr. Hendin has amply demonstrated this, and in a reductionist era, he is to be congratulated for redirecting our attention to the value for social research of extended subjective reporting in a well-defined interview context.

The interesting, and methodologically significant question here is: how do the data obtained in this twice-weekly, five interview sequence with non-patients compare with those obtained in the usual psychoanalytic situation. Are we scientifically justified in concluding that with this wonderfully brief method, applicable to an unlimited number of willing subjects, it is possible to answer the same questions which psychoanalysts have approached heretofore with the more laborious, tedious, expensive, narrowly applicable classical technique? Dr. Hendin says, yes, by stating: "Associative linkages, transference reactions, and dreams contributed to information that was at least comparable to that derived from actual patients seen over a similar period of time." He also suggests a therapeutic effect from the experience by noting that: "This picture was often in marked contrast to the self-image first presented by the subject."

Some changed self-perception in consequence of the investigative experience seems plausible on the basis of what we know about other brief confrontations. The observation of comparability of transference and related phenomena to those seen in actual patients may be more open to debate. Dr. Hendin says, the data are comparable to those derived from actual patients, "seen over a similar period of time." Is this similar time the initial period of analysis, somewhere in the middle-phase, or is it part of the end-game? Perhaps the mixture of hope and fear, of eagerness and resistance that is so characteristic of the earliest period of an analytic process will turn out to be a regular feature of non-patient research subjects as well. This may be especially true of those who, aware of inner problems, have been unconsciously awaiting an opportunity for help. But most psychoanalytic patients have gone through a long period of preliminary, unsatisfactory attempts at conflict-resolution, and have made considerable efforts to reach an analyst and to support a relationship with him. What is the influence of this preanalytic striving or its absence on the research data? What is the effect on transference and dream material of knowing that your contact with the doctor will be limited to five visits? What is the effect of knowing that it will go on for an indefinite period of time? What about the frustration undergone by patients during the long middle-stretches of the psychoanalytic voyage of self-exploration, when the shifting image of the physician may harden from time to time into that of a depriving mother or a distant and unknowing father? What about the shaping and coloring of psychoanalytic data by the patient's (and also the therapist's) awareness that the long relationship is approaching termination, with separation and independence for each from the other?

Perhaps it isn't fair to insert here, almost by a side-door, the issue of the investigator's own transference feelings. If, however, the psychoanalyst-research man is to do more than provide an open ear to his patients his own perception and feelings, at all levels of awareness, will be important as they influence the nature of his verbal interventions or silences. How does this position as investigator rather than therapist, and his view of the patient as subject rather than help-seeker, determine the subtle communications which are such an important part of the research situation? These are not unfamiliar questions. I am certain that Dr. Hendin has encountered them before. They become relevant, again, as we consider the strengths and limitations of psychoanalysis as a research method. Many of the questions which Dr. Hendin and others pose do not appear to require psychoanalysis to provide answers. They can be approached with the modified psychoanalytically oriented technique that he used with the nursing group. This produces material in depth, on the basis of which preconscious conflicts can be inferred, and on the basis of which it is possible to arrive at an estimate of the person's defensive and adaptive functioning. These are, essentially, cross-sectional data. They permit conclusions about the psychodynamics, for example, of disordered behavior with social index value, such as suicide, or of traits which appear modal for large populations; they also permit conclusions about the relationship of these behaviors, viewed psychodynamically, to the social context in which they arise. Whether or not the analytically oriented sample has the same value for the study of developmental problems of social interest seems less certain. The most traditional question in this area, stated crudely is: how do society and culture get built into personality? How can one describe in psychodynamic and genetic terms, for example, the process of acquiring—internalizing, incorporating or introjecting if you prefer— moral or ethical standards or value systems, in one family setting, in one society, or in one culture as compared with another? How is this system of self-regulation related to vulnerability under varying circumstances to certain types of behavioral disorganization? In what way are particular tendencies to organize interpersonal perceptions acquired, and how do they fluctuate, given changing patterns of threat, need-gratification and available defensive and adaptive resources. These are classical types of questions bearing on the relationship of society, culture and behavior, to which the findings from therapeutic psychoanalysis may be applied. Can they more validly and more easily be handled by time-limited interviews with non-patients? Or perhaps, do they require completely different methods, i.e., techniques of experiment or direct observation?

The fact that I raise these familiar issues does not dim my admiration for Dr. Hendin's work. I regard what he has done as tremendously significant and interesting. He brings us content, interpretation and new impetus to psychosocial research. But he also confronts us again with the need to decide just what methods are best for answering what questions.

# A Study of Basic Personality Traits of the Caribou Eskimos: A Preliminary Report*

by Joseph M. Lubart, M.D.

This report is an attempt to delineate certain aspects of the Basic Personality of the Caribou Eskimos. The various groups of Eskimos described by this title derive their name from the fact that until recently their source of food and clothing was almost exclusively the vast herds of caribou that migrated from Spring to Autumn North and South through the Barren Grounds of Canada. In recent decades there has been a marked decline in the numbers of animals ranging through this territory, resulting in severe food shortages and starvation. This has led to increasing contact with Kabloona† as the government of Canada attempts to solve the acute food problems and consequent emergent disruptions.

Since the Eskimo must increasingly face a changing economic and social environment, he is perforce confronted by new problems of adaptation to which his responses are conditioned by his fundamental character traits. It is toward increasing understanding of these traits that this study is directed, with the hope that such information might cast more light on Eskimo capacities to face change. The emphasis here is on the traditional culture and its survivals.

*This study is being conducted under a grant from the Government of Canada, Department of Northern Affairs and National Resources, for whose auspices the author is grateful.

†The Eskimo term for the white man is preferred in this report since it does not yet carry in the mind of the Eskimo the increasingly pejorative context that the term "white man" bears among other non-white peoples. By this usuage, perhaps the reader will not sense as strong an implication of caste differentiation between Eskimo and white as can be inferred with other non-whites.

Information for this study was derived from the author's interviews and observations of a group of Caribou Eskimos, supplemented by a review of the data available in the few ethnographic and sociological reports pertaining to this region. Older Eskimos were interviewed with the help of a number of younger interpreters who speak some English; missionaries were interviewed; observations were collected during a summer spent by the author in the Barren Grounds (1964) and from a previous summer in Ottawa* (1963) observing a number of Eskimos residing there; and from a few on-the-scene, well-informed administrators.†

With regard to the major problems of adaptation of the people under discussion one can do no better than to quote Birket-Smith:

"In very few places in the world will the observer receive such a vivid and immediate impression of the fundamental importance of the means of subsistence to culture as among the Eskimos and, as all know, means of subsistence in this instance means hunting and fishing. It is as if the endless struggle to wrest the daily bread from a barren and merciless country has concentrated every thought upon food and how it is to be procured to a degree only equalled by the hard struggle against the cold. If the conversation of the Eskimo does not turn upon new winter clothing, it is usually about the hunt and the contents of the meat caches. The sense for the purely expedient, without any tribute to considerations of aesthetics, which almost wholly stamps the culture of the Central Eskimos, must presumably to some extent be regarded in the light of their unusually hard struggle for existence. The worse enemy of the Caribou Eskimos in this struggle is the barrenness of the country itself."

In spite of the ferocious climate and the endless struggle against starvation and cold, this people has for centuries maintained a viable culture and the Eskimo has tended to be amiable; optimistic and hospitable individual. So long as his source of food and clothing, the caribou, was available to him in sufficient numbers, his culture remained intact and he lived by his ancient practices and beliefs.

The methodological approach to this study is derived from Kardiner's concept of psychodynamic analysis of culture. The following institutional practices constitute the data to be interpreted in this report.

*For this part of the study, the author wishes to express his gratitude for a grant from the Adele Levy Research Fund of the Columbia University Psychoanalytic Clinic for Training and Research.

†The author wishes to acknowledge his debt to L. B. J. Gunn, Northern Affairs Administrator and to Gabriel Gely, Crafts Director, at Baker Lake, Keewatin District, Northwest Territories. Their funds of knowledge and kind advice have gone farther than they know toward making this study possible.

## I. MATERNAL CARE AND INDUCTION OF SOCIAL EMOTIONS:

Infants and children are treated with quiet, non-effusive affection. During the first few years of life the child is hardly ever out of the mother's sight, always with her when she goes about, held against her skin by a band under the thighs and backside and partially covered by the spacious hood of her parka. In cold weather the baby is dressed in appropriate clothing. Feeding is on demand simply by shifting the baby to the breast under the parka. It was not uncommon for children to be offered the breast even at age three or four. Babies and children are quickly comforted if they cry both by feeding and fondling.

Parent surrogates abound, usually older female siblings, grandparents, relatives or friends, in that order. Adults, male and female, are universally kind to small children and it is considered extremely immature for an adult to lose his temper with a child. During two summers of constant contact with Eskimos, the author never once heard a voice raised in anger to a child. In fact, Eskimo women in contact with Kabloona mothers are amazed at the ease with which the latter lose patience.

Children are highly valued and adoptions are frequent. Infants are given to relatives or friends who "need" a child. Frequently older people who have no living children will adopt a youngster and several told me frankly that it was for utilitarian purposes. Nevertheless, the children in the instances noted were treated with kindness and affection. While an adopted child may be accorded low status in the family, equality is usually the rule.

Families were quite small and are only beginning to become larger in the past five or six years with increasing medical care. For example, in the 1960 census, the infant mortality rate in the Central Keewatin District was 258 per thousand as against 32 for all of Canada. From this appalling figure, one can infer the high value placed on surviving children. In interviewing women in their thirties and beyond, one became accustomed to asking how many children they *had had*. They would with distinct sadness make the tally on their fingers. In spite of the high premium on children, women do not speak in romantic terms of the coming baby and will say about giving babies away, "I do it before I become attached to it."

Sphincter control is brought about gradually and without punishment. It is with laughter that a mother will deftly swing her baby out of her parka to hold it for urinary or bowel function. She quickly gets used to her baby's habits in this regard. Vallee notes that many mothers start infants on a receptacle after meals at six months. I did not note much of this. Eskimos do not seem to ascribe any special qualities or magical properties to excreta. In fact, in the 20's, during the visit of the Fifth Thule Expedition to this region, Rasmussen reports with wry humor the un-European lack of fastidiousness that Eskimos have with regard to feces and to cleanliness in general.*

Weaning is induced gradually, usually at walking time, by introduction of adult foods cut up or premasticated. Nowadays, younger mothers object to the older womens' premasticating food for infants. Such a practice probably led to a great deal of transmission of communicable disease, particularly tuberculosis and respiratory system disease.

In the not distant past, female infanticide was practiced in times of want. In addition the mother could become fertile again and, hopefully, give birth to a male child. In cases of extreme hardship, babies and young children have been abandoned so that parents could go on and survive. This was done with great reluctance and only under dire hardship, but with the pragmatic attitude that those most fit to provide should survive. (More will be said about this in a later section.)

## II. DISCIPLINE

Obedience is instilled with quiet authority by both parents, apparently by soft voice and consistency of admonition. Eskimo children are definitely taught to accept and respect the authority of both parents, although the father is generally more permissive. Adult Eskimo males consider it unthinkable to discipline a child.

Good social behavior and habits are indoctrinated via the rewards of social acceptance and by instillation of shame. Eskimos are raised universally with strong shame responses with regard to community values and one of the worst fates that can befall one, short of physical disaster, is to be guilty of violating public opinion and being condemned by the group. One source of suicide among Eskimos is having been shunned by one's fellows. Indoctrination is very strong with regard to doing things "in the right way." In the past this involved to a high degree not only social

*By contrast with the past, Settlement Eskimos at Baker Lake now practice much more fastidiousness in their dwellings, although not with Kabloona standards. This may be due to long contact with missionaries.

behavior, but, particularly, adherence to strict taboos with regard to hunting and preparation of food and clothing. (See section on religion.) If one commits a wrong, but admits it, the group accepts and the offense is forgotten. A deceptive person, or one who had done great evil and kept it to himself, was (and still is) feared and could be abandoned by the group or even killed. While guilt is also instilled in the child, it is my tentative hypothesis that shame plays a greater role in social control.

Rage is strongly played down; to show it is to be guilty of very bad behavior, let alone bad manners. One of the most important features of Eskimo character is the repression and suppression of rage. A man in high dudgeon could be considered to be insane or could be an object of laughter and derision. (This is particularly notable when Eskimos observe a Kabloona who has lost his temper.)

If two men really disliked each other, the conflict could be resolved by a song duel. Here, in the presence of the community which would signify approbation of points scored, the two men would make up reviling songs about each other, sung to the beating of a skin drum. Major insults included accusations of incest, intercourse with dogs, keeping food from one's children, violation of taboos, and having the "cry-baby habits of a woman." No matter how deep the insults, the adversaries were expected not to attack each other and a man who would get assaultive was guilty of severe violation of custom and could be shunned. He would also be feared.

Envy, hostility and open competitiveness are strongly played down, so that all in all, the modalities of expression of aggression between individuals were, and still are, strongly impounded. From time to time, however, there have been violent individuals who would kill in an outburst of rage incident to great frustration or with regard to a particular quarrel. Such individuals were feared and outlawed. In certain instances, however, such individuals could be accepted.

Rebellion against authority was and is rare, whether among children or adults. The regional Royal Canadian Mounted Police constable noted that he hadn't had a criminal case in years and that Eskimos are strongly conformistic both to their own traditions, customs and taboos and to Kabloona law. The Eskimo is, in general, a marked conformist and conservative.

## III. SEXUAL DISCIPLINES

Masturbation in children is neither punished nor encouraged. In the past, there was much sexual liberty among children and adolescents. This has been curbed in areas of strong missionary activity, such as at Baker Lake. "Settlement" Eskimo girls in this region are now, quite moral and demure in their behavior. However, older women will speak with heartiness and humor about sex. In fact, in several instances they had to reassure 18- and 19-year-old girls who interpreted for me that such discussion was proper.

Many women with long contact with missionaries would say (as also noted by Vallee) that sex is a need that men have and that it is a wife's duty to serve him. However, from comparison of interviews with older and younger women, I hazard the impression that this attitude is mission derived and did not exist in the traditional culture, where sexual freedom and pleasure were much more frankly dealt with. (In this connection one can refer to a custom of the Polar Eskimos called "turn out the lights," in which at a signal, the lamps would be turned out in a large hut full of men and women, with obvious consequences.)

Incest between brother and sister was strictly tabooed and between parent and child was considered heinous.

One finding that cannot as yet be interpreted without further interviewing and study relates to primal scene experience. In terms of the close quarters in which Eskimos live, it would be impossible for children not to observe parental intercourse. This would be true even at present at Baker Lake where whole families live in one room, albeit in comfortable cabins. Many Eskimos stated that they have intercourse only when the children are asleep and not one out of over forty that I asked could recall seeing or wondering about parental intercourse. From this can strong repression be inferred?

While it is difficult to get all the information one would want for a solid conclusion, it is tentatively felt that there was little potency disturbance in males or frigidity in females in the old culture. That such problems can begin to exist in the mission areas cannot be doubted, but requires further investigation. A man without a woman on the trail would not masturbate, but male intercourse with dogs was not uncommon.

## IV.  SIBLING ATTITUDES

Sibling loyalties, particularly between brothers, are quite strong and maintained throughout life. Elder sons have the highest status in the sibling hierarchy. From an early age one becomes aware of the desirability of sons over daughters and the male child has more freedom and rights than do his sisters. Nevertheless, there is loyalty and comradeship between brother and sister until puberty, at which point they will often be too shy to speak to each other. A number of males and females past adolescence could remember embarrassment about sexual fantasies at puberty, but most had no such recollections and could offer no reason as to why there was embarrassment between brother and sister. Rivalry, competition, hostility and envy are strongly played down among siblings. On the contrary, they are raised to cooperate and share. Siblings are not played off against one another by parents.

## V.  INDUCTION INTO WORK

From an early age there is sex differentiation with regard to responsibilities and tasks. Hunting is left exclusively to the males and it used to be taboo for a woman to kill a caribou or a seal or a whale. The cleaning, cooking and preparation of the hides is woman's work, as is care and running of the household and making of clothes. The Caribou Eskimo woman is particularly adept and skillful at sewing hides. In the past, women have trapped birds and foxes, but when the latter became an important economic asset, the men began to attend to it. Girls are gradually taught female household duties as are the boys inducted into the practices of hunting and fishing. As boys and girls become able, they take their places in the family group performing their skills as full fledged members. There are no particular rites to mark arrival at adult proficiency, but a boy's first kill will be the occasion of much praise and parental pride. Little fuss is made of a girl's skills.

Within the sexes there is little or no status differentiation in terms of proficiency other than tacit acceptance of a particular man's skill. A good hunter never boasts and others will not elevate him. However, they will quietly go along where he selects as if it were their own choice. In most camps there is a man who is the best hunter, but he will generally not be overbearing. He is usually more imaginative, enterprising and proficient than the others.

The angakok (shaman) was the only variant from the uniformity of labor and even he (sometimes she) still performed everyday work practices and did not have the status of a professional paid for services out of surplus. The role of the angakok will be discussed under Religion.

## VI. PUBERTY

Status and duties have already been mentioned. There are no special puberty rites and entry into adulthood comes with sexual maturity and proficiency in adult tasks. Girls would be married at 15 or 16, boys a year or two later. Sexual freedom used to be practiced during adolescence, but incest to several degrees of consanguinity was strictly taboo.

## VII. MARRIAGE

Marriages are almost exclusively based on parental agreement, often made even before children are born. While males usually are older than females at marriage, the reverse is not unusual. It was, until recently, almost unthinkable not to be married, but widowhood was frequent due to an apparently earlier death ratio for males. Polygyny was not infrequent, but polyandry, while not prohibited, was rare. While girls are expected to marry the boys to whom they are promised via family friendships, theoretically the young people have free choice. In practice, however, non-fulfillment of a promised liaison can lead to dissension and broken friendships. Trial marriages used to be practiced and parents still cheerfully accept the offspring of the adolescent girl if there are any. Usually a girl will marry a boy by whom she has become pregnant. Before the missions there were no marriage ceremonies, dowry or bride price. The girl would simply go off with her man to live in his father's camp. Girls disliked leaving their own families and preferred marrying close to familiar haunts.

Wife lending or exchanging was a quite formal affair and still occurs tacitly in spite of missionary prohibitions. It could occur only at the husband's consent, usually with a close friend or "song cousin" or a welcome stranger without a woman. Taking a man's wife without consent could lead to murder or blood feud. In fact, such was one of the few, but major, provocations for aggressive behavior. There have been occasional reported murders when a strong man wanted a girl whose parents had promised her elsewhere. Rasmussen reports such an instance, where, indeed, although the girl's entire family was killed by a certain man, she lived with him happily and dutifully as his wife. It is impossible to determine whether this was a frequent occurrence by Eskimo standards. One has the impression that it was not.

Although romantic love in the verbalized and declared style of our society or in terms of an expressed magically enhanced value of the love object does not occur among the Eskimos, it is significant that a not uncommon cause of suicide among males is rejection by one's wife.

An effectual man may have several wives, often taking on a new one as the first grows older and less attractive. Usually he will take care of her and use her services in the household. In some instances he might play one wife off against the other for amusement. While the older or other wife seemingly accepts rivals amiably, my informants (older women in this instance) state that she has no choice, especially if she is old. She will tend to keep her jealousy in bounds, but can exert a sharp tongue if necessary. (I know one very effectual man in his sixties, who runs a well-fed camp. He has there "the wife he no longer uses and the one he does use." (The term "use" was provided by the interpreter.) In addition he has a third wife at present in a tuberculosis sanitarium in the South. He was an angakok and is at present, of all things, the Anglican catechist of his area! While a woman might leave her husband if she wishes, she has nowhere to go and will tend to stick out even a humiliating situation, such as the above.)

Although the woman is technically the inferior in Eskimo society, she is really in effective control of her home and can handle her husband with her tongue, usually quietly, but effectively. Seldom will a woman humiliate her husband publicly and, indeed, she will tend, at least according to the ideal, to correct him in such a fashion that he is not humiliated.* In contrast with this, Birket-Smith observes that only in the United States has he seen more henpecked husbands than among the Caribou Eskimos. The Eskimo wife is reticent to express herself and is deferential to her husband in public: he defers to her in matters concerning the household. Officially the male is in the dominant position in Eskimo society. In practice, the wife has far more influence and power in her marriage than

*I know of a number of instances from old Arctic hands in which a wife typically might correct a husband, but he will then announce the new and wiser decision as if it were his own.

is ever expressed publicly. Her role as the maker of clothes and the preparer of food cannot be overstated and her skills are as vital to survival as are those of her hunter husband. There is a saying on Baffin Island that "A man is the hunter his wife makes him." This could as well apply to the Caribou Eskimos.

## VIII. TECHNIQUES OF PRODUCTION

The Eskimo is essentially a food gatherer, garnering his subsistence from hunting and fishing, this particular group subsisting almost exclusively on the meat of the caribou. Fish are eaten if necessary, but if there is plenty of meat, fish are fed to the dogs. The Caribou Eskimos hunted the caribou with bow and arrow and lance, but came into possession of the rifle about 35–40 years ago. Much killing of the caribou, however, is still done with the lance from canoes at places where the animals cross water or are driven to crossing places. Whether the introduction of the rifle has caused the depletion of the game is a moot point. In any case, the men are experts at their task of hunting.

On the other hand, there are a number of recorded instances both in the twenties and recently, wherein traditional and conservative practices led to actual starvation when bands refused to go in search of game when, presumably, it was supposed to cross at a certain place. These groups insisted on the fact that the animals, since they always had followed certain paths of migration, must surely continue in their old ways. The amount of enterprise in a given band possibly depended on the pressure exerted by the occasional "camp boss."

The hunting range is open to all and no group ever would claim exclusive rights to a region or to the game. The catch is shared in the band, even the lazy or ineffectual being fed. It is unthinkable to let anyone go hungry, although a lazy man might be derided directly or by innuendo. He would likely be chided by his wife.

The man is the hunter and does nothing else with the game but bring it in or cache it. The woman flenses, cuts up and cooks the meat. She is expert at these tasks and, among all Eskimos, the Caribou Eskimo woman is probably the most skilled at the preparing of and the making of hides into clothes. It is striking to see the beauty of some of the parkas and boots in contrast with the squalor and general lack of material things amongst these people.

A major source of activity since contact with the Kabloona has been fox trapping for trade, an activity dependent upon the vagaries of the market in the South.

## IX. ARTS, CRAFTS AND SKILLS

Although they make implements and clothes, as mentioned, the Caribou Eskimos have had neither interest in nor any tradition concerned with production of non-ulitarian objects. Only recently has there been any craft development and this by outside stimulation by Kabloona. There are now a number of excellent stone carvers in the Central Keewatin District but every one of them told me that he carves only for money, that his desire is to simulate nature as much as possible, and that he feels that being a hunter is more in the nature of a man. In spite of frequent and probing questioning, I could elicit not one instance of an attitude that betokened motivation for carving other than the economic. (A certain man, perhaps best of the Keewatin carvers and as good as any from most parts of the Arctic, said, "Before this I was starving and feeding my family on bones. Now I do this, but if the caribou were plenty I would give this up and hunt them.") The carver has no special status in the group, in contrast with some other primitive societies, nor do other Eskimos express interest in his work except perhaps with regard to his remuneration.

All craftsmanship in the past was purely utilitarian and consisted of the making of implements for hunting, fishing, cutting, sewing, boating and cooking. As is well known, the Eskimo was virtually a stone age dweller until the past 50 years, making do with the natural resources available to him. In this regard he has always been very resourceful and most males are quite capable of making whatever they need. They put to good use all manner of scraps of metal, discarded nails and tools, etc. It is quite an experience to observe the inventory and variety of scrap put to use in an Eskimo camp, even more remarkable to note how many useful objects are made from Kabloona discards. This is not to say, however, that all Eskimos are expert craftsmen. But, traditionally, every man was capable of making the implements necessary for wresting a living from the tundra.

The woman's tasks have already been mentioned, with emphasis on her expertise in the preparing of clothing. She can measure with her eye and make parkas and boots out of hide that are perfect fits. She sews seams with caribou sinew and stitches with great precision and fineness. All in all, both male and female receive good training and develop proficiency in their respective utilitarian skills.

From the point of view of the arts, the only form of expression lay in the song which was always the property of the individual who devised it and which had no traditional significance as a folk song. These songs were often improvised, with a background of chanting by the women. They usually referred to the hunt, to past memories of good times or to tragedy. A good song maker was held in good repute and the community enjoyed hearing the singer, beating time with a drum, chanting his verses to the background of rhythmic refrains of the women, whether in the snow-house in winter or the hut in summer. This, along with the related drum dance, was one of the pleasant pastimes of the Caribou Eskimos and perhaps the only aesthetic expression aside from the skilled handwork of the women in making skin clothes.

## X. CHARACTER OF PARTICIPATION
## IN SOCIETY; STATUS, PRESTIGE

The typical group is small, usually no more than five or six families in a camp, frequently several brothers and their families in a band with their father, mother and grandparents, if living. Grouping, however, is not tribal, nor does such a sense of identification exist. Moreover, bands might consist of friends, with their married children. The average band is small for greater efficiency in hunting. When travel conditions permit there is much visiting of relatives and friends, and Eskimos like socializing and receiving visitors.

Family ties have always been strong, with increasing sense of obligation and mutual interest and sentiment in terms of degree of consanguinity, particularly between brothers, although siblings are generally close regardless of sex. Relations between adults of both sexes and their nephews and nieces are quite close as are those between children and grandparents. Relations between song cousins can be as close as those between brothers. Sharing mutual aid and obligations, while general in the given hunting band, are closer within the family itself.

Hunting the caribou is generally a group project, in which both males and females participate in driving the animals to the crossing places, but the killing was always done by the males. The kill is shared both for immediate use and for caching for later needs. No family or individual had any more possessions than others. Implements can be borrowed back and forth at will and, since food is shared, no one fares better than his neighbor.

The critical times for these people are the autumn, when the animals begin to migrate southward again and the kill must be adequate for winter caches, and the early spring, April and May, before the northward migration, when the winter stores have been fairly well depleted. Not much meat can be stored during the summer, except what is dried, because temperatures are too high for caching.

Most bands tend to have an individual male whose skill as a hunter and whose judgment about the game movements, tactics and choice of camp sites is better than the average. His views are respected, but not publicly lauded and, while his judgment might be accepted, he has no special status as a chief or formal leader. There are no such designations among the Eskimos. On the contrary, each man guards his individuality carefully and defers to no one except to his parents, both of whom he treats with respect and devotion. The term "camp boss" is a Kabloona designation, not one coined by the Eskimos. In fact, Eskimos who speak English use the term "bossy" as a pejorative description of someone who is overbearing even to small degrees, even to degrees of authority entirely acceptable in Kabloona society. The only individuals to whom an Eskimo might have deferred and whom he might have treated with awe and deference were the angakoks. The angakok was usually a man (sometimes a woman) of beyond ordinary intelligence, assertiveness and good judgment in human affairs.

The ideal goal of the Eskimo male and the major source of his self-respect is to be a good hunter and provider. He is, of course, competitive with others in this regard, but will generally play down his own attributes and skills. It is quite a contrast from our own society to offer to buy several beautiful fox pelts from an Eskimo and to hear him depreciating their value and telling one what a bad trapper he is. He obviously does not believe this, but it is the poorest etiquette for a man to extoll his own skills. Likewise, a woman will with great modesty play down her skill as a seamstress. An Eskimo likes very much to hear his dogs praised, but will state that they are inferior and of no value.

However, a source of individual expression lay in the song and in the drum dance. Here a man would tell of former hunts but, again, the songs on record seem to be nostalgic rather than boastful in statement. In the drum dance, much otherwise pent up emotion is revealed, even though the dancer does little more than shuffle about in a small perimeter in time to drum beats from his skin drum. However, it is most important to note the degree of tension in his movements, the sounds he elicits and the flushing and sweating that accompany the dance.

A measure of the degree of instilled emotional control in the Eskimo appears in ordinary conversation. One hardly ever hears an Eskimo raise his voice in discussions and, at least to this observer, he characteristically speaks gently and softly. The women may be more shrill and express more emotion, but the men are definitely reserved in their behavior.

Courage, good nature and generosity are the traits consistently cited by the Eskimo as the most desirable and admired in an individual. Courage here, however, is judged in terms of facing natural phenomena. By contrast, however, fighting in formal combat is not considered admirable, and if there were killings, they were seldom accomplished by face to face duels, such as among the Plains Indians. Killing by treachery was quite acceptable and to risk one's neck by giving warning to the enemy was considered foolish.

To have sons was of highest importance so that one could be taken care of by a hunter in one's old age. To be a widow or aged without a son was the worst that could befall one and suicide under such conditions was not infrequent.

In connection with role and status within the family, a word should be said about a practice which has perhaps been exaggerated and distorted in popular literature, namely the leaving of old people or children to die in the face of extreme food shortage. This practice has not been as widespread as stated and occurred (and may still occur) only in direst stress. The oldest and least productive would generally insist on being left or would go out into the cold alone. This was not done at the insistence of the younger and fitter, but rather on the insistence of the old parent and against the objections of the children. That the fact was accepted is true, but there was no compulsion or force. The next to go, and here by parental act, would be the infant, again with extreme reluctance on the part of the survivors. Available food would be reserved for the ones most fit to save the family, adult males. It must again be stressed that this practice was not widespread and occurred only under the direst necessity where imminent death faced all.

The author is acquainted with one old Eskimo who is not held in high repute by his fellows, who, some years ago, abandoned his two young sons in a snow house during a storm. They were found by another Eskimo also known to the author, who rescued them. To this day he does not speak to the father and other contemporaries of the father hold him in certain suspicion and contempt. Both the sons still are in contact with their father, but one son is, in the opinion of the author, an outright psychotic; the other helps support the father only because of a sense of obligation to him. That one son is psychotic and the other all but alienated from the father attests to the aberrant character of the father and he is, indeed, considered so by other Eskimos.

In studying patterns of status and, by extension, self-image and other aspects of character, mention might be made of one practice that can offer certain indicators of conflict both conscious and unconscious, namely, suicide. It is believed that there was and is a fairly high rate of suicide among Eskimos, although only two are recorded for the Caribou Eskimos in the past fifteen years. The author collected from various older Eskimos their recollections of reasons for which they had known people to commit suicide:

1. If a child dies, the parent might want to die too, particularly the father, especially if there was little food. Even if it were for other causes, the parent could never be happy again after losing a child.
2. Sometimes if a wife would not obey her husband, or disliked him or treated him with disrespect, he would not want to live and might kill himself.
3. If a man did an evil thing and the group rejected him and either left him or drove him out, he might kill himself. (Very rarely would he turn on the group and attack individuals in it.)
4. Even if someone did something evil by accident, such as inadvertently causing a death, especially of a loved one, he could be haunted by *guilt* and might kill himself. This could occur even if his fellows blamed him not at all and considered him a good person.
5. If one is old and has no son to look to, he or she might want to die.
6. When a man is too old to hunt and sees the younger men going out, he can hate life and want to die.

7. If one is old and there is little food, one does not want to see the
young ones die, and, therefore, might kill oneself to help one's family.

This brief and incomplete inventory of reasons for suicide does indicate
a potential for depression and severe anxiety in the Caribou Eskimo, a
finding which requires much more study in terms of patterns of aberrant
behavior.

Although control of aggressive behavior is an important matter in
Eskimo interpersonal relations, it must be stressed that the Caribou
Eskimo male (or female) is not an inoffensive and ineffectual individual
in his daily comportment. He is very much an individualist, quite aware
of his prerogatives as to privacy and the pursuit of his own devices. In
fact, he can be impulsive and is generally blunt and direct in making his
wishes known amongst his fellows. His capacity for anger and hostile
expression is well attested in the songs of derision. In general, however,
he is not easily provoked nor does he frequently give provocation to others.
His patience in the face of natural hardships is proverbial; so is it generally
in his social relationships.

Other than hunting and making and repairing implements, the men
passed most of their time in idleness. In contrast, the women performed
an immense amount of labor, the men not offering at all to help them.
Rasmussen mentions a typical scene in which a man lay about all day
chatting while his wife flensed and cut up fifteen caribou, gathered a
large quantity of faggots and moss for fuel on the soaking tundra, prepared several meals and did some sewing. He remarks, in reference to
the women:

". . . But to a certain extent all this labor has made its mark upon them. They
do not need to be old to have their faces marked with wrinkles. Their eyes were often
red and running with the smoke of the fire, and their hands were large, dirty work-
hands, with coarse, long nails. They had lost their womanly charm in the work, but
were always happy and content and ready to laugh, whatever one said to them."

On the other hand, when on the move, the men carry incredible loads
and often drag the sled themselves with the help of perhaps only one or
two dogs. The conception of division of labor was sharply demarcated
and strict taboos marked much of their activity. Concerning their hardiness
and the vagaries of nature, Rasmussen states:

"Their land offers them severe living conditions, and yet they think it is the best in
the world. To us the great contrasts in the various seasons were the most striking
features in their life; for they either live in a state of dire need or in an abundance
so wonderful that it makes them forget all their troubles."

With regard to hardship and disaster, the phrase, "ayanarmot" is frequently heard and means, "It can't be helped." This is not fatalism in the sense that we use in our society, embodying the idea that some purposeful force brings about an ugly event. To the Eskimo the loss is a pragmatic fact to be accepted as final and to be borne.

## XI. RELIGION, FOLKLORE

The religious beliefs and practices of all the groups of Caribou Eskimos were essentially the same, although there were some differences in the naming of the deities and some variations in their functions. The hallmark of their religion was the ubiquity of spirits, major and minor, who entered into every phase of daily life and those whose good will had to be maintained by strict observations and taboos. These observations were in no way concerned with rules of personal morality or human relations in the sense of Judaeo-Christian adherence to commandments as the means toward salvation and the reward of eternal life. Rather, they were directed toward assurance of survival and subsistence and preoccupation lay in correct observation of the details of activities in these areas. Violation of taboos pointed in only a few directions; failure of the game supply, sickness or dangerous weather conditions.

Yet, in spite of fear of and respect for the forces of nature as directed by living spirits, there was also, in contrast, a strong element of pragmatism with regard to the movements and activities of the caribou, who were thought to follow natural laws, not interfered with by the deities and not subject to magical control.

Preeminent among the spirits were Pinga and Hila, *both female*. While Hila (in some regions, Sila), was in some respects referred to as impersonal, Rasmussen's informants ascribed femaleness as did the author's.

Pinga was essentially benign, lived in the sky and watched over the souls of all living creatures. If a caribou were killed properly, she would return its soul to earth in another caribou. Similarly, the souls of dead humans were returned either in human form or as some animal. The Caribou Eskimo was quite indefinite as to whether the form in which a soul was returned depended upon the virtue or sinfulness of the human before death and it is possible that any concept of punishment in the after life was derived from contact with missionaries. In any case, there is little reference to the disposition of the souls of evil people.

Hila was in control of the forces of nature and could be most malevolent if rules were violated. It was she who sent gales, snowdrifts, darkness and cold.

There is a legend along the nearby coast that Nuliajuk (the female deity at the bottom of the sea who sends out the game) was seen by a man. He harpooned her, but she got away and dove under the sea again. The tundra was inhabited with a variety of creatures, some part human, part animal, most malevolent, a few helpful. Of particular importance was a creature shaped like an egg, female, and with one huge leg and foot projecting from the vagina. This creature leaped about the tundra with great speed, struck paralysis into anyone who saw her and, like the other malignant spirits, ate her victims. In fact, the evil spirits of the tundra generally were cannibalistic.

The angakok functioned in three ways; to cure sickness, to divine the best routes for travel, and to mitigate spells cast upon one by someone else. Casting evil spells was not common and was almost invariably ascribed to older women. The spells usually caused sickness. The cure of sickness involved the victim giving up all his possessions, which would be left on the tundra, and the angakok, after going into a trance, found out the bad spirit inhabiting the patient and expelled it. Sometimes it would be found that the victim had violated a taboo and did penance, perhaps by avoiding certain foods or activities for a time.

The angakok was essentially a benign figure who attained his status by undergoing severe hardship and privation. It was believed that only in this way could one attain the capacity for wisdom and insight. During the period of privation alone on the tundra, the would-be angakok might encounter his tornaq (familiar spirit). He might wrestle this spirit, gain control of it and, thereby, use its powers as his own. He probably also was able to go into trances easily and it might be conjectured that a good deal of self- and group hypnosis occurred during seances when the angakok performed marvels. In some, though not all, instances he had to validate himself frequently by performances. In some instances he would terrify his neighbors with implications as to his power to kill and some angakoks were very much feared. (It might be noted that at Baker Lake, a number of Eskimos interviewed, even though staunch Christians at present, would not deny the existence or powers of angakoks and hesitated to speak against them.)

There were many taboos concerning the handling of food. The general consequence of violation was the failure of the caribou to appear, partly due to their being offended themselves and partly, to Pinga or Hila becoming angry and punitive. Of significance were a variety of observances required of women soon after childbirth or during menses, non-observance of which could lead to food disaster. In these instances the woman was regarded as unclean. A number of important practices required meticulous attention in order to protect the newborn from illness or deformity. If men ate milt, they would presumably become impotent.

In terms of everyday handling of food and various articles for making of clothes, people, male or female, who from childhood had possessed many amulets, were referred to as "amulet people" and were not subject to many of the taboos, so that there was no danger in their performing various tasks that were forbidden to others. Each family seemed to have one such member so that, for practical purposes, there were few necessary tasks that could not be performed regardless of taboo.

The Caribou Eskimos did not seem to have the terror of the dead that many coastal Eskimos demonstrated. Nevertheless, there were strict observances as to burial and mourning. However, they did not fear mentioning the name of the departed as much as other Eskimo groups nor did they sleep for days after the funeral with a weapon handy. Mourners were not required to throw away their clothes nor were widows impelled to subject themselves to severe hardships.

There were varying ideas as to life after death, mention having already been made to the return of souls into living forms by Pinga. Another version of the afterlife was that people lived right on in another realm just as they were when they left life. Sometimes the dead visited the living and were greatly feared. It was also believed that the soul of a dead person hovered mournfully in space and was comfortable again only when a child was given its name. To some degree the child would acquire the better attributes of the departed, whose name it had been given. Many believed that it was dangerous to mention the name of the dead person until the name was given to a child. If a child is given the name of a dead relative, the family might address the child by the title of the dead one, e.g., uncle, grandfather, etc. Names are given regardless of sex and no names are considered sex-linked.

The following folktales are illustrative and significant of a number of factors prominent in the culture.

### 1. Kivioq

Kivioq left his parents and went to sea in a kayak while a storm was raging. Coming to a foreign land, he encountered a handsome girl with her old mother. He married the daughter and went to live in their house. The old woman, envious of her daughter, killed her while Kivioq was hunting caribou, stripped the skin from her head and pulled it over her own. When Kivioq returned, he was dragging a number of caribou behind and the old woman waded into the lake to help him. With her kamiks (boots) off, her shrunken old legs were in view and Kivioq realized what had happened. However, he feared her and went on living with her. But after each hunt, he told her he had lost his mittens or left his boots behind, so that she made him several pairs. In this way he collected many mittens and kamiks. When she became suspicious he said, "I am so fond of you, I will never leave you."

He escaped and came to a place blocked by the naked lower parts of women's bodies and could not pass until he had had intercourse with all of them.

Then he came to a place where there was only a narrow passage between two hill tops that came together and parted alternately like a mouth opening and closing. He slipped through when they opened, but just managed to escape, the tail of his parka being snipped off.

Next he came to a place that was completely blocked by thongs tied to poles (like those used for games and gymnastics). They swung to and fro incessantly and below them the ground was strewn with bones of those who had attempted to pass, were caught and perished. But Kivioq got by safely.

Then he came to an enormous bubbling pot that blocked the road and threatened to boil the unwary alive. He balanced on the edge and got around it safely.

Next he encountered two bears fighting savagely, their great jaws snapping fiercely and dripping, but he slipped between them and got away safely.

He then came to a dwarf woman cooking food in her house. He collected his spittle and let it drip down on her through a hole in the roof. She said, "What is that standing in my light?" and she cut off one of her cheeks and put it into the pot. He did it again and she cut off the other cheek and dropped it into the pot. He did it a third time and she cut off her nose and did the same. When he did it a fourth time, she ran out of her house enraged, with her ulu, ran it over some large stones and cut through them as if they were meat.

She said, "I would skin you just like that if only I could reach you." But Kivioq raised his lance and cried, "I could harpoon you just like that," and, as he did that, the inflated bladder attached to the lance burst and the old woman dropped down dead, killed by the sharp crack.

Then he came to a house where there lived a woman with a tail made of iron. Kivioq remained there for the night, but before going to sleep he laid a large flat stone on his breast. When she thought he was asleep she rose and let herself fall on him so as to pierce him with her tail, but it broke on the stone and she fell down dead.

Then he continued on his journey and came to a place where the water was blocked by a huge mussel which opened and closed its shells. He paddled through quickly as it opened and made it by such a narrow margin that the rear of his kayak was nipped off. The mussel said, "The giant mussel almost had you there," and it sank to the bottom of the sea.

When at last he recognized that he had come to his own land he began to sing loudly with joy. His old father and mother had been sitting on a large rock waiting for him ever since he had left and had worn two hollows in the stone. And when they saw him they were so happy that they fell over backwards and died. After this Kivioq was so unhappy that he didn't care to stay in his own land any more and went back to live in the lands he had visited.

2. *Igimarahugjuk*

Igimarahugjuk ate human flesh. There were no caribou in the country or salmon in the lakes where he lived, for they had gone off elsewhere. So, often there was nothing to eat in the region and people would starve to death. But Igimarahugjuk would not starve and so he ate his children. His wife, however, ate lice and kept herself alive that way. He sent her out into the country to gather moss and twigs and killed their children and boiled their flesh. And the wife fled to her brothers and told them that her husband had eaten their children. They hid her and soon Igimarahugjuk came with grief and said that his wife and all their children had died of hunger. His brothers-in-law consoled him and said they would hold a song feast when evening came. And they ate and played games with the stretched thongs and sang songs and were glad and Igimarahugjuk was the noisiest of them all. Then his brothers-in-law sang:

"Igimarahugjuk eats men's flesh!
Igimarahugjuk eats his children!"

During the game they had tied his arms fast to a piece of wood. He broke it in his rage and stabbed himself in the stomach with it and the brothers-in-law killed him. But then no one would believe that his wife had eaten only lice and they killed her too, and cut open her stomach and saw that it was truly filled with lice. But all the lice turned into mosquitoes and flew out over the land and it is said that that is where the mosquitoes came from.

3. *Creation of the Sun and the Moon*

A brother and sister had incest and were ashamed. The sister walked off mournfully followed by her brother and they walked off the end of the earth and into the sky. She became the sun and he the moon and they can never come together again.

4. *Creation of Thunder and Lightning*

A brother and sister stole a caribou skin and a piece of flint. They became ashamed and fearful of what would be done to them if they were caught. They decided to change into something else, but each animal they thought of could be killed and eaten. So they became thunder and lightning and were invulnerable and when they shake the skin there is thunder and the stone makes lightning.

5. *Creation of Fog*

A man was carried off by a bear, but pretending that he was dead he sprang up and killed it with an axe. The bear's wife had a human skin filled with fat and the man cut a hole in it so the fat ran out. He ran off and she stayed to lick up the fat. Then he drew a line on the ground with his finger and a great river sprang up. She asked how he got across and he said he had drunk it all up. So she did so too and burst open and all the water she'd drunk became fog and that's how fog was made.

6.

Once when there was no food a man and woman caught one willow grouse and began to eat it. Two children came and the man asked the woman if she wasn't going to give them some to eat. She said she'd already given them one foot, half for each. There are a number of tales of canibal ogresses and many stories of animals outwitting each other. As has been mentioned, many of the humanoid creatures believed to inhabit the tundra are cannibals.

## INTERPRETATION OF THE FOREGOING DATA

Any attempt to understand the characterological traits of individuals in this or any society must give primary consideration to the balance of forces that summate into the homeostatic pattern of the society. Regardless of negative and divisive factors, a culture will remain viable if there is a sufficient quantum of satisfaction of basic needs, effective superego formation, an adequate range of permitted activities and effective modes of social control of antagonistic mechanisms. Although there is character individuation in any group, there is, nonetheless, a broad spectrum of personality traits common to all members of a given culture since all were exposed during development to a variety of practices to which all must respond and more or less conform. Deviations will give rise usually to some degree of negative reaction by the group as a whole and there will be recognizable systems of expression of sanction and disapproval. Moreover, even the nature and boundaries of individuation are in many cases governed by institutionalized sanctions.

It is to the patterns of shared response that the term Basic Personality refers in this study and it is to these traits that the following analysis of the data addresses itself.

No one can define how any culture started, but it is possible to take a cross section at any given point in time and to study the relevant relationships between the problems of adaptation of the group as a whole, emergent institutionalized practices directed toward adaptation and basic character traits resulting from interaction between the individual and these practices.

The most striking single fact in this culture is the necessity for tremendous preoccupation with getting food and keeping warm, to the exclusion almost entirely of activity directed toward other modes of action and thought. The fierce climate and the intense efforts required to secure game and shelter seem to have subordinated all activity and to have conditioned the development of institutions strikingly vectored about the needs for cooperation, playing down of hostility both inter- and intrafamilially, and the growth of a "philosophy" of life and the universe that protects one as much as possible from anxious awareness of the true precariousness of existence. Yet, juxtaposed to the latter, is at the same time a large capacity for pragmatic recognition of the vagaries of life and ability to find pleasure and satisfaction in spite of an environment of great hardship.

A survey of the foregoing inventory of institutionalized practices reveals that these needs have been subserved by the following modes:

1. Sharing of the hunting grounds and game.
2. Impossibility of accumulation of wealth.
3. Group attitudes against display of rage, envy, overbearing behavior or marked competitiveness.
4. Socially sanctioned means toward handling disputes via the song duel.
5. Group readiness to accept even a wrongdoer so long as he admitted his error and was not secretive.
6. Wife lending and exchange.
7. Promising children in marriage.
8. Adoptions.
9. Nominal equality between adult males and absence of formal chieftainship or leadership.
10. Non-interference with another's privacy unless a transgression had been committed of significance to the entire group, such as violation of hunting or food taboos.
11. Easy acceptance into the group by role fulfillment.
12. Permissive child rearing and the use of the reward system for teaching of necessary skills.

13. Indoctrination of both guilt and shame systems with regard to social norms.
14. Playing down of sibling rivalry.
15. Abundance of kind parent surrogates.
16. Clear distinction between male and female roles, with each in effective control in his own sphere.
17. Institutionalized means whereby more assertive or superior individuals, usually males, could utilize energies without threatening group stability, namely, by becoming an angakok. Superior hunters could be tacitly accepted as "Camp Boss."

On the positive side of the coin, these factors lend themselves for both male and female, to personality traits conducive to a high degree of capacity for cooperation and confidence in group membership. The individual, assured that basic needs for food, sex and companionship will be gratified and that there will be a minimum of negative attitudes overtly expressed toward him, emerges as an amiable, hospitable person, expectant of and ready to offer good will and assistance cheerfully. He has confidence in his capacity to handle everyday functions and severely trying conditions as well. He is essentially optimistic, calm in the face of either minor or severe difficulty, little given to overt anxiety or panic, and slow to anger or violence. He is anything but an anxious, suspicious, conniving or quarrelsome person. He derives his self-esteem from his proven capacity at role-fulfillment and from tacit group approval for living by accepted values.

The product of kindly child care and adult protectiveness, he is strikingly stoical and calm in the face of pain or illness. This is not merely a product of pride (although this element does exist), but is rather a projection of unconscious magical and reality oriented expectations of help derived from gentle and willing parental care during his infancy. Although in the old religion disease was partly believed to be visitation by evil spirits and could therefore be interpreted as caused by someone casting a spell, such belief was not widespread. That it could exist is attested by the fear of women, especially old ones, so rife in the folklore. It is worth observing that the wishing of and fear of evil between people seems to have been far outweighed by expectations of good will.

That a goodly element of stoicism derives from other than some of the salubrious sources enumerated above goes without saying and leads to discussion of some aspects of Eskimo Ego defenses. As has been strongly implied, one of the most important areas of Eskimo social control lies in the mechanisms of suppression and repression of rage, which, coupled with the Ego defense of isolation of painful feeling, protects him from otherwise unbearable emergency states.

In terms of his stoicism, the previously mentioned term "ayanarmot" is to be noted. This phrase, meaning, "It can't be helped," represents one of the most frequent expressions of Eskimo attitudes in the face of disaster. It is not of the order of magnitude of fatalism as known in our culture. To us, the concept of Fate implies some purposeful order and, therefore, protects us from fear of oblivion or total loss by implying some positive end. The Eskimo has no such notion. In the face of his enormous mortality rate and the rigors of a harsh and dangerous climate, he is a pragmatist about the things of the earth which he wishes to enjoy while he can. The need to isolate feeling in order to bear frequent and dreadful disasters, particularly the death of loved ones, becomes a most useful mechanism against anxiety, despair and depression. This system might serve, in part, to explain Eskimo behavior, which, in some circumstances might appear to the uninitiated observer to be indifferent and cold, when such is truly not the case.

Thus far, the positive aspects of the integrative systems listed have been discussed. What might lie on the other side of the coin for people who, in order to achieve the high degrees of cooperation necessary for survival in their clime, must pay for the price of conformism, with its concomitant necessity for marked repression of rage and its derivitives such as envy, overt competitiveness and self assertion? While further field observation is necessary, some tentative hypotheses might be offered, which appear to be substantiated by current evidence and, in certain connections, from the old folklore. While, on the other hand, permissive child rearing can lead to an adult addicted to acting out and impatient with frustration, it can also lead to an individual quite capable of cooperation and highly skilled in cirumscribed areas, if the permissiveness is confined and per-formance rewarded, while unwelcome modalities are gradually inhibited. It would seem that the Eskimo child, particularly the boy, while permitted a wide latitude of free behavior, also learns social conformism via the indoctrination of shame. While not all Eskimos are the same, of course, by and large the repression and suppression of blatant assertiveness seem to have been practiced among the Caribou Eskimos, according to Birket-

Smith, before the Missonary era. The camp boss, however, has been common among these people, indicating a need for a leader.

The recorded instances of inertia, confusion of purpose and disaster when the caribou herds began to fail to follow traditional routes of migration, attest to constriction of imagination and binding of initiative incident to conformist patterns. Can such tendencies be the product of impounded capacity for self-assertion? In our own society, certainly, the obsessional individual, bound to an obedience system and fearful of asserting himself, shows marked inhibition of initiative and imagination. Can this be true as well for the Caribou Eskimo, described even forty years ago by Birket-Smith as a great conformist? There are indications that such traits are present in this group. Unlike the sea Eskimo who ranges farther and wider for his food, the Caribou Eskimo for centuries waited patiently at the known crossing places for the seasonal migrations and frequently went hungry, even starved, when the animals did not appear on schedule. There are numerous instances when the herds were known to be not more than twenty to thirty miles in a different situation.

The potential for passive goals must be seriously considered as a future hazard for a group of people who are beginning to face the need to adapt to new economic and social conditions. At Baker Lake this potential has shown evidence of its presence by the ease with which a goodly number of Eskmios seem willing to seek government handouts as compared with others who scorn coming to the Settlement. While such character possibilities might seem paradoxical in men who are otherwise hardy, resourceful and proud of their abilities, these traits might attest to a certain precariousness in the self-esteem structure of the Caribou Eskimo male, who must constantly validate himself in one of the few areas about which life vectors in his world, namely, successful hunting.

For other indicators of Ego functioning, attention may now be drawn to the rich sources in the old religion and folklore.

Firstly, in the religion a major feature is that everything is alive, nothing is inanimate, and living things are reborn provided proper form was maintained in the hunt. The concept of the return of the caribou after they are killed (just as among the sea Eskimos the sea mammals are never depleted) constitutes a powerful system of defense against the major primary problem of the Eskimo, fear of starvation. The fact that everything is animate reinforces the defense system against the fear of death.

A most striking aspect of the religion and folklore is that in this overtly male dominated society the female figures stand supreme as sources for both good and evil. The supreme deities Pinga and Hila (as is Nuliajuk along the coast) are female, representing the projection of the good and the dangerous mother. In fact, the projective systems present a seeming paradox in this society, for the female mythical figures are for the most part malevolent, cannibalistic, sexually exploitative and castrating; yet, there is no question that the Eskimo mother is permissive and kind with her children.

It might be noted that for the most part, as in the legend of Kivioq, the evil females are older women. It has been stated that the fate of an aging woman in this society has not been a happy one. Without a son, she has been totally dependent on the graces of other people, she has had no status, and is discarded sexually as well. Such folk tales may then be the expression of the pent up resentment of the aged woman as well as representative of male fear of women in general. In the tale of the willow grouse the mother is represented as a selfish person who deprives her children of food. In the story of how fog was made, she appears as an outright cannibal. Such stories are common in the folklore.

How then can the maternal figure appear as so malignant in a society well known for its good child care? Recognizing the present state of incompleteness of explanation, nevertheless several tentative ideas might be considered.

In the first place this is a society with profound food anxiety, wherein even in good times, families may go for days without food, particularly in the autumn before the caribou return south and in the spring before the northward migration. In the face of hunger the child may blame the parent. In addition, since breast feeding is frequent and on demand whether for hunger or as a pacifier, and is often continued until age three or four, the oral incorporative fantasies of the infant have ample time and stimulus for development. This, plus bouts of true starvation or severe hunger might well stimulate the infant's cannibalistic fantasies with concommitant fear of retaliation.

In the second place, the mother is the source of what discipline there is and indoctrinates the socially derived foci of guilt and shame.

Thirdly, although the male is dominant outside the hut, the female very definitely is in command of most familial functions. It may be recalled that Birket-Smith referred to Caribou Eskimo husbands as henpecked.

Fourthly, primal scene experience must have occurred in every individual's life and was subjected to strong repression. How much of an effect this might have had on male potency is difficult to ascertain as yet; it might be hazarded that the Eskimo male can worry about potency, even though there is much denial on direct questioning. The epic of Kivioq surely points up fear of the female on sexual grounds and the male taboo against eating milt also reinforces the possibility of some degree of potency disturbance among Eskimo males. The notions of the female as "unclean" during mensus and after childbirth are also indicative of fear of the vagina. In contradiction to this, is the fact that sexuality outside of incest was free for adolescents and there were no controls and prohibitions against adolescent sex play. The absence of strict taboo on childhood sexuality could protect the individual from potency disturbance in spite of male fear of the female.* This question must remain open, pending additional data.

Regardless of source, the presence of fear of the female on sexual grounds and at the level of oral deprivation represents weakness in the male Ego. The significance of these male anxieties lies particularly in the potential for grave difficulty in his adjustment if faced with disappearance of his greatest source of self-esteem—to be the good provider. His Ego is more precarious than that of the woman in this culture, since her own pride can actually be increased if she lives in a settlement and can raise her children with better shelter, food and security than ever before. Signs of difficulty in this culture are already in evidence in areas where Eskimo girls have had exposure to Kabloona personnel and no longer wish to marry Eskimo men. (A future report on this subject is planned.)

Various factors in the old culture contribute strongly to female resentment of her role, among which are her traditional secondary position and subservience to the male, the harshness of her tasks in tundra life, the potential for discard as she ages and her obsequious status if she becomes a childless widow. Evidences of this resentment include her sharp tongue directed at her husband, albeit within the igloo, and, in a more

---

*In this connection reference might be made to Kardiner's observations concerning absence of potency disturbance in Marquesan males in spite of their great fear of females. Here too there was no taboo or punishment connected with childhood sexual activity other than for incest.

subtle sense, her readiness to give up children in adoption "before I become attached to them."

It is of interest at this point to note the various tension-relieving functions of the practice of adoptions both as to the giving away and receiving of children. The woman can be relieved of the pressures of providing for and caring for too many mouths and demands, or by receiving a child, can fill an otherwise lonely household and insure provision for future reciprocal care as she grows older. Both of these factors are consciously accepted and frankly stated by women interviewed. In terms of the community bonds, the giving of such gifts is an instrumentality for cementing family relationships with other families in the community. With regard to the children themselves who are given in adoption, preliminary observation so far reveals that those given in infancy seem to have no evident conflict as to being unwanted or abandoned, since they were fully accepted in the family to which they were given. However, the knowledge that such a practice exists might have some weight in the fundamental fear of the woman, since the giving away of children is generally by her choice and decision. The possible conflicts of adopted children might be the basis for fruitful future study.

Regardless of the areas of resentment of her role, the woman's general behavior with children certainly stimulates in them capacity for affection and cooperation, idealization of parent figures (especially notable in the deity Pinga who is truly benign) and a potential for self-confidence.

The remaining noted folktales are illustrative of taboo systems in this culture.

The legend of the creation of the sun and the moon is an obvious prohibition against brother–sister incest. It is also, it should be added, an expression of the potential rifeness of such attraction. That incest is the product of contiguity rather than based on the inheritance of a guilt-bound ancestral experience, is supported by the facts of the close quarters of Eskimo living and the emergence of the aforementioned legend. The lack of memory of primal scene experience among these people is indicative of repression of something once viewed and forbidden.

The story of the children who stole is indicative of Eskimo attitudes about thievery. It also points up in a sense the close relations between siblings, in this instance, brother and sister again.

Finally, the story of Igimarahugjǔk illustrates the horror of cannibalism and, significantly, something of the lower status of the young female in this society, wherein the girl is completely subject to the suspicions of her older brothers. It is to be noted, however, that she has her permanent revenge for her ill treatment by loosing the mosquito scourge on the Arctic. Again the female is made the source of something obnoxious.

In these folktales, the male is in general cast as good and heroic, strong and adventurous, but subject to ill treatment by women.

Another focus for observation of factors in the character structure lies in the area of affective disturbances, or, rather, in what we might discern as potentiality for such difficulties. The author is not prepared at this time to discuss actual clinical syndromes, since, so far in the present project, such material was uncovered incidental to the broader purpose of the study. However, a few comments might be made concerning the information garnered with respect to the former high suicide rate. The information is as yet meagre and is derived from the recollections of older people. Even if their observations are not statistically accurate, their thoughts on this subject are quite significant, since they represent what for them are sources of depression, severe anxiety and desire for death.

According to the consensus that added up to the list of causes previously mentioned for suicide, the precipitating patterns seem to cover a wide gamut, including shame and guilt, with fear of community rejection and abandonment high on the list; depression with fear of maternal abandonment as expressed in reaction to rejection by one's wife; anxiety and rage, the latter retroflexed, in the aged person, male or female, who feels useless and discarded and, particularly, is highly charged with envy of and resentment toward younger people who can function well. This attitude on the part of old people seems born out in religious beliefs and practices concerning the dead. The latter are feared and propitiated, particularly via the tradition of never mentioning the name of the departed until that name is given to a new born child. The envy and resentment that the dead bear toward the living disappears when they are reborn by having their name is given to a newborn child. The envy and resentment that the dead only be touched upon at this time, furnishing some indicators of points of sensitivity and potential breakdown in the Eskimo's personality.

Finally, on balance, despite rather severe underlying conflict patterns implicit in this culture, particularly with regard to the areas of male–female relationships and the vagaries of impounded aggression, it must be reiterated that this people not only survived a ferocious climate, but lived essentially with a good capacity for pleasure and productive human relations. Patient parental attitudes, permissive play involving imitation of adult activities, and universal affection toward children, enable the Caribou Eskimo to grow with pleasurable investment of skills necessary for survival and of human contacts. He emerges with self-confidence and capacity for responsibility coupled with readiness for cooperation and hearty enjoyment of life with his neighbors. He shows certain implicit foci of conflict, but these have so far in no way been crippling, nor have they disrupted the social homeostasis of the world he has known.

The potential tragedy of adaptive failure may appear if his food supply is not restored under conditions of nature or if the Kabloona culture cannot help him to retain the dignity of being a provider by helping him to learn new skills. He is at the moment on a cold and hard anvil.

It is hoped that this report of a pilot study might help to open further understanding of Eskimo Basic Personality, hence to cast more light on his capacity to adapt to his changing world.

## Bibliography

1. Birket-Smith, K. Kaj. *The Caribou Eskimos*. Report of the Fifth Thule Expedition, 1921–24, Vols. I, II. Copenhagen, 1929.
2. Birket-Smith, K. Kaj. *The Eskimos*. London, 1959.
3. Carpenter, E. S. Witch-fear among the Aivilik Eskimo. *Amer. J. Psychiat.* 110, September, 1953.
4. Carpenter, E. S. Space concepts of the Aivilik Eskimos. *Explorations*, No. 5, Toronto, 1955.
5. Hanbury, D. T. *Sport and Travel in the Northland of Canada*. London, 1904.
6. Kardiner, A. *The Individual and His Society*. New York: Columbia University Press, 1939.
7. Kardiner, A. *The Psychological Frontiers of Society*. New York: Columbia University Press, 1945.
8. Lantis, M. Nunivak Eskimo personality as revealed in the mythology. *Anthropological Papers of the University of Alaska*. 2: 109–174, 1953.
9. Mowat, F. *People of the Deer*. Toronto: Little–Brown, 1951.
10. Rasmussen, K. *Across Arctic America*. New York, 1927.
11. Rasmussen, K. *Intellectual Culture of the Hudson Bay Eskimos*. Report of the Fifth Thule Expedition, Vol. VII (Parts 1 and 2). Copenhagen, 1930.
12. Rasmussen, K. *The Netsilik Eskimo*. Report of the Fifth Thule Expedition, Vol. VIII. Copenhagen, 1931.

13. Steenhoven, van den, G. *Legal Concepts among the Netsilik Eskimos of Pelly Bay,* *N.W.T.* Canada: Dept. of Northern Affairs and National Resources, Northern Co-ordination and Research Centre. Report N.C.R.C.-59-3, 1957.
14. Turquetil, Mgr. A. *L'Eskimau.* Editions du Devoir. Montreal, 1927.
15. Vallee, F. G. *Kabloona and Eskimo in the Central Keewatin.* Canada: Dept. of Northern Affairs and National Resources, Northern Co-ordination and Research Centre. Report N.C.R.C.-62-2, 1962.
16. Van Stone, J. W., and Oswalt, W. *The Caribou Eskimo of Eskimo Point.* Canada: Dept. of Northern Affairs and National Resources, Northern Co-ordination and Research Centre. Report N.C.R.C.-59-2, 1959.
17. Weyer, E. M. *The Eskimos.* London, 1932.

# Summary

# Retrospect and Prospect: Review and Evaluation of Developments at Columbia Psychoanalytic Clinic

*by George S. Goldman, M.D.*

The chain of events that brings us here today started in 1945, when a small group of distinguished psychoanalytic educators took an unprecedented step and for the first time established in a university setting a psychoanalytic training institute affiliated with the American Psychoanalytic Association.[10,2] The occasion was accompanied and preceded by some controversy. Intermittently since then, the question of analytic training in universities has been subject to debate within the national psychoanalytic community. In recent years this discussion has been focused somewhat more clearly on the actual experience of the Columbia Psychoanalytic Clinic and the three other analytic institutes that have subsequently developed in universities.* Recently analytic educators, not connected with university-affiliated institutes, have expressed the opinion that the future development of new psychoanalytic training institutes will probably occur predominantly, if not exclusively, in university settings. Thus, in addition to the strong impetus generated by the Twentieth Anniversary, our own contribution and our sense of responsibility to psychoanalytic education impel us to review our history—our beginnings, growth and development, and indications for the future.

*Cleveland Psychoanalytic Institute of the School of Medicine, Western Reserve University; Division of Psychoanalytic Education, State University of New York, College of Medicine at New York City; and Pittsburgh Psychoanalytic Institute, School of Medicine, The University of Pittsburgh. Since the Twentieth Anniversary Conference an additional university affiliated institute, the Psychoanalytic Training Committee: University of North Carolina–Duke University, has joined the other nineteen institutes of the American Psychoanalytic Association.

The group that started the Psychoanalytic Clinic for Training and Research was composed of outstanding psychoanalytic educators: Dr. Sandor Rado, previously a leader in psychoanalytic education at the Berlin and the New York Psychoanalytic Institutes, brought his brilliant analytic mind, his exciting and stimulating quality as a teacher, a persisting doubt about the finality of any answer and the insistence that all theory and therapeutic method must be capable of validation.

Dr. Abram Kardiner, in addition to his work as a psychoanalytic teacher, had already carried out many of his well-known psychoanalytic studies of culture and had demonstrated how different cultural practices and child-rearing methods influence personality development.

Dr. David M. Levy had produced many original and significant contributions in the field of child development and child psychiatry. His work uniquely emphasized the application of experimental method to human and animal behavior.

Dr. George E. Daniels had pioneered in the application of psychoanalytic knowledge to general hospital medicine. Modern interest in psychosomatic medicine began when Dr. Daniels and his group started their teaching and research programs at Columbia-Presbyterian Medical Center.

Dr. Nolan D. C. Lewis, then Chairman of the Department of Psychiatry, supported the development of this first university-affiliated institute, and provided important organizational guidance and wisdom.

It is not possible to refer to the specific contributions of all who participated significantly in the early development of the Psychoanalytic Clinic. Such a list would include: Drs. Nathan Ackerman, Robert Bak, Viola Bernard, Carl Binger, Raymond DeSaussure, George S. Goldman, Henriette R. Klein, John A. P. Millet, Nathaniel Ross, Fanny von Hann-Kende, and Frederick Weil, as well as others.

The staff members of the newly established Psychoanalytic Clinic, for the most part, had been trained abroad. Younger staff members had had their training in the New York Psychoanalytic Institute during the 1930's or early 1940's.

All those involved in the new venture were, first and foremost psychoanalysts, interested in providing the best possible training and in stimulating psychoanalytic research. These aims were incorporated in the official title: The Psychoanalytic Clinic for Training and Research. Also, they were interested in bringing analytic training into a university and in utilizing the academic and clinical resources of a university medical school and department of psychiatry. Several decades before, in the early years of psychoanalysis, the organized medical profession and universities generally had rejected psychoanalysis. Understandably disappointed, Freud nevertheless in 1918[3] and again in 1933[14] indicated the desirability of psychoanalytic training in universities. However, in the 1940's, many analysts viewed the new institute at Columbia with doubt—some with suspicion.

It is important to emphasize that the staff members at the Psychoanalytic Clinic did not all have the same views. What they did have in common was an interest in an endeavor that was unique, and the willingness to experiment and explore innovations in psychoanalytic teaching methods and to re-examine some aspects of therapy and theory. There was a strong feeling that psychoanalysis and medicine would each benefit through a closer relationship and also an interest in the possibility of ultimate cooperation with other academic or scientific disciplines.

A special aspect of the academic and clinical setting was the availability of patient material for candidates. A major innovation was the utilization of patients in clinical teaching. Hitherto, case presentations in "Continuous Case Seminars" were entirely from written notes. At the Psychoanalytic Clinic, it was felt that patients should be presented in person so that students may have their own observations in addition to the selected material presented by the therapist. The general assumption that presentation in conferences would be injurious to therapy and to the transference has not been the case at Columbia Psychoanalytic Clinic where special procedures ensured review of the patient's reactions.*

The latter 1930's and early 1940's was a period of much ferment in the psychoanalytic movement and in psychoanalytic education in the United States. There was controversy and confusion about theoretic and therapeutic concepts which decades later would be discussed in classical psychoanalytic circles under the heading of ego psychology, but which at that time were rather suspect.

One cause of the turmoil and troubles was the difficulty and the reluctance of many analysts to accept change. Having mastered and utilized a set of concepts and an approach to the infinitely complex problem of

---

*Follow-up studies showed that the appearance and interview at conferences usually became a useful and sometimes catalytic experience in the analysis or psychotherapy.

human motivation and behavior, it then became very difficult for many to accept and utilize changes in these concepts, even when suggested by Freud. For example, the major revision in the libido theory introduced by Freud in *Hemmung, Symptom* und *Angst*[5] in 1926 was soon known in this country, but it did not seem to have much impact on the then current theoretic and operational concepts. In his lectures at the New York Psychoanalytic Institute, Rado[12] repeatedly emphasized this point and partially as a result of this stimulus, an authorized and approved translation finally appeared in 1936 under the title "The Problem of Anxiety."[6] A lag of 10 years in the translation and publication of an important revision in the libido theory does not suggest ready acceptance of change.

The changes suggested by Hartmann, published in German in 1939[8] seem to have been accepted by many analysts without the opposition that arose in response to presentation of the adaptational approach by Rado or Kardiner. This held true in spite of the fact that some of Hartmann's suggested revisions of the libido theory were quite profound—such as the conflict-free, autonomous areas of the ego and the indicated and implied change in ego-id relationship as referred to in today's paper of Dr. Karush. Hartmann preserved the structure of the libido theory by utilizing concepts such as "desexualized libido," "deaggressivized aggression" and "neutralization" to help account for the existence of ego functions that were not initially drive-related. Nevertheless, the original paper, which was published in 1939, was not translated into English and published in book form until 1958.[9] Again, this would seem to be a rather long delay in making available and convenient an English translation of a distinguished major presentation suggesting significant change in psychoanalytic theory.

It should be emphasized that the foregoing reference to the sometimes slow acceptance of change is not intended as a critical or polemic remark. This kind of lag is often characteristic of institutions and organizations and awareness of its presence is necessary in understanding the history and development of the Columbia Psychoanalytic Clinic, which by its very existence in a university constituted a major change in psychoanalytic training institutes. No doubt lags of this sort have already occurred in our own brief history.

During the past twenty years our staff has gradually changed. Currently only two of the early group are still fully active on the staff. Approximately

90 percent of the present faculty are Psychoanalytic Clinic graduates. The Clinic clearly has been coming of age as new generations of teachers have emerged. In planning this conference, Dr. Willard Gaylin and his Program Committee agreed that the most appropriate celebration of the Twentieth Anniversary would be presentation of a cross-section of the thinking and research of staff members who are graduates of the institute. Collectively the material presented reflects the adaptational approach to psychoanalysis as it is currently conceived at Columbia.

It may be useful to remark about the way in which the various presentations do reflect some of these concepts and attitudes. The first three papers (Drs. Aaron Karush, Lionel Ovesey, and B. Ruth Easser and Stanley R. Lesser) present a spectrum of clinical and theoretical material that contains similarities and a general conceptual agreement, but also differences. One does not find a "school" of thinking, but, we hope, individuals who think and who question.

Dr. Karush's presentation is an attempt to assemble and assess some theoretical considerations about areas of the psychic apparatus as seen from the adaptational viewpoint—that is, with emphasis upon the biological function of the organism, and upon the motivational factors, as the organism interacts unceasingly with its environment. The paper is a careful, imaginative and scholarly attempt to probe with reason and speculation into a highly abstract area where only minimal factual knowledge is currently available. Relatively few Columbia graduates have done much of this kind of exploration. Perhaps we have been held back by a bias that stemmed from a concentrated and too immediate insistence that every clinical and theoretical concept must be subject to validation in accordance with the usual rules of scientific method. We still adhere to this principle. Just as an object should not be defined only in its own terms so must the validation of a concept include more than its own hypothetical frame of reference. However, it is methodologically sound to divide concepts into those which can be validated in the "here and now" and those which serve as useful exploratory hypotheses that can only be validated at a future time when new information is available. Hypotheses of this type are frequent in science, e.g., in astronomy. We are pleased to see efforts in this direction. We continue to emphasize the importance of developing concepts and hypotheses in such a way as to make them capable of validation, either now or in the future. Note Dr.

Karush's effort to develop concepts in a direction that provides for a possibility of validation, e.g., in some areas by means of perceptual research, as suggested in the discussion of Dr. Pumpian-Mindlin.

Dr. Ovesey's paper immediately brings to the forefront a special interest and emphasis of the Columbia Psychoanalytic Clinic since its inception; —that is, not only the development of knowledge and skill in clinical psychoanalysis, but also the ability to use psychoanalytic knowledge in reparative psychotherapy. Only a limited percentage of the patient population meet the criteria for full-fledged psychoanalysis. Conversely, many patients whose severity of illness, rigidity or ego-weakness may preclude analysis should have therapists analytically trained to utilize pertinent analytic knowledge. Therefore, supervision of patients in reparative psychotherapy and didactic discussions of the contrasts and comparisons between psychoanalytic and reparative methods are included in the curriculum.

It should be said unequivocally that we differentiate clearly, and emphasize the contrast, between the operational processes of psychotherapy and psychoanalysis. We consider the proper and successful use of transference and transference interpretation to be a unique and powerful instrument in psychoanalysis. While we consider analysis the most advanced form of therapy, capable of achieving the most far-reaching goals, we also have high regard for psychotherapy which aims at lesser goals but can make special demands upon the therapist's skill, resourcefulness and emotional capacity. We have been criticized for retaining the teaching of reparative psychotherapy in a psychoanalytic institute. Thus far, whenever this question has been reevaluated, the staff and candidates have agreed that this particular experience is far different from, and superior to, that available in any other training situation.

Dr. Ovesey stresses the importance of clarifying the psychodynamics and diagnostic groupings of agoraphobes who are often so difficult to treat successfully. He relates this diagnostic classification to treatment methods, i.e., psychotherapy or psychoanalysis.

The presentation of Drs. Easser and Lesser offers a glimpse of psychoanalytic technique with a particular clinical type, the hysterical character. The focus is sharply on transference behavior and the way in which this may constitute a stubborn defense against the development of a therapeutically useful analytic transference. If the analyst, in a countertransference, responds to the defensive emotionality or resistance as if it were basic emotional response, then he misses the defensive nature of the "quasi-transference," a concept that can help clarify a subtle but crucial interference in analytic treatment.

The next three papers could be grouped under the heading of Research. The work of Dr. William Goldfarb et al., in addition to its general excellence, utilizes the experimental approach that has been so consistently and ingeniously exploited by his co-author, Dr. David M. Levy. Information is sought in the here and now with the hope that it will be presently useful in the understanding and in the treatment of schizophrenic children and families. Just as we feel that the best reparative psychotherapy is done by those who can bring to it the seasoned utilization of psychoanalytic knowledge, so we feel that Dr. Goldfarb's research, which offers very real promise, is appropriately being conducted by a team of psychoanalysts.

The project reported by Dr. Arnold M. Cooper et al. also seeks to obtain information in the here and now—specifically a method of measuring ego strength through intensive individual studies using the Adaptive Balance Profile. This project is extremely complex, not only in the volume and intricacy of its detailed studies, but especially because the group soon found that attempts to assess, to define, to classify and to particularize forced them to restudy, reconsider and refine basic concepts and ideas. Dr. Joseph Sandler of the Hampstead Clinic has reported that the same phenomenon occurred in connection with work on the Hampstead Index and that the enforced reconsideration of concepts became a most valuable byproduct of the research. [15]

The project of Dr. John J. Weber et al. constitutes the first attempt at a psychoanalytic institute to use computers and electronic data processing methods in dealing with large numbers of psychoanalytic case records (1,348 patients, of whom 588 had been in analysis). The previous experience of Drs. Weber, Jack Elinson, and Leonard M. Moss had prepared them for the possibility of exploring the use of Ego Strength Scales in large numbers by coding directly from case records instead of conducting intensive multiple interviews as in the Ego Strength Project. A different order of data would be expected and has been described. Both approaches will be continued. A point to be emphasized is the wide range of exploratory methods that tend to develop at a university psychoanalytic institute with the history and background of the Columbia Psychoanalytic Clinic.

The final category, "Applied Psychoanalysis," would include the account that Dr. Herbert Hendin presented of his work with suicide, with the Scandinavian cultures and with other applications of psychoanalytic understanding to social problems. Another paper in this category which could not be read for lack of time, but is included in these proceedings, is the report of a field study of the Caribou Eskimos of northern Canada by Dr. Joseph M. Lubart. These presentations reflect the continuation of the Psychoanalytic Clinic's traditional interest in the interaction of society and individual, a tradition started by Kardiner's original studies and carried on by Kardiner and Ovesey's *Mark of Oppression,* Hendin and Willard M. Gaylin's work with non-patients, and the two current papers.

Many other studies are in process but could not be included in a one-day scientific program. These include, among others, several dream studies, longitudinal studies, investigations in psychophysiology, genetics, psychosomatics and emotional problems of contraception.

To get another perspective, let us turn from staff activities to a glimpse of the total graduate body of our institute. During these twenty years 167 candidates have graduated. Eight graduates have been appointed chairmen of departments of psychiatry in universities. A total of 19 graduates have been appointed full professors in medical schools. At this time, of all analytically trained chairmen of departments of psychiatry in American medical schools, twenty-five percent had their analytic training at this institute. A recent survey indicated that, aside from the foregoing, at least 49 additional graduates had become chiefs of psychiatry in hospitals or psychiatric organizations—or research, training or clinical directors. Every graduate, so far as we were then able to determine, had served in academic positions or in research, or had provided service to the community through work in hospitals or psychiatric institutions.

A particularly striking and significant point is the way in which a group of analysts, trained to carry out the most refined, complex form of individual therapy, has at the same time remained interested in and involved with the broader form of psychiatric and community activities and the ways in which psychoanalytic knowledge and principles can be effectively utilized at the widest level of application. Even in the field of community psychiatry, seemingly the furthest removed from psycho-analysis, we find that a staff member of our institute was the leader in establishing the first training school for Community Psychiatry. A second staff member is a chief assistant and others are in charge of Community Psychiatry activities at other hospitals.

The reference to community psychiatry leads to a consideration of the dramatically changing psychiatric scene and the place of psychoanalysis and psychoanalytic training in the total picture. Twenty years ago psychoanalysis was just about the only shining light in a large dim psychiatric scene in which there seemed no way of knowing when, if ever, the resources could begin to meet the needs. Since then, as a result of untiring efforts by professional leaders and government officials, tremendous amounts of planning and work have been done and huge sums of money have been, and will be, spent to provide more and more resources. We have seen the arrival of more effective drugs, open wards, group therapy, therapeutic communities, and at the same time a tendency toward granting research funds to projects that utilize the concepts and languages of chemistry, physiology and sociology. We have seen the increase of analytic training groups, a few in New York affiliated with the American Psychoanalytic Association, and very many not in that category (at least eight in New York City). There has been an explosive proliferation of non-medical therapists—psychologists, social workers, teachers, sociologists, group workers, or individuals who could help. Twenty years ago every resident wanted psychoanalytic training. Now, some think of a career in the physiologic or biologic approach, some in child psychiatry or community psychiatry. There are more choices. In this complex situation what will be the future of psychoanalysis and psychoanalytic training? Will psychoanalysis be lost—through sheer dilution? Will the concern of some analysts come to pass—the disappearance of the pure gold of psychoanalysis as it combines with other metals to form alloys? The answer is definitely in the negative. The pure gold of analysis cannot be used up. It does not exist in a finite quantity. It is as infinite in its amount and presence as love, or life, or any creative, recreative or integrative human activity.*

*The following quotation from Freud does not express concern but seems rather to present a positive attitude to the broadest utilization of psychoanalysis in psychiatric therapy: "It is very probable, too, that the large-scale application of our therapy will compel us to alloy the pure gold of analysis freely with the copper of direct suggestion. . . . But, whatever form this psychotherapy for the people may take, whatever the elements out of which it is compounded, its most effective and most important ingredients will assuredly remain those borrowed from strict and untendentious psychoanalysis."[4]

From another standpoint, the utilization of computors, drugs or electrodes in brain cells will hardly replace the human capacity and need to feel and make decisions. We need not fear the "man with the hypodermic," who Freud correctly predicted long ago would be "on our heels."[1] Our working relationship with this man in a university setting sometimes enables us to learn from him and sometimes to teach him. Some who do psychophysiological research have been analytically trained at this institute, and, I presume, at other institutes. We hope to call upon the psycho-physiologist to collaborate in the testing and validation of concepts.

As a result of collaboration in other directions throughout the University, there has been in operation a permanent Columbia University Seminar which meets regularly on the general topic of "Human Maladaptation in Modern Society." In addition to analysts, participants have represented the fields of sociology, psychology, social psychology, animal psychology, social work, economics, law, architecture, housing, and others.

Ten years ago, at the Tenth Anniversary of the Columbia Psychoanalytic Clinic, the interesting and impressive program was centered around the "veterans," those who participated in the establishment of the Clinic.[13] During the past decade, as indicated above, the cast of characters has changed almost completely. It should be noted that such changes have occurred not only in the Psychoanalytic Clinic but also in the Columbia University Department of Psychiatry, within which the Psychoanalytic Clinic is located. In 1955, Dr. Lawrence C. Kolb became Chairman of the Department. Thus, the Psychoanalytic Clinic has gone through three changes in directorship and one change in the administration of the Department of Psychiatry. The latter event is of particular interest in view of the fear expressed by some analysts that university-affiliated institutes are subject to a special danger, namely, that a departmental chairman friendly to analysis may be succeeded by one who is hostile to the field. On the contrary, we have long been convinced that any departmental chairman who assists in the development of a psychoanalytic institute in his own department is bound to be succeeded by a chairman who is at least equally cooperative, if not more so. A well functioning analytic institute is certain to provide personnel and leadership from its staff, graduates and candidates for the department's training, treatment and research programs. Any movement can logically be only towards better mutual understanding and collaboration.

Our own experience has been precisely that. Dr. Kolb, Chairman of the Department of Psychiatry during our second ten years, continually gave help and encouragement to the staff of the Clinic and welcomed more and more Clinic personnel into key roles as the Department's programs expanded at a remarkable pace. Thus, the Department received the benefit of specially trained Psychoanalytic Clinic graduates, and the Clinic staff had the advantage of early teaching experience on a series of levels: medical students, state hospital residents, departmental residents, and analytic candidates. Dr. Kolb served regularly on the Executive Committee of the Psychoanalytic Clinic and at the same time appointed the Director of the Clinic to the Executive Committee of the Department of Psychiatry, thus assuring the opportunity for effective collaboration. In these favorable circumstances the Psychoanalytic Clinic and its staff have developed and matured in many ways, only a few of which have been presented. The sense of individual initiative and active participation has grown with the years. There has been a renewed and increasing interest in the experimental approach to teaching methods—for instance, with team teaching and also with the videotape machine. During its second ten years, the Columbia Psychoanalytic Clinic, losing its irreplaceable "founding fathers," became a young group that wanted to find its way and establish its own identity, a major step towards the goal of true maturity. The success that has been attained can be credited in large measure to the Chairman of the Department of Psychiatry, Dr. Kolb, who participated in our operation and at the same time provided the favorable environment.

As I look upon the depth and breadth of activities of the Columbia Psychoanalytic Clinic, I am moved to emphasize that these developments and achievements could not have come to pass were it not for a truly extraordinary group of men and women—the staff of this institute. Never, at any time or any place, have I seen a group of colleagues so dedicated, so giving of time and energy, spread in so many directions as they strive to encompass their many responsibilities: teaching, research, reading, committee meetings, selection interviews, supervisory sessions, reports, association meetings, out-of-town professional meetings, writing papers, and always the major commitment: the treatment of patients with psychoanalytic therapy. They have all been overextended, but they have never said "no" to a new task or challenge that was necessary or significant.

I know of no way adequately to thank this devoted and highly motivated group of colleagues.

Another group that has our gratitude includes those who established the Psychoanalytic Clinic. From them we received what wisdom we could absorb together with the scientific attitude of asking questions, seeking validation, trying innovations, all with a touch of the unconventional and the maverick. The qualities that we received from this group of leaders, combined with the advantages of university affiliation, have equipped and prepared the Columbia Psychoanalytic Clinic so that it could live, grow, contribute and develop an entire new generation in this changing psychiatric world.

It is that new generation which will shape and mold the future of this institute. In fact, they are already doing so. They presented today's program with a variety of personal style in the consideration of clinical, theoretical, research and applied aspects of psychoanalysis. You did not hear representatives of a "school" of thought but individuals who share a general conviction and commitment towards further understanding and utilization of psychoanalysis. They intend to maintain their flair for the experimental and exploratory, and they have learned the necessity and appreciation of tolerance—tolerance of differences with which they disagree, and tolerance amongst their critics. They look to the future with confidence and with the feeling that they are increasingly a part of the mainstream of psychoanalysis, a method of treatment and study which still, after seventy odd years, continues to open new doors to the understanding of man.

## References

1. Daniels, G. E. Comprehensive Medicine. In Rado, S., and Daniels, G. E. (Eds.) *Changing Concepts of Psychoanalytic Medicine*. New York: Grune and Stratton, 1956, p. 47.
2. Daniels, G. E., and Kolb, L. C. The Columbia University Psychoanalytic Clinic: an experiment in university teaching in psychoanalysis. *J. Med. Educat.* 35: 164–71, 1960.
3. Freud, S. On the teaching of psychoanalysis in universities (1919 [1918]). *Standard Edition*, Vol. 17. London: The Hogarth Press, 1955, pp. 169–73.
4. Freud, S. Lines of advance in psychoanalytic therapy (1919). *Standard Edition*, Vol. 17. London: The Hogarth Press, 1955, pp. 157–68.
5. Freud, S. *Hemmung, Symptom and Angst*. Vienna: Internationaler Psychoanalytischer Verlag, 1926.

6.  Freud, S. *The Problem of Anxiety*. New York: Psychoanalytic Quarterly Press and W. W. Norton, 1936.
7.  Goldman, G. S. Reparative Psychotherapy. In Rado, S., and Daniels, G. E. (Eds.) *Changing Concepts in Psychoanalytic Medicine.* New York: Grune and Stratton, 1956.
8.  Hartmann, H. Ich-Pscychologie und anpassungsproblem. *Internationale Zeitschrift fur Psychoanalyse und Imago.* 24: 62–135, 1939.
9.  Hartmann, H. *Ego Psychology and the Problem of Adaptation.* New York: International Univ. Press, 1958.
10. Klein, H. R. The Columbia Psychoanalytic Clinic: a development in psychoanalytic training. In Rado, S., and Daniels, G. E. (Eds.) *Changing Concepts of Psychoanalytic Medicine.* New York: Grune and Stratton, 1956.
11. Lewin, B. D., and Ross, H. *Psychoanalytic Education in the United States.* New York: W. W. Norton, 1960, p. 369.
12. Rado, S. Lectures, New York Psychoanalytic Institute, 1931–35.
13. Rado, S., and Daniels, G. E. (Eds.) *Changing Concepts of Psychoanalytic Medicine.* New York: Grune and Stratton, 1956.
14. Rosenbaum, M. Freud-eitingon-magnes correspondence. Psychoanalysis at the Hebrew University. *J. Amer. Psychoanal. Assoc.* 2: 311–7, 1954.
15. Sandler, J. The Hampstead Index in Psychoanalytic Research, presented at Research Seminar, Columbia University Psychoanalytic Clinic, March 30, 1963.

# Index